THE WORLD OF TEILHARD

The World of Teilhard

Edited by

Robert T. Francoeur

With a Preface by

John LaFarge, S.J.

HELICON PRESS
Baltimore

Helicon Press gratefully acknowledges the kind permission of Harper & Brothers to quote certain passages from *The Phenomenon of Man* (New York, Harper, 1959).

Library of Congress Catalog Card Number: 61–14676

Dedicated to
three teachers whose intellectual zeal
and warm humaneness
inspired, germinated and nourished
this and many other works:

Leo Buss, University of Detroit

Paul Stokely, Ph.D., College of Steubenville

Edward Wenstrup, O.S.B., Ph.D., St. Vincent College

PRINTED IN THE UNITED STATES OF AMERICA BY THE NORTH CENTRAL PUBLISHING COMPANY, ST. PAUL 2, MINNESOTA

CONTENTS

THE WORLD OF TEILHARD

PREFACE

An ever-increasing body of literature clusters around the person and the ideas of Pierre Teilhard de Chardin. Such growth is a witness to the originality of his thought. The question of how far religious faith can be reconciled with the exacting, quasi-miraculous triumphs of the strictly scientific method of hypothesis, investigation, and empirical analysis is of course a perennial topic of interest, one that has already given birth to a small library of comment. Solicitude in this connection will doubtless explain some of the curiosity about Teilhard's ideas. The extension in our epoch of the observable universe into inconceivable immensities of time and space and complexity combines with the doctrine of evolution to give a new and dramatic turn to this whole cast of religio-scientific questioning. The new cosmogony's incredibly vast perspective of the evolving world — inanimate, animate, subhuman, human, and societal — as may be gathered from the fragmentary records of the rocks, raises the question with particular intensity as to how all this can be fitted into the schedule of creation, redemption, final transcendence, as proclaimed in the teachings of the Christian faith.

Joined with this inquiry is the subtler and much more searching question of reconciling the view of the continually progressing universe with the agonizing uncertainty of free human choice and action. Every step in the path of progress, every new conquest of disease, ignorance and human misery seems only to emphasize the fundamentally ambiguous situation in which that progress finds itself. This inner contradiction between the glorious prospects of human progress and the strange impasses into which it is continually leading us is symbolized by the apparent inability of the human race to establish even the most elementary guarantee of stable unity, peace, and freedom from the ever more lurid specter of war.

As a scientific observer — not merely a faithful but also a highly creative student of nature and nature's inner dynamism — Teilhard de Chardin won the enthusiastic admiration of countless fellow scientists. Yet he was an outstanding man of God, of cloudless faith, of utmost simplicity and integrity of heart, who had pondered for a lifetime over the contending aspects of the problem. Hence he seemed to be the person who of all others could succeed

3

in penetrating this cosmic riddle. Moreover, Teilhard makes emphatically clear that there is no question of colorless blending or fatuous compromise. Any concordism, any notion of "proving" faith from science, is as alien to his philosophy as would be its medieval contrary: that of attempting to prove truths of "natural philosophy" from the data of theological revelation.

He does, however, propose a Christian meaning to the total natural cosmogony, and his thoughts upon this matter are passionately debated by his admirers as well as by his critics. How valid are his conjectures, how far he can claim a logical, philosophical sequence of ideas, how far his theological perspective is widely comprehensive, and not just conveniently selective — these are all matters of continued debate.

Is there an inherent contradiction in the picture of an optimistically progressive universe moving ever to the point when it will be ready for a transcendent consummation, yet always threatened with total disaster from the wrecking force of human perversity? Here, again, is the subject for a continued discussion. How far has Teilhard stated the question in all its integrity, and how far has he shed light upon its solution through his many-branched concept of the Tree of Life's "complexity consciousness"? He always relates this concept to the mystery of man's social structure: his humble littleness yet incredible dignity of origin and personality.

As Robert Francoeur remarks in his Introduction to this collection,

> . . . There are some enthusiasts who do much harm by their reckless acceptance of everything in Teilhard's thought. There are others, probably more numerous, who hide behind the fear of any "novel" thought and ignore the challenge evolution presents to the modern thinker. Some enthusiasts will claim that Teilhard has solved all our problems, while others will refuse him any consideration because he failed to clarify some points. Yet if we remember that the thought of Teilhard de Chardin was never meant to be a definitive thing, that it is open and pregnant, undeveloped, that it was meant to stir up thought rather than to answer all questions, then we shall be able to examine his work with profit.

One's judgment of a person's thought is never quite isolated from one's impression of his person, for traits of personality enter into even the most abstract reasoning, particularly in a type of speculation that profoundly affects human experiences and emotions. One can hardly issue a certificate of complete intellectual integrity to a good man merely on the basis of his personal holiness. On the other hand, one cannot lightly write off the purely personal factor. The man whom I knew, and entertained as a guest at the time he first came to the United States in 1948, to begin work with the Wenner-Gren Foundation of New York, was no ordinary "good person." He was a man of unalloyed holiness, manly personal integrity and deep human sympathy, and of an astonishing degree of childlike conscientiousness and humility: a trait witnessed to by his immediate superiors in the community of his own order. He kept the rules of the Society not with ordinary correctness, but with intense delicacy of childlike exactitude. He also suffered mental agony from the suspicions cast upon his work by persons who were thoroughly honest and sincere in their convictions, yet unfamiliar with the sequence of ideas and experience that laid the groundwork for his assertions and hypotheses. Moreover — and I think this is important for an understanding of Teilhard de Chardin, as it has been the case in a number of somewhat similar instances in history — the mental isolation, the absence of sound critical companionship and healthy, normal give-and-take, outside of his professional specialty — an isolation that this atmosphere of suspicion imposed upon him, succeeded in driving him in upon himself. For this reason, as I said in reviewing *The Divine Milieu,*

> . . . The discussion, it seems to me, cannot stray very far from the complex reality if certain outstanding characteristics of Teilhard's motivation are kept in mind.
>
> He was a man consumed subjectively by three noble and not incompatible passions, each of which has a long and honorable ancestry in Christian history.
>
> From early childhood he was consumed with a *scientific passion*, a desire to know, especially about what the earth's record had to say about its past history and the history of humanity. Again, he was moved by a deep *moral passion*, an inner urge to justify this exacting devotion to scientific lore from the standpoint of his own equally exacting standards of goodness and holiness; to assimilate this intellectual passion to his own quest, and the quest he wished for all mankind, for the capital virtues of purity, fidelity, universal charity. Finally, he was equally consumed by an authentic *mystical passion*: the longing to reach and to commune with the living God, with the center of his own personality, the center of all mankind and the goal of all history. With equal intensity he rejected, as some of the following interpretations have made plain, any notion of a pantheistic mysticism. For him the ever increasing "convergence" of human intelligences and communications meant an intensification of the individual human personality, the utter opposite of a merging of the individual in a pseudo-mystical All *(America,* Nov. 12, 1960).

To unite in one person, in one all-comprehensive scheme, all these varied and outwardly conflicting passions, is a task that demands a philosophical and theological equipment which Teilhard's preoccupation with the intricacies of his purely scientific research did not fully permit him to acquire. In his humility I think he was more conscious of this deficiency than his critics give him credit for. But such a handicap, though it would warn us against blind worship, does not detract from Teilhard's true importance as a very great intellectual explorer.

Our present generation is anxiously questioning the inner value of a world which is ever passing, yet is destined for ultimate transfiguration in Christ. Linked with the intrinsic value of the world is the cognate question of the value of man's work in the world. Does the *opus Dei* derive its worth only from the intention by which it is performed or has it also an intrinsic value of its own, in the Creator's immeasurably far-seeing plan? This was the question Teilhard asked himself and answered in his *Divine Milieu.* How far will his answer be accepted?

Teilhard, says Paulinus F. Forsthoefel in this volume,

> saw in all the stages of evolution a constant seeking after greater consciousness and spontaneity which was to culminate in the reflective ability and freedom of man himself. He interpreted the course of evolution according to the light thrown on it by considering man as the goal of evolution. . . . The biologist who is convinced that an Intelligent First Cause exists as the explanation of the ultimate origin of the universe finds it inconceivable that this Intelligent Being would be unconcerned with the progressive development (evolution) of his creation. . . . He will still disagree with Teilhard as to the mechanism of evolution. . . . He will, however, agree with Teilhard that this mechanism of itself cannot explain the plan behind the course of evolution. . . .

A Preface, however, that attempts to anticipate the considered judgments of the contributors is out of place. The brilliant series of interpretations that form this volume speak from a wide range of intellectual interests. They emphasize the importance of Teilhard's works not as manuals of ready answers, but as tentative explorations of a problem that cannot be avoided, any more than great Christian thinkers of the past could avoid exploring the realms that new scholarship and the revival of ancient scholarship opened up to their inquiring minds.

Père Teilhard is buried under the traditionally plain headstone of his Society, in the lovely graveyard adjoining the Jesuit Novitiate of St. Andrew-on-Hudson, near Poughkeepsie, in ground that as a young priest-novice, over fifty years ago, I had (most ineffectively) pretended to help excavate. It is a blessed spot, and we who did our part in creating it love it, and hope that as we each come in turn to lay our bones within the secluded circle of rocks and trees above the banks of the Hudson River, we may make it a seed-ground of the Resurrection, not only for ourselves, but for all mankind. Teilhard de Chardin saw that ultimate triumph in a completeness and originality of vision which he tried to convey to the modern world. I hope we may all gather from it at least some precious fragments.

— JOHN LAFARGE

January 19, 1961

1

INTRODUCTION: A NEW WORLD VISION

Robert T. Francoeur

Some writers have called him "the new Galileo," "an architect of great thought." Others have viewed him as "the Thomas Aquinas of our age," "a clandestine theologian" whose thoughts and works will supply a new dimension in our religious thinking. Still others have given him such epithets as "the equal of a Teresa of Avila or a John of the Cross," a man "in whom the flame of a Paul of Tarsus and the ardor of a John of Patmos seem to be reborn."

Background

He was a leading scientist, a world-renowned paleontologist, a visionary whose lyrics and mystical writings speak of love and union, a Catholic priest, and a Jesuit. Europe is ringing with the challenge of his thought, and now American thinkers are facing the challenge of Pierre Teilhard de Chardin and his striking vision of the world.

The scientific specialist is well acquainted with his work on the fossils of the Peking Man and the Java Man, and with his scientific labors which, for over fifty years, carried him to every corner of our globe. But beyond the hermitage of science, Teilhard de Chardin is a strange name just now beginning to be heard. *The Phenomenon of Man* and *The Divine Milieu*, the most important works of Teilhard, have now appeared in English. Several works about Teilhard are also either in preparation or already published, including *Pierre Teilhard de Chardin, His Thought* by Claude Tresmontant, Nicolas Corte's study, and the authoritative biography by Claude Cuénot (soon to appear in English). These are opening the door to a new vision of man.

When we introduce Teilhard with the glowing and somewhat brazen audacity of the epithets quoted above, you may naturally respond with a frown of disbelief. True, these quotations have been drawn from European sources. Teilhard is respected by many abroad and his thought praised by such scholars as Arnold Toynbee, George Gaylord Simpson, Julian Huxley, André Malraux, and Jean Wahl. Still, wisdom is universal, and the thought of a great man cannot be confined to the Continent. A man who has stirred

7

the spiritual thought of a materialistic world so deeply and powerfully that he has been compared to Paul of Tarsus, John of the Cross, and Thomas Aquinas should be better known in America. To make him better known is the whole purpose of this anthology. We have asked scholars in various fields to give their impressions of Teilhard and of the influence of his thought on their specialty.

But before we bring Teilhard de Chardin out of his French milieu, it would be enlightening to glance back over the history that preceded him.

That history is from the outset the record of man's continuous preoccupation with the idea of motion. Twenty thousand years ago, man began to paint the walls and ceilings of his caves with beautifully proportioned sketches of animals; and from these paintings it is easy to deduce that these early Aurignacian and Magdalenian people of southern France and Spain were very conscious of the reality of motion and progress in a definite direction. Their attempts to portray motion are indeed intriguing — drawings of eight- and twelve-legged bison and reindeer. Motion, development, unflowering, evolving — that is the line of man's thought.

Later, when the Aryans migrated into India about 1,000 B.C., this fundamental idea of motion and change was given its first cosmological application in the writings of the *Rig-Veda*. Primeval waters contained the primordial germ of all life — a floating world egg from which all other things would evolve. Then about 500 B.C. Confucius wrote his famous *Yi-Chang*; even the title of this work points to the idea of an evolution. In the *Yi-Chang* Confucius tried to show that everything in the world was derived from a simple original substance by a gradual unfolding and blossoming. At the other end of the Fertile Crescent, the Egyptians also had a form of evolution in their primitive religious cosmology.

When we come to the leaders of early philosophy, the Greeks, the evidence is very clear. Thales, Anaximander, and Anaximenes were ardent evolutionists. Haeckel went so far as to term Anaximander "the prophet of Darwin and Lamarck." And even though in this primitive stage man's thoughts of an evolving cosmos were vague, confusing, and for the most part without scientific evidence, they were definite in their basic idea that we live in a world of development.[1]

In the Christian era that followed the decline of the Greek schools of philosophy, three scholars stand out as exponents of an evolving universe. Basil was the first really noteworthy defender of Christian evolution. After his death his brother, Gregory of Nyssa, developed Basil's ideas and propounded an evolutionary interpretation of the universe which seems more absolute and far-reaching than the Darwinian. The *rationes seminales* of Augustine are known to almost every scholar, but we seldom realize that this evolutionary view of the world was fairly dominant in Christian thought until the end of the eighth century and probably even to the end of the twelfth. Little known, too, is the letter written by Pope Anastasius at the end of the fifth century to the bishops of Gaul in which he clearly stated that the common and general interpretation of Genesis was this: that in the beginning God created everything "potentially and causally" [2] and that only later on with the passage of time did the distinction and arrangement of species come about. Christianity is in fact a synthesizing influence: Paul, Basil, Gregory of Nyssa, and Augustine only tried to synthesize and harmonize the secular knowledge of our world with the revealed wisdom of the Word made flesh: "And I, if I be lifted up, will draw all things to myself."

A strange symbiosis of opposing concepts is present in this early stage of human thought. As Fothergill and Osborn have shown, the Greek philosophers and the early Christian writers expressed many evolutionary views in their cosmological and religious writings. Yet at the same time, this same evolutionary view was paralleled and limited in its application by cyclic theories of time and the myth of an eternal return. This has been pointed out by Mircea Eliade and Walter J. Ong, S.J., and exposes a deep dichotomy in primitive thought. The orientation of Biblical thought has always been that of a process; it is opposed to any fundamental cyclism. Thus the early Christian cosmology could easily adopt the evolutionary view of the Greeks, fit it in with the historical process of creation/ incarnation/ redemption, and arrive at a synthesis of evolutionary science and Biblical thought such as Basil, Gregory and Augustine expressed.

But after the culmination of 13th-century learning in Albert the Great and Thomas Aquinas, dichotomies arose between science and the philosophy of the schools; theology, philosophy, and science became separate entities completely independent of one another. Then Luther stressed the essential corruption of man's physical nature; later, Jansenists proclaimed the deadliness of all physical reality. Materialistic naturalism became the vogue when the natural was divorced from the supernatural. With Descartes, Spinoza, Kant, Hegel, Auguste Comte, and Marx, science and philosophy became agnostic and even atheistic while religion and theology often withdrew to the heavens above only to leave earthly man untouched and unmoved by their message.

After the decline of scholasticism and science in the 14th century, philosophy took its turn in the driver's seat. But the evolutionary concept of our world did not die. It only passed from the realm of theology and Greek "physics" to the hands of the natural philosophers. In the 19th century another change took place. At that time science was beginning the ascent which has given it the highest place in the modern world.

The man who took evolution out of the field of speculation and theory was Jean Baptiste Lamarck, who published the first scientific exposition of evolution in 1809. Fifty years later Darwin and Wallace presented the members of the Linnean Society of London with a "complete" theory of evolution based on the struggle for survival and existence. Of interest in Lamarck there had been hardly a ripple beyond scientific circles. But as for Darwinian evolution, no deluge or flood ever swamped the land faster or more furiously. The time was ripe. Everywhere men's minds were gaping and open for a new explanation of our world. Atheists pounced on the theory and forged it into a cudgel wherewith to pulverize their mortal enemy, religion. Theologians went on the defensive and withdrew into their fortress. Two camps pouring out the proverbial fire and brimstone — a deafening roar with little or no light. Lamarck had been a religious man, a Catholic. Darwin, at least, was not completely irreligious. And yet evolution had become the tool of mechanists and atheists.

Almost fifty years after Darwin's *Origin of Species* another milestone in the history of evolutionary thought appeared, Henri Bergson's *Creative Evolution*. A Jew most of his long life, toward the end of it he was certainly Catholic in thought. He was the modern prophet of the "spirit" among the scientists, and his whole mind was to restore the proper position of the spiritual in evolutionary and scientific thought.

The advances of the last decade have occurred somewhat like a double-pronged spear. For eighteen months after its release, Pierre Lecomte du Noüy's *Human Destiny* topped the nonfiction "best-seller list." This was in 1947. *Human Destiny* was the first modern major attempt to synthesize theology and science available to American readers. Despite many shortcomings and not a few theological errors, it is a valuable essay at synthesis. Though quite independently of Bergson, Lecomte du Noüy actually extended the trend of thought of his French compatriot.

At the same time another French scholar was on the same path: Pierre Teilhard de Chardin, Jesuit, mystic, and scientist. This is the man we wish to introduce in this anthology. At least, we should like to introduce the influence his thought has had on various fields of human learning, for in the man Teilhard stand out a "philosophy," a "theology" and a scientific conception which will alter our vision of the world.

George Gaylord Simpson declared in his study *Evolution: the Modern Synthesis* (1942) that: "The time is now ripe for a rapid advance in our understanding of evolution. The need today is for a concerted attack on synthesis." Basically the need of our modern "wisdom" is for a new synthesis uniting once again the compartments of knowledge which up till now have been pigeonholes where we could store our little facts in isolation. But this need for a new synthesis is not limited to the realm of science. It is vital for our modern philosophical and theological knowledge as well. Has not Bruno de Solages, rector of the Catholic Institute of Toulouse, identified this as the

prime need of modern Christian thinking if it is to be fruitful? After examining the evidence for an evolutionary universe he wrote:

> It is necessary then for the Christian thinker to adopt the evolutionary
> outlook and to present the facts of Revelation within the framework of an
> evolutionary concept of the universe, . . . just as St. Thomas in the thir-
> teenth century presented them in the framework of the ancient cyclical rep-
> resentation of the world.
>
> But is there nothing better for him to do than to accommodate himself
> to this concept as best he can, and to correct — as if from outside — the me-
> chanistic evolution which others work out for him? If he could only start
> with this perspective and show how the Christian message is harmonious with
> it, if he could show that he can believe in the spirit even though he may be an
> evolutionist, would not the position of the Christian scholar be infinitely
> better? Do I need to mention Bergson's *Creative Evolution* and where it led
> him? The last works of that brilliant scholar, Lecomte du Noüy, pursued the
> same course. — Another name, which is indeed becoming famous, is now on
> the lips of all when they speak of spiritual evolution: it is the name of Father
> Teilhard de Chardin.[3]

A New Synthesis

Essentially the thought of Pierre Teilhard de Chardin is synthetic. It is
not what we should ordinarily call "science" and yet it does not fall into the
category of metaphysics or theology. Sometimes poetic to an extreme, it is
more than mere fantasy and different from mystical ecstasy. Teilhard terms
his work a "phenomenology," a study of the cosmic phenomena. Actually
none of our commonly known categories of human knowledge fits the work
of Teilhard. About the closest we can come to categorizing his thought is to
liken it to the thought of the ancient Greeks. At that stage of human consciousness the divisions between the various branches of knowledge were not
so definite as they are today. Knowledge was one. Does not Aristotle call his
work a "Physics" at the very moment that he introduces his arguments from
reason for the existence of God? For the scholastics, this would be a "cosmology," a metaphysics. But Teilhard rejects any attempt to classify his
thought in airtight compartments, for his synthesis is not a "system" nor a
closed syllogistic discipline of one branch of knowledge. Teilhardian thought
is *fecund, open, free, and all-inclusive*. It is not definitive, cut-and-dried.
It is based on the findings of modern science but is not confined to the experimental methodology of the laboratory. Its scope leaves room for "scientific extrapolations." The concepts of duration, time and evolution are the
very foundation of its synthetic viewpoint.

Following the spirit of the great scholastics and the "nouvelle théologie,"
Teilhard tried to synthesize and reunite the scientific contributions of the
20th century with Revelation. This is the first time since Albert the Great and
Thomas Aquinas that a scholar has attacked the problem of the unity of all

knowledge on so broad a scale. The attempt is there, but it is not definitive, for it is only an essay, a beginning. As Jean Guitton has said, Teilhard de Chardin is more the prophet of a new vision than its master.[4]

Modern science looks upon the tangible universe as a series of syntheses or unions that tend to gather together into new bodies more complex than the original components. Simple precedes complex in the history of life. Atoms are born of a union of electrons, protons, and neutrons. From the atoms come molecules, then cells, organs, and organisms — the plants and animals. The progression is clear, for the whole story of matter strikingly exhibits this grand law of evolution, the law of increasing complexity. This is the basic interpretation that Teilhard found in the history of matter. There is a meaning, an orthogenesis in evolution — a birth which has a goal and direction.

Analyzing the structure of the world in the light of modern physics, as we are tempted to do in this atomic age, often gives us the impression of complete dissolution. The phenomenon of atomic disintegration overwhelms us just as the sidereal immensity does on the other end of the scale. In the world of chemistry and physics the changes that bring atoms together in molecules, cells, and organisms do not produce any new energy. In fact, even though there is an apparent "newness" in the living organism, it is a parasitic thing, living off matter until the second principle of thermodynamics, the law of entropy, finally dissipates all its utilizable energy in heat. If this flow of entropy downward were the only force at work in our universe, then our only forecast would be the ultimate death of our world, a state of absolute and uniform cold where all motion would be annihilated.

But is this the true picture of evolution? Can the stream of evolution dissolve into nothingness? Is the flow only a senseless abortion, a miscarriage of nature? Or is it possible that beyond the tangible world of matter there is another force at work in the universe? Is there possibly another form of energy in the world?

Bergson spoke of two streams in evolution: matter, which tends downward, and spirit, which rises upward to freedom. Lecomte du Noüy likewise spoke of this "opposition" between entropic matter and freedom-aimed spirit. Much farther along the same line, we find Teilhard's recognition of the value of the spiritual. Besides matter, which is only the external aspect of the universe, there is also a *"dedans,"* the "within" of things. Everywhere in the world we can find this parallel of the *within* and the *without*. In the inorganic this duality is only a scientific extrapolation. Among the plants and animals, though not very evidently, it is present. Here we might clarify Teilhard's position by comparing his concept of evolution as an increase in consciousness with Lecomte du Noüy's view of evolution as a development of physical and moral freedom. The two seem complementary and compatible.[5]

Extrapolating into the past history of evolution from what we know of man himself shows us the relation of the *within* and *without,* for in mankind consciousness, freedom, spiritual liberty — the *within* of things — are just as evident as the *without* of matter and physical freedom. Complexity increases on the exterior until the limitations of matter halt it. Then the law of increasing complexity/consciousness changes its level but not its direction. In man the growth is on the interior, in his moral consciousness and freedom. But throughout all matter we have a parallel between complexity and consciousness. The lower the form of matter — whether it be animal, plant, or mineral — the smaller its physical and psychic freedom. At the base of the tree of life, consciousness is disassociated and dispersed only to rise in man to the level of moral freedom. This is the great law of evolution, the law of complexity/consciousness.

And just as there are two faces to the coin of matter so also do we find a duality of exterior/interior in energy. In fact, matter is only "canned light or bottled-up energy." These two forms of energy — Teilhard asks if perhaps they might not be just that, two forms of the same energy — have separate but related functions in the movement of evolution. Radial energy or spiritual energy draws an element towards a higher degree of complexity and consciousness. This is the real force behind evolution. This is the force behind the rise from simple to complex and from dispersed consciousness to centralized consciousness. Tangential energy, which corresponds to the *without* of matter, binds the members of a group together. It is the cohesive force in a phylum. It is through the interplay of these two forces that Teilhard tries to explain the universe and its history on the phenomenal level. Atom, molecule, cell, plant, animal, man: a steady progression in complexity ever more centered around its core of consciousness.

This apposition of spirit and matter, of the *within* and *without* of things, of extrapolated radial and tangential energies, and of the scientific parameters of complexity and consciousness, creates many implications (as well as many problems) which may prove fruitful in our understanding of the world. But they will require an abundance of thought to be properly evaluated. Some of these implications (and problems) will be touched on in the essays to follow.

From Atom to Man

A spiral nebula of dispersed gases, a monstrous world atom slowly contracting . . . A whorl of whirling, flaming stars, new born in space . . . A chunk of molten, incandescent matter slips from our sun into the void of space. Crystalization follows and our own earth is born with its mineral world. And on this earth crystalization is widespread, almost universal. But here and there over the cooling globe some matter is polymerized under the influence of radial energy. Molecules clump together. Organic compounds are formed and those complex compounds of carbon which are so close to viruses and proteins — the megamolecules — appear for the first time.

Teilhard claims that there was an era when the megamolecules formed a much denser layer over the earth than they do today, a time when this covering was so dense that there was a state of chemical hypertension unknown in the world today. This hypertension ultimately culminated in a critical point, a point where prelife and its consciousness could finally breach the limitations of matter. When the combined impetus of tangential and radial forces climaxed, certain elements on the surface of the earth leapt the critical threshold that separates life and nonlife.

At this point the ordinary believer may be puzzled. "Can the scientist create life?" For Teilhard, this chemical state of hypertension was something that would happen only once in the ordinary course of nature. Once the radial energy that caused the piercing had found its natural release in the expanding world of life, this critical point became only an object of historical study, a unique event in the past. The chemical world of prelife will continue to change but it will not evolve. The axis of evolution has passed beyond that stage. Henceforth it is concerned only with the living. This situation, however, does not eliminate the possibility that scientists (such as Wald and Miller) may produce the arrangement or order of a living thing in the laboratory.[6] On the phenomenal level, the scientist may be able to re-create this hypertension, to which the creative concurrence of the Absolute would answer.

The primeval waters teemed with new life — fragile, simple, and often shapeless forms. These first sparks of life spread like a flood over the land to form a new covering, the "biosphere." Life is difficult if not impossible to define in the laboratory. But we can at least attempt a description. The three immanent activities of nutrition, growth, and reproduction give us the elements for our concept of a living thing.

At first sight reproduction, wherein a part of the parent develops into a new whole, may not seem to be an immanent activity. But in its earlier phases it clearly is so. Both nutrition and growth are also present in any form of life. (Because the cell is more plastic and more sensitive than the simple molecule, it can adapt to circumstances. It can join with other cells in an organism where diversification and specialization reign.) To these three characteristics Teilhard added a fourth, which borders on a scientific extrapolation though it is not such. As cells multiply and associate together, they do so along a definite path. All living things follow much the same pattern in their development. This "unconscious purpose" or oriented evolution the biologists call "orthogenesis." These are the essential qualities of all living cells.

With this we meet another problem, that of entelechy, the expansion of life as a whole in an orthogenic evolution. The various branches of the tree of life spread out more like a bush, and for this expansion three things are required: grouping, ingenuity, and indifference. First of all, life, or a particular form of life, must grope its way in the void of chance, weaving here and there to open up new possibilities: a hit-and-miss affair wherein everything is tried in order to fill all the possibilities and where all the possibilities are filled so that everything may be tried. Then ingenuity — in order to gather the various forms into stable and coherent unions. And finally, an indifference for the individuals left behind by the stream of evolution. Evolution must tread over a hecatomb of outdated forms of life. Life "passes over a bridge of accumulated cadavers." The arrowhead moves onward only to leave the past to a lingering death.

Yet, as we mentioned above, one of the characteristics of evolution and the growth of life is that it displays a definite form. There is a direction to the evolutionary stream, an orthogenesis, a true birth and not a miscarriage. This, of course, is contrary to what most biologists hold, as Michael Polanyi has pointed out [7] (a fact that makes the enthusiasm of many scientists for Teilhard a real puzzle). For many scientists the history of life has no direction; chance alone produced the seeming "direction" of evolution toward greater consciousness.

As life expands, the various groups of animals develop. From an initial point thin groping lines spread out to outline the final stage of a particular phylum. When all the various possibilities have been explored, a phase of expansion sets in where the outlines are detailed, and the phylum spreads itself like a fan. Groping to explore is followed by ingenuity to bind together. When each ray has reached its perfection and is at rest, the whorl becomes stagnant; it loses its creative instability, its ingenuity.

Subatomic particles join to form atoms; atoms associate together in the molecules, which in turn unite into living organisms of varied complexity and consciousness. Syntheses arise in the form of associations and unions in most of the forms of life, particularly at the extremities of the two main branches of the animal kingdom among the insects and mammals. At times this socialization is so extreme that it destroys the individual in order that the group may survive. Many instances of such destruction may be found among the social insects: the ants, bees, and termites are perfect examples. Association is really not a tool of evolution. It is simply a defense mechanism that attempts to consolidate and perpetuate what evolution has already produced.

Evolution itself, though, cannot and does not halt just because a phylum has adjusted to its environment. Even though a particular whorl may be situated at the head of the stream, it soon reaches its limitations. It matures and slips into senility just as it passes the spark on to a higher level. One or two rays in a whorl will not become specialized. They will not be affected by the general decline of the whole group but will retain their creative instability. Eventually these will find a fissure in the stabilized group only to break out in a new form of life. Through creative instability evolution advances onward. The pile of cadavers grows with each step and year. Some species pass into oblivion with the dinosaurs, others linger on in man's shadow.

Within/without, radial/tangential, complexity/consciousness: these are the measuring sticks that disclose the growth of the tree of life. But to reconstruct this tree we must try to read the history of the past. Here we find that the tips of the branches, especially those closer to us, are very distinct, while the origins are blurred. Like the first wheel, the first car, and the first model of any invention, the earlier and less advanced forms of life have left us only scattered, fragmentary evidence. When we realize that much of what once was land teeming with life is now beneath the ocean waters, and what is now land was once the seas, when we realize that the step from one species to another occurred in only a few creatively unstable individuals out of millions in a whorl, we can easily understand why the "missing links" are missing. The chances that any animal or plant will leave its imprint on the sands of time for us to read are very slim indeed. Yet every scrap of evidence we find fits into the gaps in our evolutionary schema, and nothing we have as yet found contradicts that schema.

Despite the problems we face, there is a certain pattern in the facts we know which helps us reconstruct the tree of life, at least in its general outlines. Mankind cannot be an isolated figure in this tree. We must consider man as the newest shoot, breaking through into the world of reflection but at the same time still bound to the lower levels of consciousness from which he sprang. Within the whorl of the primates from which he came, man is still the least specialized in his organs. "Specialization paralyzes, ultraspecialization kills." Among the primates and placental mammals man alone has retained his creative instability because he has remained unspecialized. At the same time evolution has concentrated all her energies, as we shall see, in the human brain and consciousness. The zigzag line of man's ancestry winds back through the placental mammals, through the reptiles, to the amphibians, where life emerged from its aquatic origins. Below the primitive fish, the earliest and lowest vertebrate level, we find a tangled mass of weak and often shapeless forms of life like the sponges, sea slugs, polyps, hydras, amoeba, and euglena. Here the division between animal and plant almost disappears. In fact, even the distinction between living and nonliving becomes so clouded that chemists and biologists alike claim the virus in their domain. Plant and animal, living and nonliving — in practice these are distinctions valid only in the outer branches of the tree of life. Any descent to the source of life means a descent to the minute, the frail, and ill-formed, as well as a return to water, where life first sprang forth from the nonliving. This decreasing definiteness explains the vagueness we meet in any picture of the earlier phases of evolution.

Teilhard has shown that the advance of the evolutionary stream is the equivalent of a progressive increase in complexity and consciousness. As the external material side of the universe grows in complexity, the spiritual or interior side also is swept along in the flood. The more matter undergoes mutations and expands in its complexity, the more do consciousness and liberty of action increase. Mutations in the tangential seem necessarily to react on the radial. In this light, our problem is to find the link between the tangential and the radial, the material factor in every being which seems to provoke the blossoming of consciousness. The only system that fits this situation, as Teilhard points out, is the nervous system. Throughout the history of life, and particularly among the vertebrates, a study of the development and concentration of brain tissue will reveal the place of any animal in the tree of life. Dinosaurs for instance, with their massive bulk, had very small "brains," sometimes not even located in the head but in the sacral region. This in itself would place them long before the mammals in history. Ordinary common experience tells us that the more developed and centered the nervous system is in the region of the head, the more consciousness succeeds in reaching the exterior world with instincts that become more and more adaptable and complex.

The tree of life has three main branches: the plant world, where consciousness has gone into a deep sleep in simple tropisms; the insect world, with consciousness imprisoned in a shell of chitin; and the vertebrates, where consciousness blossoms in sense perception.[8] The insects have succeeded in concentrating nerve fibers in their brain region and at the same time they have developed a marvelous depth of instinctive social life. Yet this social life has a strange quality about it — it destroys individuality. Despite this progress, the insect can get only so big before the weight of his exoskeleton halts his advance. Perhaps this is the reason for the excessive social life of the insects.

The few individuals involved in the genesis of a new branch of evolution must possess a creative instability; they cannot be perfectly adapted to their environment without losing their power to evolve. The insects, which have branched off the main stream of evolution, have done just this. They have so specialized their consciousness and physical structure that further evolution is impossible for them. On the other hand, among the mammals instinct has remained fluid and unspecialized. More than this flexibility of instinct (consciousness), the primates have retained a flexibility and lack of specialization that extend even into the physical: they have all three types of teeth — canine, incisor, and molar; they have retained their ulna and fibula, which animals like the horse have abandoned in order to specialize in speed; their hands with opposable thumbs and four fingers can grasp any object; their diet is un-limited. The primates represent a phylum of "pure and direct cerebrali-zation." Thus it was from this least specialized, most conservative, and most conscious group, the primitive primates, that man's body probably came.

According to Teilhard, those animals that branched off and left the main stream of evolution have gone far down the road of specialization. Their limbs, teeth, claws have become so adapted to their environment and its re-quirements that they are expert runners, rodents or flesh eaters. But they are limited to this specialty. Specialization is the necessary tool of adaption, but at the same time it kills creative instability. The side branches specialize and adapt while the main shoot remains conservative with very little specializa-tion. The primates have changed very slightly since their first appearance. Yet these unspecialized animals have not lagged behind in their development. Among these forms "evolution is concentrated in the brain, leaving every-thing else plastic." This lack of specialization is of great importance, for when applied to the hands, which can grasp anything, it reduced the need for strong jaw muscles and permitted the development of a larger skull and brain. With this development, the eyes could converge and unite their vision. Bifocal vision could become binocular. A world of three dimensions appeared for the first time, and the hands became a key to many doors theretofore locked.

Slowly consciousness began to turn in on itself — at first only on the external physical side. Everything in this world enters by way of a birth, and that birth requires a gestation period where hibernation and preparation are the rule. The mammals and particularly the primates prepared for the birth of thought by turning consciousness in on itself, by making it possible for the animal to observe his own hands in action in a three-dimensional world. Such a stage we may call only a prelude to thought, because reflection consists primarily in "knowing that you know"; the animal only "knows." Conscious-ness began as a diffused circle of reflection which little by little centered on itself. Just as the atom is organized around its nucleus, so is the grain of thought gradually centered around its core. Around the mammal "an 'aura' of freedom begins to float, a glimmer of personality." Then, when a certain stage of cerebralization is reached, a sudden change in nature occurs on the phenomenal level. Reflection reaches the term of its gestation period in the birth of individual reflection. (Much later, as we shall see, individual reflec-tion will reach its maturity in the birth of an "ultrareflection" centered around the Omega Point.) Thus are individual man and reflection born.

We may never be able to place the exact origin of man either in time or in space. Again the reasons are the same as with many of the "missing links." The fossil story does, however, indicate that at the end of the Tertiary Era, just before the appearance of man, the primate population of the world had reached a state of hypertension very similar to that which occurred before the birth of life. Some of these primates, such as the Australopithecus and the Proconsul of South Africa, were closer to man anatomically than any monkey or ape of today. Somewhere among this mass of primates an instantaneous mutation took place and evolution jumped to a new and higher form of life. Teilhard has been criticized for not mentioning the direct creation of the human soul, but remember — this is phenomenology, not philosophy or theology. Science can tell us nothing about the origin of the soul, nothing of Adam and Eve. From the whole history of evolution, the indications are that mutations have always been individual affairs. From the scientific standpoint, Teilhard is *inclined* toward the birth of man from a single original couple. But scientifically we cannot prove one way or the other. Naturally because of other beliefs of religious or philosophical basis, he held for monogenism. Pure science can tell us nothing of an instantaneous creative impulse of God hiding under a phenomenal veil to produce man's soul.

Little by little after the birth of life, the earth was covered with a cloak of life, the biosphere. In the birth of man, the earth adds a new and higher covering. "The earth builds a new cloak. Better still, it finds its spirit." This is the "noosphere," the layer of thought which slowly expands and spreads the radial over the surface of the earth. Henceforth evolution is concerned only with the development and interdevelopment of thought.

A few fossils scattered across the eons are about all we know of the story of man today. As usual, origins disappear in haze, relations are tenuous, branches splintered off from the main stem become isolated and finally are wiped away. This is the position of the Java Man (Pithecanthropus) and Peking Man (Sinanthropus). They flourished for a time and then gave rise to new leaves that overran the parent. Midway between a primate of the chimpanzee type and modern man, Peking Man used tools and fire in his life along the banks of the Yangtze River in North China. Of Java Man we know less, since his remains are found in alluvial deposits rather than in caves as were those of the Peking Man. Above these primitive forms of man rose the Neanderthal Man of Western Europe. And somewhere in the many rays of Neanderthaloid men rose the first man of our modern type (*Homo sapiens* — Cro-Magnon and Mousterian Men) from whom the four races of present-day mankind probably developed.

After the initial branching and exploring during which *Homo sapiens* came not only to Europe but also to the world, the human phylum followed the same general laws of expansion and radiation as all the other creatures born in our evolving universe. From somewhere in tropical Africa, the Near East, China, or Java — in what we can call the "fertile crescent" — modern man spread so rapidly that at the dawn of the New Stone Age he had worked his way across the Bering Straits bridge into America.[9] About this time, social life made its first significant appearance. The syntheses of the past are important but the synthesis of man is of vital importance. Man first appeared as a family, then as a tribe. Finally after long centuries of individual nations, another step occurred. Political and cultural unions sprang up all over the rising verticil of mankind, unions in which the powers of the spirit and mind began to dominate. Gradually and almost unnoticed, the radial supersedes the tangential, the interior shoves the exterior and physical into the background. The evolution of thought supersedes the evolution of the body. Evolution has reached its limit of freedom in the physical side of man and is lifted up to continue its advance on the level of the spirit.

Yet individual reflection is not the end of evolution. A further synthesis lies ahead. With the beginning of civilization mankind changes from expansion to coalescence, from divergence to convergence. And the development of social consciousness is part and parcel of the growth of civilization. With physical contact, there naturally comes a mingling of the radial, of consciousness. Everywhere in our world, individual isolated consciousness is yielding to the formation of the "ultrareflection," the new union that will synthesize all human consciousness, without destroying individuality and personality, into a new "body." This development of a social consciousness in man or, perhaps better, this coalescence of human monads into a "superatom" or "ultramonad," is integral in the continuation of evolution.[10]

With this mention of "ultrareflection" and a cosmic "body," we enter the field where Teilhard de Chardin reached his particular claim to our attention. Above we have presented a sketch of his scientific thought, but a sketch truncated like a triangle without an apex. The "cone of time" rises from the dispersed elements of the subatomic where consciousness (physical freedom) is scattered in the mist to the coalesced elements of the human where physical consciousness is at its highest and interior consciousness has its beginning. But Teilhard did not stop with a half-socialized humanity.

Looking ahead at the course of physical evolution, we may conjecture that anatomical changes will probably continue even in man. His little toes disappear. His wisdom teeth are already passing, and his appendix and little fingers may have entered the road to disuse. But these changes are minor and of no importance for the real evolution of man. New races may be formed but this does not seem probable. The human rays that expanded so rapidly over the world at the birth of man have now entered a phase of convergence. The modern inventions of travel and communication, the radio, television, jet plane have so shrunk our planet that the layers of the noosphere are being bound together in an ever tighter mesh.

The drawing of the cone of time based on a study of the phenomena only portrays these facts. But the picture is incomplete. Our modern stage is at a critical point. Actually we are just now beginning to feel the immensity of our universe and the "coalescence" of mankind. And these two pressures are the cause of the ennui, the "fear and trembling" we all experience. We are at a critical point, the point where humanity passes from divergence to convergence. And in the interpretation of this "stage of convergence" lies our problem. As man converges, his independence (even though this was only a delusion) seems to shrink. More and more we have come to depend on our fellow man. We can no longer claim the relative independence of the American pioneer who settled in the primeval forest. Even our independence as a nation has passed into history. The not-so-old policy of "isolation and hands off" has given way to international and even intercontinental blocs.

And this loss of our independence — where will it lead us? To the mechanization of an anthill or a beehive? To the impersonalism of totalitarian dictatorships? To a "Big Brother" type of society?

To answer this question Teilhard resorts to the facts and criteria he discovered in the earlier stages of evolution. Evolution is not just an ascent of consciousness in the world. With man, consciousness became individualized, and hence evolution is also an ascent of individual consciousnesses. The real axis of evolution is an ascent that not only continues the rise of consciousness on the cosmic or global scale but also protects and expands the individual consciousness it has engendered. Marxism, totalitarianisms, and materialistic creeds pulverize personality. They destroy individual consciousness in the collective and impersonal state. But, if we rule out the "religions of the up ahead," does that mean that the cone of time has no apex? That it is a truncated thing? That evolution halts at the critical point?

If the universe is to converge, it must do so in its most evolved elements. Furthermore, we can expect some consistency with the past. The general laws of logic and evolution which we have found in the previous stages of evolution should appear also in the evolution of man. If there is one thing that the phenomenon of biological evolution has taught us, it is this — that man is not something tossed into a world without warning or preparation. He is not an epiphenomenon but an integral part and at present the leading shoot of an unfolding universe. Logically, then, there ought to be a supreme consciousness which will embody all human consciousnesses without destroying their individuality. But this point of convergence, which Teilhard calls the Omega Point since it lies at the apex of the cone of time, has certain definite characteristics that can be determined by extrapolation from the general laws of subhuman evolution. We can eliminate any idea of the pantheist's "great all," which fuses and dissolves personality in the peace of nirvana. Our Omega Point of evolution must unite human consciousness but at the same time perfect them in their higher life.

In every step of evolution, tangential energy binds an element with all other elements of the same complexity while radial energy leads the same element on towards higher levels of complexity and consciousness. And even here, certainly we must admit that of all the forms of radial energy, love is the highest and the only form that will allow man to reach the level of a new synthesis. A man must grow in his personality, in that which is most vital and essential to his being, while in the same movement he is universalized in this ultrasynthesis. Through love our personality can expand in the union of a higher and fuller life, which we then have in common with other creatures. If love is not at base the motivating force of an association, then that union will only destroy personalities. Hence the force that attracts all evolution must be a power of love. The Omega Point cannot be just an algebraic symbol at the apex of time. It must have a personality that we can love and that will attract us.

This is the first characteristic of the supreme consciousness, of the Omega Point. But then man has been on this land for at least a half-million years. Surely the lack of abstractness or impersonality in the Omega Point must extend not just to its personality but also to its place in time. To be loved by all men, it must coexist with all men. Simply, this Supreme Consciousness must be external; it must shine on the earth at every moment of its unfolding. That is a second attribute. But there is a third and it is this: our personality, that incommunicable ego, is the most vital element in each of us and it is this which, above all else, evolution and the ultrasynthesis must preserve. We can hand on to our posterity the fruits of our labors and thoughts, our works of art, our writings, our inventions, but these are inconsequential when compared with our individual personalities. Hence the Omega Point must also be the principle of our immortality. In it we must find our consummation as well as our permanence. If by extrapolation we can attribute these qualities logically to the point of convergence, then our picture of the world is complete.

Whatever may happen to the world, whether it reach the dissipation of its tangential energies in a cold death or be transformed in some unknown way, does not matter. All that does matter is that man has found through death and the attraction of the Omega Point the liberation of his radial energies in a union with God the Omega who constitutes ahead of us "a universe, the collector of consciousnesses."

Question Mark in No Man's Land

Any summary of Teilhard's thought necessarily loses much of its life in transposition. Still, summaries are necessary.

In the beginning we spoke of Teilhard's place in modern thought. There are some enthusiasts who do much harm by their reckless acceptance of everything in Teilhard's thought. There are others, probably more numerous, who hide behind the fear of any "novel" thought and ignore the challenge evolution presents to the modern thinker. Some enthusiasts will claim that Teilhard has solved all our problems, while others will refuse him any consideration because he failed to clarify some points. Yet if we remember that the thought of Teilhard de Chardin was never meant to be a definitive thing, that it is open and pregnant, undeveloped, that it was meant to stir up thought rather than to answer all questions, then we shall be able to examine his work with profit.

The studies comprising this symposium are interpretations. They are attempts to portray and develop the thought of Teilhard while always remaining faithful to his spirit of ever pushing forward the frontiers of human knowledge and understanding. Time may prove that some of the interpretations and reflections presented here are not really in keeping with his mind. With only a fraction of his complete writings available, this danger is inevitable. The attempt to plumb the depths of any human soul is a trial-and-error affair, and the attempts made here to penetrate the mind of a man at once mystic and scientist present even more problems. Consequently we do expect, and in fact we warn the reader, that he will not be able to agree with all that is said in this study of Teilhard de Chardin. But if these essays encourage and awaken minds to the dimension of time, if they bring a foundation of hope and optimism to the many who would like to see legitimate bridges connecting the diverse disciplines in the realm of knowledge, then this work has served its purpose.

As we mentioned before, Teilhard de Chardin is more the prophet of a new world vision than its master. Dr. Oppenheimer recently remarked that the real frontiers of science, and, in fact, of all knowledge, lie in the interdisciplinary realms where one branch of science coalesces with another. If the evolutionary concept of biology has invaded and overrun the fields of chemistry and physics, so too have statistics and chemistry entered the field of biology. In fact today it is often impossible to draw distinct lines of separation between various branches of natural science, e.g., biophysics, biochemistry, statistical biology. Here in the no man's land between realms that have been isolated too long, we will find the Galileos and Darwins of the 20th century. And this is exactly the position of Teilhard de Chardin. He is a bridge builder spanning the gaps between science, philosophy, and theology. He has set the piers, he has sketched the plans, and like the architect's drawing his work has inspired men to join him on the frontier. But as with the architect's sketch, some of the details will not stand up as time and the bridge progress. The qualities of Teilhard de Chardin are those of a seer. Like one of his own evolutionary prototypes, he is one of the men who stand out in the 20th century as beacons. In this he was, as one admirer has remarked, "a head and shoulder above those of us who are left here to carry on the work and to mourn the passing of a noble scholar and a great gentleman." [11]

2

AT WORK IN THE FIELD

George B. Barbour

When the Sino-Japanese War ended, Père Teilhard was free to return to France. One day, soon after his arrival in Paris late in June, 1948, he went to the Institute, only to find it almost deserted for the summer. But in the hallway he met Pierre Pruvost, professor of geology at the Sorbonne, who had been with us on a cross-continental trip after the Washington International Geological Congress. Pruvost greeted him warmly, saying how delighted he was to meet his globe-circling friend again. Teilhard said he was equally delighted, adding with a twinkle in his eye, "But I assure you it is for an entirely different reason."

"What do you mean?"

"Well, for *me*, you see, it proves that the earth is round after all!"

The Round Earth

Teilhard and I were together in the field from the days of his first collaboration with Père Emil Licent, six years before he joined the Cenozoic Research Laboratory which Davidson Black organized in Peking in 1928, after Bohlin's work confirmed the importance of Zdansky's earlier finding of the first *Sinanthropus* tooth. We were in the field at intervals thereafter, and an intimacy, begun then in the Far East, continued on three other continents after the War.

It was an exciting time to be in the Old Chinese capital. At that time the Chinese warmly welcomed the help of the truly international group of scientists that acted like a magnet to attract a steady stream of visiting experts in all fields of learning.

In 1916 J. Gunar Andersson had come from Sweden to serve as Advisor in Mining to the Chinese government. Andersson was a giant of a man, of great physical strength and indomitable courage, an ideal prospector in rough places. He still carried on his thigh a scar marking the bite of a rabid dog which had attacked him on an earlier expedition far from medical help of any kind. Andersson had heated a poker in the fire and without hesitation had plunged it into the flesh, effectively cauterizing the wound. The actual finding of the Peking Man site was incidental to a visit he paid in 1918 to the coal seams behind Choukoutien ("the Inn at Chou's Gap"), where local fuel was used to make quicklime from the bedrock limestone in which the caves had formed. Anderson realized that the time was ripe for the establishment of a national geological survey and strongly supported the new organization.

Fortunately, during the preceding years a number of brilliant young Chinese had gone overseas to study in the universities of Western Europe and North America, and were beginning to come back to their homeland. This group of "returned students" formed the nucleus of the movement, which developed as the literary renaissance, codifying the spoken language for use in newspapers, poetry and scientific prose, in place of the complex classical literary forms that were unintelligible to the bulk of the people.

In this group was V. K. Ting, who had studied at Glasgow with Gregory and who was peculiarly well fitted to be the first director of the new Survey. Ting spoke several foreign languages fluently, understood the psychology of men, Eastern and Western alike, and won the co-operation of everyone. On one occasion as toastmaster he introduced a half-dozen speakers each in his own tongue — French, German, British and American varieties of English, Japanese and Chinese — but he did it with a wit so delicately gauged that while each man in turn felt complimented at the praise heaped on his head, he just failed to detect the subtle barb about his foibles that was not lost on those of the audience who were at home in the language being used. As the one man who might have been able to lower the ugly tensions rising in Shangai, Ting was sent there as mayor. His successor as director of the Survey was Wong Wen-hao, who had trained as a seismologist in Belgium and spoke French like a native, a fact which made for an immediate rapport with Teilhard.

A. W. Grabau had gone from Columbia University to join the Survey as advisor and also as a teacher at Peita National University in Peking. Grabau was a prolific writer constantly hatching new ideas. He seemed to be the foster parent of the Palaeontologia Sinica, the Geological Society of China and the Peking Society of Natural History, and inspired a succession of young stratigraphers and paleontologists. It was Grabau who coined the scientific name of *Sinanthropus pekingenis* ("the Chinese anthropoid from Peking") — a model term, since it makes no attempt to describe the creature specifically (as does *erectus* or *crassidens*) and does not prejudge its relationship to the genus *Homo*.

In many ways the most brilliant member of the team working with Teilhard was Davidson Black of Toronto, whose position as anatomist at the Peking Union Medical College, established by the Rockefeller Foundation, enabled him to secure support for the Cenozoic Research Laboratory of the

Geological Survey. Teilhard became attached, at Black's urging, to this group when it became clear that the Choukoutien deposits needed the help of an expert in the mammal field. It was Teilhard himself who acted as director during the months after Black's untimely death until Franz Weidenreich was appointed.

There were also a number of younger Chinese specialists, notably C. C. Young, a vertebrate paleontologist trained by Schlosser in Germany, who was Teilhard's closest associate in the laboratory. Since Teilhard never tried to learn Chinese, and did not feel happy in German, they always used English as the least common denominator.

Today the best known name among the younger men is that of W. C. Pei, a student of Grabau's who showed such promise as a field worker that before his final year at the university he was entrusted with the excavation of the cave when Bohlin's meticulous work proved that *Sinanthropus* teeth were embedded at different levels in the cave-filling.

As many of the facts about Peking Man gained attention in Europe, thanks to Teilhard's pen, it was not unnatural that his name became associated with the find. In France he was often referred to as the discoverer of *Sinanthropus*. Teilhard himself was much disturbed at this and was at pains to disclaim credit for finding the precious skull. From my field notes for October 17, 1929, it is clear that we and other members of the Survey were together at Choukoutien that day, and stood within a foot or two of the spot where five weeks later Pei was to expose the side of the cranium.

In most discoveries relating to man's ancestry, the problem arises of setting a date to any particular fossil evidence. In recent years the rate of natural decay of radioactive elements has come widely into use as a means of estimating the antiquity of whatever is found. Thirty years ago no such technique was known and other lines of approach to the problem had to be followed. The most obvious was by a study of the associated animal remains which might be correlated with fossils found at other sites where the precise geological age had been established. Any such assemblage is likely to contain some extinct forms along with more developed types that are closely related to living or recent species. This was a type of detective work after Teilhard's own heart. He seemed to have a kind of second sight that let him see the probable implication of a faint protuberance on a cervid molar as he turned it over between his right thumb and index finger with a sensitive touch, and recalled its resemblance to one he had handled in some collection in Paris, London, or New York years before.

One difficulty with this paleontological approach was the fact that Peking lies far from the nearest points of the globe which have yielded any rich fauna of comparable age. The environment at Choukoutien was very different from that of the Trinil river beds, from which the Java Ape-Man had been retrieved. Hence a second line of attack was opened by working out the successive steps through which the land surface had evolved its present contours. Over the last million years the landscape has been shaped and reshaped, here by weather and stream action stripping off the surface, there by filling up the hollows with erosional debris. It fell to me to try to decipher this sequence of events.

We had already been able to recognize a series of stages that had left their record of cut and fill over much of North China, and field expeditions were planned to extend these findings up the Yangtze and Yellow River to the Tibetan and Mongolian border, into Manchuria to the Russian frontier and over as much of the coastal China as time allowed. Davidson Black had laid the ground work for a reconnaisance expedition north of the Himalayas into South Central Asia. On Black's death this plan had to be abandoned, and Dr. Helmut de Terra asked Teilhard to join his expedition into the Siwaliks instead.

It was into a growingly stimulating environment that Teilhard was to find himself plunged when he went to China in 1922. Père Licent had established the Musée Hoangho Paiho at l'École des Hautes Études in Tientsin, a port city eighty miles from Peking, and he enlisted Teilhard's co-operation in a study of his fossil collections in the hope of adding to his exhibits by new trips into the interior. Licent was at heart a collector and less interested in the scientific implications of his finds, which was Teilhard's consuming aim. Licent kept journals of everything that caught his attention in the field, and hoped to publish the account of his journeyings as a commentary on the route maps he sketched. The two savants usually traveled with a "Peking cart," a driver, and a cook-boy who went into action when they pulled in for the night, unless they had arranged to sleep at one of the mission stations, where they were always welcome.

Licent made a practice of writing to the Chinese Fathers at these missions, urging them to send to Tientsin any fossils they or any of their parishioners found. He even claimed on this basis that anything picked up became automatically reserved as property of the Museum. The request was at times a source of puzzlement to the Chinese, who knew that such "dragon bones" are a recognized item in the classical pharmacopeia. Ground to powder, they are prescribed as a sovereign cure for all digestive troubles and much else besides. After all, they have an indestructible quality not shared by bread pills! I have often been asked whether the Reverend Fathers at the museum were not running a profitable dispensary counter on the side. And if so, would it not be possible to prevail on them to send something for little Third Bear's sore eyes or grandfather's backache!

French, British, and German army service maps, varying greatly in accuracy and coverage, were still purchasable, but of little use away from the main caravan routes. The new Chinese military map series was not yet generally procurable. One Belgian Catholic mission had brought out a good road map of the part of the province which was their care. Licent hoped to produce something similar for his museum. He charted his travels in Hopei province in the simplest manner, gauging distances between bends of the road by counting the turns of a marked spoke on the wheel beside which he was walking and measuring the rim, or by clocking the time elapsed on his watch. At each bend of the road a back-bearing to the previous bend, and a forward sight to the next, gave the change in direction. Experience had shown that the speed of the cart seldom averaged more than ten Chinese *li* (3.3 miles) per hour, dropping below eight on rising ground but reaching even twelve *li* when the beast or his driver espied a village ahead that promised hope of a bucket of water or a cup of tea with a chance to relax.

After Teilhard came to Peking, our mode of travel was more variable. Peking carts are all right for roads on the plains or along main caravan routes, but in rough country pack animals had to be used and much of the ground was covered on shank's mare. For our expedition on the middle Yangtze we used in turn rail, river steamer, motor launch, sampan, plane, and sedan chair. Beyond Chungking it was ricksha, model-T Ford, and bus, the latter always crowded well beyond capacity, the roof piled high with bundles, bedding rolls and wicker baskets of vegetables and poultry. Bicycles were hooked over the bumpers or tied on the roof. When we struck bad going, the passengers got out and shoved, and if a tire punctured, as happened several times a day, we all sat by the roadside and offered advice while the patch dried.

In the field Teilhard exchanged his clerical garb for a khaki suit of military cut, with a close-fitting collar. For headgear he preferred a hard-used, dark grey felt hat, varied by a beret or brown pith helmet for summer and a high black fur cap with earflaps for the bitter winter weather with its chill blasts from Mongolia. His eyesight was keen, and only later on did he begin to use steel-rimmed glasses for reading. He liked to travel with a padlocked black metal kit box which probably dated back to his days of military service in the first World War. It was three feet long and a foot deep, and carried everything that did not go into his bedding-roll or pockets. The contents varied with the expedition. Folded maps and papers lay on the bottom. One or two tin cylinders held rolls of so-called Mexican silver dollars, which always were valid even in districts where the latest paper currency was not yet acceptable tender. The tubes were stuffed with newspaper to prevent the clink of coins from arousing curious investigation. When bound for a district where he was likely to be asked to celebrate Mass at one of the missions, he included a lightweight cassock. For cool evenings he took a cape that served also as an extra blanket at night. Penknife, hand-lens, padlock key, marching compass and small cash went in his trouser pockets, leaving the tunic pockets for the little black quadrille notebook, pencil and pen, and the breast pockets for his breviary on one side and cigarettes and matches on the other. He used a short-headed hammer and always brought a chisel for excavating fossils.

Usually his field notes were brief and to the point, illustrated only by line-drawings aimed not at reproducing what he saw, but at interpreting in a generalized way the relation between the rock units whose structure was often only partly exposed. He used to regret that he could not make relief sketches of the landforms we saw. Whereas I took photographic equipment and used colored pencils to emphasize features in field sketches and maps, Teilhard preferred to dispense with field glasses, camera, and aneroid, and eschewed gadgets of any kind. Once when he was starting for the Gobi Desert I gave him a neat fuel-charged cigarette lighter, thinking it would reduce his heavy consumption of matches and could be refilled from any motor fuel can. On his return he apologized for having left it somewhere in the middle of the desert. Evaporation in that dry region had proved so rapid that he had to refill it from the expedition supply cans every second morning. So he wisely discarded it. "And even the Renier technique wouldn't work after dark!" On the C2 Congress cross-continental trip, Professor Renier had entertained us all by using his pocket lens to focus the sun's rays on the tip of his cigarettes until the tobacco began to smoke, when he would pull vigorously until it was well lighted.

The C2 party crossed the United States in two Pullman cars that were coupled to a succession of trains overnight and shunted into sidings by day while we went off into the field. Standard Pullmans have only a single drawing room, which was always reserved for a married couple. In our car the royal room was assigned to Sir Arthur Smith Woodward, Keeper of the British Museum of Natural History, and his wife. The rest of us slept in section berths. At night all our belongings had to be repacked into bulging suitcases and stowed under the seats. One afternoon, Teilhard, changing his shirt after a hot day's work, and noting ruefully the greater convenience of baggage space in the drawing room, drew Renier aside and twitted him with malfeasance for not having managed things better, adding, "Couldn't you have used your well-known diplomatic powers to secure for us at least half a wife apiece!"

China

In the field, Teilhard's spare figure covered the ground at a steady pace with a faintly uneven gait, since one foot — I think the right one — turned out a little more than the other.

The years during which we traveled together saw a marked spread of new roads in China, and it was interesting to note the effect on the people in the hinterland. The Chinese farmer and coolie carry on their heavy physical work by resting frequently during the day, but unlike Westerners they do not need to release tension lying down. They seem to relax equally well squatting. The Shansi farmer achieves the same result standing storklike on one leg, resting the other on the spade with which he is digging. In early days his reactions to strangers on the road tended to be slow. If you wished to inquire about the road ahead from a passing peasant, you soon learned to hail him twenty yards before you met him so that by the time you came abreast you had caught his attention. Often a smile would then spread over his face at the surprised discovery that the queer foreigner was speaking his language! When the road for automobiles first opened down the Fenho valley of central Shansi, the slow reactions to approaching buses led to frequent spills on the part of pack-laden coolies and wayfarers. Three years later, thanks to the road, the country-side had awakened, and you could count on alert responses to questions by the way. On my visit to the same Taiku district in 1934 it was as guest of H. H. Kung, the seventy-fifth direct lineal descendant of Confucius, in a plane that took his entire family for their first ride in the air over the very slopes where we had worked out on foot the physiographic stages by which the rift valley of Central Shansi had assumed its present day landscape. Teilhard's *Lettres de voyage* attest to his keen interest in the way the people were awakening.

As a rule we were on the road early in the morning and tried to find a place for the night well before dusk, unless aiming for a settlement where we were expected at a mission or railway rest house. Often we found quarters in an inn — either in the open courtyard or on a corner of the mud platform which served as bed for all comers — or better, in the outbuilding of a temple or on the elevated stone platform of a village theater. The latter had the special advantage of keeping the curious at a distance of four or five feet. Our appearance was probably the talk of the month as far as the villagers were concerned. Sheet glass being unknown in such settings, the window frames are stretched over with white paper. This is translucent, but doesn't afford the interested audience a chance to inspect the funny foreigners. But a well-moistened finger can be worked round and round until a small hole is made in the paper affording a peephole with a ringside view. After dark behind each such peephole shone an eye reflecting the light of our candle, and we knew we had company.

In the loess highlands of Shansi and Shensi, where dust and silt have piled up in layers of two hundred feet and more, half the population sleeps in homes dug into the hillsides. Such catacombs were welcome shelters when the monsoon rains broke.

Expense was kept down by living as far as possible off the land. When we pulled in for the night and had found a spot to set up our camp cots, the cook foraged for eggs, noodles, millet, rice, and an occasional chicken or whatever else the place offered. A wooden supply-box carried the extras — coffee, sugar, condensed milk, jam, marmalade, canned fruit, chocolate, and such essentials as candles, matches, soap, and insect lotion. Water was boiling for a cup of tea by the time we had washed and cleaned up. Teilhard hunted for a dilapidated pair of brown slippers and began to relax.

On the road during the day, when traveling with a Peking cart across a stretch of country that offered no problem, the driver would be evicted from his perch and Teilhard would climb aboard to sit propped against our bedding-rolls, with his legs dangling over the left shaft, take out his breviary and read the office for the day or sit silent in contemplation for half an hour. In districts where we were moving with pack mules he fulfilled this same obligation at dusk or before we struck camp in the morning. I have related elsewhere the occasion when what looked like a serious accident prevented his completing his office for the day and he allowed me to read it to him since he could not use his eyes for reading.

After supper we discussed the day's observations, completing our field notes while things were still fresh in mind, and laid plans for the morrow. Teilhard lighted another cigarette and I hunted up my pipe. If a Chinese colleague was with us, he would go out and inquire about the next stage of the route, the condition of the road, the state of the fords and mountain passes ahead, and pick up any gossip he could about the hazards of the way, the local military situation, bandits, and possible quarters for the next night.

Spreading an oilcloth or newspaper on the floor to stand on, we would undress and climb into our blankets and blow out the candle. It was then, as night fell and the day's work was over, that Teilhard would speak of the germinating ideas that were to appear later in his writings. Much of what he said did not seem so new at the time, and my training was inadequate to follow his profounder thought, especially when he sought to look into the future. What seemed important was that he was restating for a new generation an interpretation of human life that has to be carried forward progressively as men become aware of new truths, regardless of the original source of any particular contribution.

For some reason that I never fathomed, Teilhard (as noted above) made no effort to learn Chinese. He had therefore to depend on his companion of the moment for an interpretation of what was being said: Even his pronunciation of place names led to confusion at times. The French romanization of Chinese words seems less close to the original sounds than the British Wade or the standard German pronunciations. By convention, though spelled "pei," meaning "north," the Wade form is pronounced "bay," which comes closer to the North China sound than the aspirated "pay" of the French "Pékin." In consequence there were occasional misunderstandings due to his failure to learn the language. But Teilhard's belief in human nature always made him find a kindly interpretation of such contretemps. He could never bring himself to impute to other human beings a selfish motive or underhanded action, and preferred to let himself be swindled or misdirected.

It is interesting to note that comments on his writings tend to fall into two sharply separated groups. Many are glad that a scientist has confirmed their religious beliefs and pointed the way towards higher truths, even if they are unable to go with him up to the highest level to which he guides them. Others consider that he is guilty of "muddy thinking" and uses a framework of scientific structure to bear a weight of "proof" that it cannot support. In these analyses, the critics are in reality judging themselves rather than Teilhard, who was at pains to make clear that he offered no final answer to many of the problems of life and was only pointing out the direction in which he was convinced more nearly final answers would ultimately be found.

English readers of his works are at a disadvantage in that they are dealing with a translation instead of the original, which was cast in the personal essay style that was characteristic of the man. Teilhard was writing against a background of French, predominantly Catholic, intellectual thought. Some critics seem surprised that he does not cite the writings in English and other languages by authors who a generation ago had put forward ideas he adopts. These critics overlook the fact that, whereas most philosophers spend days in libraries tracking down parallel ideas in the works of others, Teilhard's energy was being devoted to field and laboratory work, and to a prodigious output of sound research publications on a wider range of specialized subjects than most scientists would venture to tackle. In all, according to Claude Cuénot's bibliography, he was responsible for some five hundred printed writings, of which nearly two hundred deal with geological subjects, in addition to several dozen other writings of miscellaneous types.

Africa

Our field season in Africa, in 1951, was in marked contrast to the journeys we had made together in China two decades before. Early in 1947 we had been invited to join the University of California Expedition to study the sites from which Raymond Dart and Robert Broom had recovered the fossils of *Australopithecinae*, the South African Man-Apes, contemporary with Peking Man. The invitation was pressed by C. Van Riet Lowe, director of the Archeological Survey of South Africa, partly at the suggestion of Abbé Henri Breuil, who was spending the year at Johannesburg. Our seats had been reserved on the same plane when word came of Teilhard's heart attack. It was too soon to know whether he would ever be able to go into the field again, and so the party, which was to work for one summer only, needed a geomorphologist. In the end it was decided that I should go ahead without him.

Thanks to the generous help of the South African scientists, the directors of the Bernard Price Foundation, and Alex Du Toit, dean of African geologists, I saw all the localities of importance and much else besides. In August, 1950, I visited Teilhard at Les Moulins in the Auvergne country, and amplified the reports I had been sending him at intervals. Our discussion seemed only to increase his resolve to see the field evidence for himself as soon as his doctors allowed him to travel. By 1951 he had recovered so thoroughly that his desire was granted, and the Wenner-Gren Foundation for Anthropological Research made it possible for him to travel by boat via Southampton to Capetown. We met in London. On July 12, I saw him off on the boat train, took the plane myself for Uganda, the Congo and Angola, in time to meet Pierre's train on its arrival at Johannesburg at the end of the month. On this trip he was relieved of the nuisances of travel by Mrs. Rhoda de Terra, an author interested in African affairs and a devoted traveling companion, who took charge of all the details of reservations, baggage, tickets, and minor purchases.

This time Pierre was under strict doctor's orders not to overexert himself in the field. Johannesburg is a mile above sea level, and he was advised to start slowly. But he was pleased to find that he adjusted to the altitude at once and suffered no breathlessness. Our first trip was to the Sterkfontein and Swartkrans caves near Krugersdorp. He stood it well and was impatient to go further afield. Some days later Van Riet Lowe organized an expedition to Makapan and we followed this by visits to the Vaal River, Kimberley, and the Norlim quarries at Taungs, where the first *Australopithecus* had been found. Teilhard was thus able to see each of the vital Man-Ape sites in turn.

Travel was always by car or rail. It was even possible to coax a jeep onto the ridge above the Historic Cave at Makapansgat and then clamber down to the excavations from above before continuing the descent to the track at the base of the valley. The Dutch type of village inn in South Africa is less primitive than its Chinese upcountry counterpart. By careful planning it was always possible to arrange for a siesta after lunch, and, though Teilhard protested vigorously at this "restriction of human freedom," he accepted the situation, throve on it, and was always eager to start out again the next day. As a result he ended the season in better physical condition than he began it.

The days in the field were interspersed with visits to Dart in his laboratory at the University of the Witwatersrand and Robinson in the Transvaal Museum at Pretoria. The South African scientists were no less stimulating than the group with which he had associated in Peking. He had retained his gift of sharing enthusiastically in the interests of each new man he met. Having prepared himself in advance by extensive reading, he could discuss their problems with understanding, and was always ready to offer advice when they turned to him. In the field his eye had lost none of its keen vision, and when Van Riet Lowe took us to the Vaal River in the Orange Free State, it was Pierre who at once spotted two water-worn Early Stone Age implements in a layer of river gravel that was supposed to have been picked clean.

In the intervals between our trips, he worked on a statement on convergence and reflection to be translated into English for use in connection with lectures he had promised to give on his return to New York.

Some time must elapse before it will be possible to assess the full significance of Teilhard's ideas in their impact on human thought and belief. His ideas began in his fertile mind as he worked in the fields of China and Africa with his many colleagues. We can only be thankful that he has left a wealth of writings that seem to have no equal in our generation.

3

TEILHARD AND THE COSMIC CHRIST

Claire Huchet Bishop

The world-wide reputation of this French priest of the Society of Jesus makes it superfluous to introduce him to the readers of this anthology. He was that rare combination of a mind dedicated to inflexible scientific discipline and a heart rooted in the Messias. Had he renounced or at least compromised with one or the other side of himself, life would have been far less rich but far easier for him, and the chances of his being misunderstood would have greatly diminished. He had the temerity to assume himself whole with, so to speak, his double allegiance. It was an uncomfortable and challenging attitude.

Teilhard's work falls into three broad categories: (1) his strictly technical contribution as a paleontologist; (2) his scientific synthesis; (3) his Christology. I shall attempt to call attention to that aspect of Father Teilhard's contribution more particularly relevant to his Christology. It should, however, be realized at the outset that, had not Teilhard been such an outstanding paleontologist, neither his scientific synthesis nor his Christology would have the same value. As it is, all his thinking rests on the solid rock of a specialized and exacting science. It is not irrelevant either that from 1922 until he died in New York on Easter Day, 1955, Teilhard roamed the world for scientific purposes. Long before traveling was as swift and easy as it is now, Teilhard literally walked the earth; sometimes alone with natives, going to places no white man had ever been before, sometimes participating in important scientific expeditions under European or American auspices — Egypt, China, Africa, Birmania, India, Java. Between 1929 and 1937 he studied firsthand the human fossils recently unearthed — the Sinanthropus (Peking Man), the Pithecanthropus (Java Man), the Australopithecus (South Africa Man). A measure of the rigor of his scientific approach is revealed when we recall that he persistently refused to vouchsafe for the authenticity of the Piltdown Man discovered in 1912. He declared that fossil *"anatomiquement impossible,"* long before it was recognized as a hoax in 1953.

His paleontological research led him to further studies in geology, chemistry, physics. He was appointed to the College de France. His work is now being published in France gradually, under the auspices of a committee composed almost solidly of internationally known scientists of many countries. These simple facts should be borne in mind should the reader be drawn into a controversy over Teilhard de Chardin. The background of his work is such that his contribution cannot be made light of, whether we like it or not. Incidentally, should any imperfect or erroneous statement be found in this present article it should be attributed solely to the inability of this writer to convey Teilhard's meaning.

The scientific synthesis grew out of his work as a paleontologist. This particular kind of work, which deals with millions of years, revealed to him a pattern of evolution in space-time which grew from the multiple and undifferentiated to the complex and personalized, from geogenesis to biogenesis to psychogenesis. He *saw* (he insists on this word) in nature complexity increasing, and with it, consciousness. The passage from one plateau to the other is accomplished through a *jump*; it is a threshold, a discontinuity of continuity in evolution from prelife to life, from life to the thought-step, from "materialization to vitalization and to reflective process." It appears that in order that the jump may take place, it is necessary that a certain level of complexity be reached at each threshold. Here, Teilhard does nothing but read the signs of nature. He does not discuss how the jump is accomplished, whether or not a divine creative action intervenes within the process; we are purely on scientific ground, which in itself is neither affirmative nor negative of faith. Faith is of another order.

The reflective process brings us to the study of the human phenomenon, as expounded in the book bearing the title *Le Phénomène Humain* (in its English translation *The Phenomenon of Man*), first of Teilhard's works to be published in English. Incidentally, for those who want to get a brief but rounded acquaintance with the breathtaking thought of the author, the short essay of Claude Tresmontant, *Pierre Teilhard de Chardin: His Thought*, will prove most valuable. Written between 1938 and 1940, *The Phenomenon of Man* bears the mark of a relentless, exacting, uncompromising, and provocative search for truth which will still intensify and clarify itself further in subsequent works. Already one cannot help being moved by the fearlessness of Teilhard's intellectual integrity, which reaches grandeur. Here are, briefly stated, some of the significant points of the demonstration:

Consciousness having culminated in the reflective process (man), from then on its ascent becomes the ascent of consciousness. This may appear simple evidence, but has in fact a far-reaching effect, namely that, whereas all other species diverge, man, as a species, is converging. The ascent is convergent. A purely material and obvious emphasis of this can be found in our age with the rising of population, the use of technology, and the development of communication media. *Nolens volens*, people are converging physically. Whole countries are on the march to a deeper consciousness. Finally, in all sorts of fields, movements toward better understanding and fellowship are afoot which, fifty years ago, not benefiting from the converging physical and material influences of today, were impossible as mass movements, the idea they embodied being perceptible to but a few seers.

Far from being a leveling, melting down process, convergency of consciousness is highly personalizing: *"L'union ne confond pas, mais différencie."* This process being contained and engendered by space-time, it follows that the nature of space-time can be neither a closed whirl, nor an endless spiral nor a scattered explosion. It has to be convergent. The ascent of consciousness has to result in One Consciousness, union, unity. Here some scientists departing from Teilhard contend that his observations and method, rigorously exact and valid concerning the past and present, cannot be applied to the future, which is no scientific domain. In other words, they refuse to join Teilhard in discussing the meaning of evolution, its ultimate direction. On the contrary, other scientists vouchsafe that it is possible to search for the direction of a given phenomenon without ceasing to be on scientific ground.

The physical demonstration of Teilhard can be schematically summed up in his own short, incisive, potent phrase, *"Tout ce qui monte converge."* Convergent space-time can be viewed as a cone. A maximum of consciousness in consciences results, *per se*, in a convergence within a hyperpoint of consciousness which itself is, of necessity, hyperconscious, that is hyperpersonal. Indeed, universal energy cannot possibly be less developed than the terms animated by its very action. Universal energy has to be a thinking energy. For this reason, the point of convergency called Omega Point by Teilhard cannot come to existence solely by the convergence of thinking monads. It is their very principle and cause without which they could not converge. Therefore, already, Omega Point is.

It does not follow that, fatally, the whole of humanity will make the jump into the age of convergence, oneness, the age of spirit, noogenesis. The reflective process includes for man the freedom to say No. What is evident is that now, as never before, has man been surrounded by better conditions for his developing from reflective process to union.

So far Teilhard's demonstration has not entered religious ground. When he does, it is with a special message to Christians. It is natural that non-Christians and unbelievers part company here. That they do so without bitter antagonism and without feeling the necessity of questioning anew Teilhard's previous conclusions, points not only to the soundness of his work but to its hospitable character — in fact, as hospitable as his own person was; he who, according to those who met him, took exception to no one and was able to discern the spiritual ascent in anyone regardless of race, creed, or the absence of creed.

That Teilhard has a special message for Christians does not mean necessarily that Christians will understand it, nor that they shall not be disturbed by it. Far from it. It may happen that, failing to grasp his meaning, we distort it unwittingly. It may be too that, being a pioneer, a breaker of trails, Teilhard himself may fail sometimes to find the words and expressions that could convey what he has perceived. It is well to remember that, in those matters, much is a problem of semantics. Therefore a great deal of circumspection is required in this study. We can be helped in it if we come to understand better the state of mind that was Teilhard's during his half-century of research.

Teilhard was grounded in scientific rigor and, at the same time, he was a man of faith. To many, this sounds incompatible. To some it may mean that his scientific search was vitiated at the start. To others it may mean that his faith was bound to be adulterated. Yet the scientific student discovers that his rejection of Teilhard's ultimate interpretation of his synthesis does not endanger the validity of the synthesis itself. On the other hand, the religious student finds that, far from interfering with his faith, Teilhard's broad and unsentimental vision anchors him deeper than ever in Christ, the Messias, and the one Lord.

How is this accomplished? Is it that Teilhard safely maintained science and faith in separate compartments? Or is it that he indulged in concordism, finding science in the Holy Scriptures, or fitting his faith to science? He did neither. Never did he raise a partition within himself, never did he try to evade and avoid the issue. Refusing any shelter, any spiritual ghetto, Teilhard, God's magnificent gambler, staked his whole. He let science and faith live fully within himself, never knowing from day to day what might happen, never attempting to influence one by the other, neither forcing them together nor pushing them apart. As he tells us himself, "In utter freedom I let react, within my innermost self, the two apparently contradictory influences."

That this insecurity was highly uncomfortable, no one will doubt. All his life, Teilhard, the explorer, knew spiritual as well as physical stress and duress. Teilhard lived dangerously. It is this very intrepidity that gives his synthesis its irreplaceable value. He was almost the detached witness of the outcome: "After thirty years I discovered that a synthesis had taken place naturally between the two currents." Though his scientific integrity does not allow him to reject entirely the possibility of an unconscious conditioning into Christianity on his part, yet it is evident that there is a maximum of effort at an unbiased approach. Had Teilhard backed away slightly at one time or another, not only would he have mutilated himself but neither his scientific work nor his faith could have authentically survived in their entirety.

Of this cosmic synthesis ending into Christianity, Teilhard spoke modestly as "an introduction to an explanation of the world." For him, Omega Point and Christ are one. It is impossible here to analyze the incomparable pages Teilhard devoted to Christ. Cosmic Christ and Incarnated Christ, One. Creation, Incarnation, Redemption, One. The Body of Christ that should be "wholly understood as a physical reality," a living Organism more real than physical organisms as we know them. Physically and literally, convergence takes place "*per Ipsum, et cum Ipso, et in Ipso.*" This is the Messianic expectation in which St. Paul saw the whole creation participating. Though we may be overwhelmed by suffering and evil and sin in the world as we see it today, yet the converging process is at work, whether or not we acknowledge it as Christ. It is for us to say Yes or No as co-workers in the vineyard. Only such an end is worth man's effort — to labor on an ascending road that leads to a summit from which life will never fall back. The labor is not encompassed within our works, no matter how accomplished in the physical, intellectual, or artistic domain. The labor is the ascent of our consciousness, our very self, toward and in the One.

The grandiose eschatology of Teilhard has inspired some of his most profound pages of lyrical beauty. Through the years several texts were written at Easter time, *Pâques* being the liturgical time most fitted to singing the Glory of Oneness. At Easter of 1923, Father Teilhard, then plodding along in the Gobi desert, wrote the following prayer, which might well be a rallying point for all Christians and an inspiration to all men of good will:

> Since once again, O Lord, in the steppes of Asia, I have no bread, no wine, no altar, I will raise myself to the pure majesty of Reality, and I will offer to You, I, your priest, upon the altar of the entire earth, the labor and the anguish of the world. . . .
>
> Receive, O Lord, this Host, that the whole creation, moved by You, presents at this new dawn. This bread is our effort, it is nothing in itself but an immense disintegration. This wine is our grief, as yet alas but a dissolving beverage. But at the base of this shapeless mass You have placed, I am certain of this because I feel it, a blessed desire that makes us all cry out· "O Lord, make us one!"

4

"UNIVERSUM DEI"

Karl Stern, M.D.

The student of evolution works like a detective. He collects his pieces of evidence on a world-wide scale, a jawbone here, a tibia there. A fossil appears, fixed in rock like a cosmic fingerprint; a fish believed extinct is taken alive from the sea, like a star witness who had been presumed dead. But quite in contrast with the common detective story, the more the fragments of evidence fit, the more our detective must refrain from looking for a perpetrator. The scientific theory of evolution is like a thriller without a whodunit. The sleuth must trace everything back but never to a culprit (this would betray a "metaphysical bias"), and he must introduce all working assumptions except a motive (this would amount to a "teleological bias").

The scientists who impose such frustrating and paradoxical rules are justified up to a point. Here, as we shall presently see, the aim transcends the method — a special case in that detective story that we call scientific discovery. There are other reasons for which the rules of the game have to be strict. The theoretician of evolution is related to the ordinary biologist as a theoretician of history is to a historian; as Toynbee or Sorokin or Spengler are to Ranke or Mommsen or Trevelyan. Now there exists a deep distrust of the specialist toward the man with the unifying approach. The basis of the distrust is not always objective: it often contains a hidden human element. Some of the critics of Professor Toynbee among his fellow historians have been more passionate than the occasion would warrant, and one is justified in suspecting a personal resentment. And part of it is this: scientific research implies an attitude of mental asceticism. It is much more fun to indulge in the philosophy of nature than to do a decent bit of experimental research. It is more fun to speculate about the meaning of history than to assemble data. Therefore those who spend their lives as humble diggers resent the sweeping gesture coming from the direction of an armchair. Incidentally, it seems that those who are the more fortunate in the "sweep" are frequently men who themselves have gone through a long apprenticeship in the patient groundwork of science.

Thoughts like these occurred to me on reading Teilhard de Chardin's work, and the controversial literature concerning him. It is always fascinating to look at a scientist *sub specie temporis* — i.e., within the setting of a certain phase of history. The fact that the *Zeitgeist* expresses itself similarly in the divergent fields of human activity appears understandable when we remain confined to the aesthetic. It appears more difficult to accept the conclusion that science, too, should be a part of the same historical process. We think we can see why Picasso, Joyce, and Stravinsky were contemporaries and did, in three quite different fields, things that are strangely comparable. But the fact that Newton "belongs" with Bach is more puzzling, and more suggestive of coincidence and idle speculation. The reason is probably that we are inclined to underestimate the objective element in the aesthetic creation, and the subjective element in the scientific creation.

When we look from this point of view at the theory of evolution we see that, quite independent of the question of its truth or untruth, it "belongs" to the 19th century. The reasons, however, are strangely contrasting. The beginning of the Industrial Revolution was associated with an extraordinary emphasis on progress. Thus, it is not at all surprising to see that the concept of an advance by improved workability should have inspired biologists. The idea that in the vast workshop of nature things that don't work so well should be discarded in favor of things that work better arises quite understandably out of the mood of the time. That faith in progress, however, belongs at the same time to another modality altogether. To 19th-century thinkers human history was a process of unfolding. The Christian eschatological idea of history, as a temporal series with an immanent and transcendental goal, had gone underground long ago, and now lifted its head, strangely disguised, in the world of Herder and Hegel, Marx and Nietzsche.

These two aspects of progress, the one of mechanics and the one of historicity, have both entered into the theory of evolution to varying degrees at various times. Before we go further into this we must first make another distinction. We encounter the theory of evolution under several aspects. There is a working hypothesis for the use of the biologist which serves to explain otherwise puzzling phenomena — such as the geographical distribution of plants and animals, the extinction of certain species and the survival of others. This was the theory that the passenger of the *Beagle* originally developed. Such a theory has no philosophical implications, and it is hard to see how anyone who is not a well-trained biologist can venture to take a stand one way or another. But then there exists that other *global* aspect of the theory of evolution. There the theory answers questions about the creation, and the nature and destiny of man, his being and his becoming, and his position in the universe around him. In most cases this theory attempts to replace religious concepts by something "closer to truth." We are told that in the atheistic museum of the Soviet Union the story of the universe is presented pictorially for the enlightenment of the onlooker, to demonstrate that scientific research has done away with religious notions, which are held to be the manifestations of archaic and superstitious thinking. The same tenets are found in a great deal of the literature of evolution since Thomas Huxley and Ernest Haeckel.

Let us, for the sake of argument, present this global concept of evolution in an extremely positivist formulation. Then we would have to say something like this: At a certain moment of time the temperature of the earth was such that it became most favorable for the aggregation of carbon atoms, and of nitrogen with hydrogen, and of the carbon atoms and oxygen with the nitrogen-hydrogen combination, and that from random occurrences of large clusters such molecules occurred which were most favorably structured for the coming-about of life, and that from that point it went on through vast stretches of time until, through processes of natural selection, a being finally occurred which is capable of choosing love over hatred and justice over injustice, of writing poetry like that of Dante, composing music like that of Mozart and making drawings like those of Leonardo. Of course, such a view of cosmogenesis is crazy. And I do not at all mean crazy in the sense of slangy invective but rather in the technical meaning of psychotic. Indeed, such a view of the history of the world has a lot in common with certain aspects of schizophrenic thinking. I shall not pursue this idea any further here.[1]

The only important thing in this connection is to see *why* such a view of cosmogenesis is absurd. And the very first and most obvious objection is that no degree of development and structurization of matter explains the phenomenon of consciousness.

We could, theoretically, build a huge electronic memory machine that stores and "processes" all events in the world from now until some indefinite time; but we could not give it consciousness. (Cybernetics, as De Broglie pointed out, has left the phenomenon of consciousness as mysterious as it was before.)

All materialistic theories of evolution had to make a cautious detour around the problem of consciousness. The reason for this is simple. A theory, to remain strictly scientific, has to treat the world around us, the stars and the nebulae, the rocks and the seas, the trees and the herbs, the fishes and the anthropoids, as an object, as some huge, monstrous *res extensa* which I can analyze experimentally and mathematically but into which I cannot enter intuitively. If I insist on treating the universe around me as such a scientific object I have to assume a strange attitude: I have to cease to belong to the universe I am studying. At first sight this seems paradoxical. Are we not told that the "biological (Darwinian) insult" (as Freud called it) was so hard to take just because it kicked man from a lofty anthropocentric position right into the animal world and made him part of the biological series? In reality, the moment we look at something purely scientifically we are alienated from it. We are confronted with it as with a reaction in a test tube. The cosmos we look at may be infinitely more complex than the process of $CaCO_3+ZHC$ but it is, in principle, still the same. It is an object, a *Gegenstand* (literally something opposed to me), a matter of pure existence, hopelessly and forever estranged.

Besides this view of nature as a huge *res extensa* there is another view of, or rather relation to, nature. Man can grasp nature intuitively, by inner union. This attitude prevailed in rural civilizations, wherever man was imbedded in nature, rather than piercing it with analytical tools. It still prevails in certain Eastern civilizations and philosophies; it prevailed in Europe during the Middle Ages. On the religious plane, at least in the West, it came to its greatest flowering in Franciscan spirituality; but it would be quite wrong to regard the attitude we are talking about only as a "religious experience." One thing is true: this relationship cannot be scientifically objectivated. It takes place in what Professor Northrop calls the *aesthetic continuum*. Indeed, ever since the rise of science in our Western civilization this particular relation to nature has gradually become limited to the artistic and poetic experience.

Such nonscientific relationship to nature presupposes a sense of belonging, a knowledge of intimacy, which the method of scientific inquiry must strictly avoid. Dürer's presentation of a rabbit or a clump of grass conveys a knowledge of nature which no scientific inquiry, on account of its very method, can ever give us. The reason most of us hesitate to apply the word "knowledge" to the insight within the "aesthetic continuum" and want to reserve it strictly for scientific knowledge is that our minds have become so warped by the positivist bias that we cannot think straight any more. I do not say that one knowledge is more superficial or more profound than the other. But they occur on two different planes. Of course, Dürer's rabbit, no matter how long I contemplate it, will not save me a course in the natural sciences. On the other hand, all the thousand observations from the fields of comparative zoology, embryology, cytology, biochemistry which we have accumulated about the phenomenon "rabbit" will never, if added up, amount to the insight that Dürer's rabbit conveys. The aesthetic experience is an immediate experience of essence, a *Wesensschau* in the sense of Husserl. The scientist elucidates an object of nature as it *exists*; the artist elucidates its being.

Dionysius the Areopagite and St. Thomas have used the term connaturality only with reference to human qualities, such as virtues and vices. (I can achieve a knowledge of courage and cowardice in others because I know these qualities from within myself.) Actually there is a form of knowledge by connaturality also with reference to animals and plants. What distinguishes my

naïve expression of the rabbit or my experience of Dürer's rabbit from the
knowledge gained from a research handbook on the rabbit is an inner participation, a relatedness which is perhaps best described with a term that
Max Scheler uses (though in a different connection) — *Kreatürlichkeit* (creatureliness). I am co-natured with an animal by my creatureliness. I know
perfectly well that in a treatise on evolution this statement means begging
the question. But this is just the point. Nothing of the historical order can
be understood by the cumulative sciences. To understand the life history of
a single individual we need, besides the mosaic of externally observable facts,
our understanding by connaturality. To understand world history the facts
accumulated by historians are not enough. We have to add the function of
Einfühlung (empathy), as Wilhelm Dilthey has pointed out. And now we
see that for the historicity of nature, too, a reconstruction of causalities is
not enough. Thus, there exists a phenomenology of nature which enables us
to know a living universe not by analytical penetration and disassembling, not
by *Gegenständlichkeit* (objectivation) but by union, by connaturality. This
is a universe to which I *belong*. While in the natural sciences the living objects
are opaque and denatured by conceptualization (Haas), in the aesthetic continuum they remain translucent and I can interiorize them. To most people
the only authentic component in the aesthetic experience is something
vaguely emotional.[2]

To the naïve beholder of nature every phenomenon — whether it be a
lion or a rose, a lizard or a fir tree — conveys a sense of completion in itself.
The ensemble of these phenomena conveys a sense of order, even to those
who have never heard of ecology or such things. The idea that all these living
things are random points of arrestation, as it were, in a blind mechanism of
physical occurrences, governed by pragmatic advantages, is difficult to accept.
We forget only too easily that the burden of proof is on those who want to
impose a mechanistic explanation on phenomena which, to our *Wesensschau*,
have the immediate, irreducible quality of createdness.

Let us then summarize by stating that there exist two methods by which
we can approach the phenomena of nature: the poetic-intuitive and the
scientific-analytic, and that they are of equal validity, each on its own plane,
but not of equal applicability. Then we realize that the scientific-analytical
method, with all its breath-taking results, cannot possibly be applied to a
great number of questions, such as the mystery of creation, the infinite variety
of living forms, the destiny of man, the presence of hate and corruption and
their coexistence, in the same world, with love and beauty. As is well known,
many contemporary positivists go so far as to deny the validity and genuine-
ness of these problems. At any rate, the problems belong to a category that
cannot be objectified; they belong to the *inwardness* of things.

There is such an inwardness to the process of becoming. We do not have to go as far as cosmogenesis. I myself have a certain number of years ago been a single cell, microscopically small, and now I sit at a desk, writing. Millions of data from the cumulative sciences form a fearfully intricate net of causalities to tackle this mystery but my being and my becoming are not caught in the meshes of the net.

This is equally true about cosmogenesis. The tissue of causalities is still more vast, still more intricately interlaced, truly unsurveyable for any single human being; no matter how many threads one unravels, what one is looking for remains forever elusive. Creation and redemption, if they are real, must be free acts, simple and unique; and millions of causalities do not add up to one free act. This was probably the deeper meaning of Bergson's reaction against the mechanistic concepts of evolution of his time. Only Bergson (at least at the time of *L'Evolution créatrice*) did not find the solution in the inner historicity of Christian anthropology which is experienced intuitively and affirmed mythopoeically. ("Mythopoeic" in this context does not mean "invented and imaginary," therefore untrue.) But, to define the criterion of truth in the mythopoeic as compared to the scientific in history would go beyond the scope of this article.

At any rate, an "inner anthropology," a concept of man which considers his position within the hierarchy of living forms, and with this the world of anxiety and happiness, guilt and atonement, loneliness and acceptance, love and hatred, can never be clarified within a *res extensa*, a sequence of mechanisms (from water and ammonia to the highest organic structures) which only explains the world without comprehending it. It is clarified only by a historicity (from the Garden of Eden to the Garden of Gethsemane) which comprehends the world without an attempt to explain it.[3]

Incidentally, this does not mean that the symbols and languages of science cannot be used to hint at things of the inward order. It has often occurred to me that the doctrine of the Fall, for example, would be taken seriously by scientists if it were presented as a scientific hypothesis, instead of as a revealed truth. Ortega y Gasset once remarked, when speaking of biographies, "Every life is, more or less, a ruin among whose debris we have to discover what the person ought to have been." One could say the same thing about the history of nature. That strange juxtaposition of harmony and perfection on one hand, and of spoiledness and discord on the other is, hypothetically, explained by a past occurrence that introduced a movement opposed to harmonious structurization. This could be made to sound nicely scientific — but as related to the "inward" aspect of the human experience it becomes a "legend."

Moreover, there exists about historical events a scale of *inner relevancy*. This scale mounts in the direction from natural to secular to sacred history. Whether polymerization occurred in this or in that way subsequent to the clustering of atoms, whether the birds branched off the reptiles in this or that fashion or at this or that period has no relevancy to my being. No matter how much I may be interested in evolution — so far as the immediate questions of my personal life go, I could not care less. Not so with secular history. The battle of Philippi, the Thirty Years' War, the American Revolution are much more personally relevant. They have shaped, no matter how remotely, my life. The question as to their veracity has a certain indirect bearing on me, at least causally. The intended sacrifice on Mount Moriah, the consummated sacrifice of Mount Golgotha, the Resurrection — these are events of the highest personal significance, a final significance. Every life is interiorly related to these with an immediacy that makes even secular history seem pale by comparison. Whether those events of sacred history are true at all, whether they occurred as told — nothing could be more personally relevant than these questions.

Will the two worlds of which we spoke initially, the world of objectification and the world of inwardness, forever remain incompatible? Will with the progress of science the Cartesian chasm be further widened and man still more fearfully alienated from himself? The victory in our time, of dialectical materialism in the East and of positivism in the West seems to indicate just that.

This is precisely where men like Father Teilhard come in. Teilhard's most original and persistent idea, that of complexity/consciousness, amounts to nothing less than a formal attempt at a welding, a confluence of the world as *res cogitans* and the world as *res extensa*. The very term "complexity/consciousness" symbolizes this quite neatly. Together with this goes, quite logically, his other central theme: the hierarchic structure and polarized flux of the universe. Thus, Father Teilhard's work — though tentative and fragmentary — will remain as a great sign to show that we are in the middle of a crisis, a wholesome crisis that ought to heal the split in our soul. No matter how many of the details of Teilhard's work may succumb to later criticism (this is not important), his chief impulse is anti-Manichean. And this is of a significance that cannot be underestimated.

Even a man like Teilhard de Chardin will never completely succeed in welding faith and science by a formalized procedure. It is a good thing that this should be so. But he has fully welded them in the depth of his own person. This created loneliness. He was a man misunderstood by his fellow scientists and his fellow theologians alike. From all that has been remarked here it is quite understandable why scientists regard *The Phenomenon of Man* as unscientific and theologians regard it as "unsound." Pascal once remarked that Christ is in a no man's land, rejected by Jews and Gentiles alike. This no man's land is today, more than ever, the natural habitat of the *chrétien engagé*. There is, about all Teilhard's attempt at reconciliation, something deeply touching. Compared with it so many of the hackneyed treatises on "science and religion" (by sceptics and scholastics alike) seem like cold intellectual games. In Father Teilhard's work one feels a movement of love, like that of a language interpreter who frantically tries to help two opposing camps to come at least to a linguistic *entente*. Even his terminology betrays this, and one cannot remain unmoved. (The term "Omega Point" has a scientific connotation: the symbol of Greek letter and "point" suggests a graph — and at the same time an evident scriptural connotation. It is the language of love which creates these semantic bridges.)

The interpreter from no man's land, rushing frantically back and forth, is bound to appear as a traitor, first to this camp and then to the other. This, too, is one of the marks of the *chrétien engagé*, and cannot be avoided. The heroic attempt to bring hostile armies to meet on a terrain of truth makes the go-between appear to be a double agent. His language is bound to slip. Hence we should not be surprised if Father Teilhard talks at one time like any one of a dozen of his scientific colleagues.

> Left for a long time to itself, under the prolonged and universal play of chance, matter manifests the property of arranging itself in groupings which are more and more complex and, at the same time, more and more enclosed in consciousness. Once begun, this double movement, coupled with cosmic involution (corpusculization) and psychic interiorization (or "centration"), is continued, accelerating and pushing itself forward as far as possible.

On other occasions he talks like this: "While masking a higher stage in the gratuitousness of the divine operator, are not creation, the Incarnation and the Redemption each so many acts indissolubly linked in the apparition of participated being?" The first quotation does not sound much different from statements by Professor Haeckel which had such bad influence on the church attendance of the *fin de siècle* bourgeoisie. It is hard to believe that the second quotation comes from the same pen. These are the hazards of the conciliator. He is easily caught in cross fire. Compared with him the scholastic philosopher of our time is like a man tacking little paper flags on colored maps.

Teilhard's idea that man is as yet embryonic and unfulfilled is also typical of a precarious role with dual commitments. As far as it is eschato- logically inspired it is Christian. As far as it is biologically inspired it smacks of the 19th-century optimism of progress. As we have pointed out, the idea of progress by evolution is pragmatic. It becomes questionable the moment we introduce aesthetic and moral values. If we do this we perceive heights and ebbs in history but no "cone." The cave drawings of ten thousand years ago are more "advanced" than all the academic art of Darwin's contemporaries. The sculpture and architecture of the 19th century are far below Greek sculpture and architecture of two and one-half thousand years before. It is quite conceivable that our times, with its tremendous burst in technological progress, will in the judgment of history be related with the lowest phases of moral human development.

Thus, within recorded human history at least, there is no unequivocal evolution. Moreover, the Christian fulfillment is entwined with history and, at the same time, is mysteriously outside all historical progression. While I am writing this, a state of sanctity is being attained by "little souls" anonymously scattered on the globe. Ever since the Incarnation, fulfillment is free, *hic et nunc* — it cannot wait for occurrences on the timetable of an extraneous process. "Out of these stones God can make children of Abraham." The Pauline idea of freedom from the law pertains also to the laws of historical sequence. The idea of an ultrasynthesized mankind which, as a developmental stage, represents the Mystical Body, appears like Comtean optimism in a baptized version. It seems to go against the Paulinian idea of freedom. Such an externalized concept of cohesiveness does remind us of present-day forms of collectivism, no matter how much Teilhard and his commentators object against such interpretation. The spirit will always be fed from the twin sources of loneliness and society. The Garden of Gethsemane and the Upper Room are two typical images of our inspiration.

None of these observations is made just for the sake of criticism. On the contrary. It is quite possible that later generations may look on Teilhard as a St. Augustine of natural history. The naïveness and the time-conditioned limitations of some of Teilhard's work favor this comparison. St. Augustine was the first one to introduce the Christocentric theme into human history. Father Teilhard does so with natural history. Many of the details of the *civitas Dei* appear today just as naïve and time-conditioned as many aspects of Teilhard's work. Yet the genius of Augustine succeeded in introducing a metaphysical *timor* into the reading of history, and the idea of history as a drama with hidden content has never completely disappeared since then. It is quite conceivable that Teilhard de Chardin's *universum Dei* will mark the same milestone in the philosophy of nature.

Of course, the spiritual drama immanent in history was stated long before St. Augustine — namely, in Scripture. St. Augustine has only elaborated on it in the language of the historian and philosopher of his time. And something quite similar is true in the case of Teilhard. He has made the spiritual drama of cosmogenesis eminently palatable to the modern taste. But in a different language it has been stated long before. And, as in some of the best stories, the thrill is maintained although the whodunit has been given away on the first page: "In the beginning God created heaven and earth."

5

A STUDENT OF THE "PHENOMENA"

James P. Reilly, Jr.

The invitation to philosophize to which wonder beckons man has in the history of the human experience met with a variety of responses. The pre-Socratics answer the invitation differently from a Plato, and an Aquinas differently from a Kant. But it is not only the individual responses that differ; more importantly perhaps, the attitude of mind each respondent brings to this invitation and the nonphilosophical factors that have shaped this attitude determine in great measure the direction of that inquiry we call philosophy. Disclaimers to the contrary, that philosophy is a scientific discipline admitting of no other than an unbiased starting point, are contradicted by the conflicting testimonies of the philosophers themselves. Even the Cartesian attempt to purify the starting point of philosophy succumbed to the psychological predilections of its innovator.

The Invitation to Philosophize

Whether or not philosophers have always been sufficiently aware of the role that the nonphilosophical elements of their experience have played in their total philosophical formation, certainly many of their disciples have often ignored these elements. More frequently than not, a given philosophy has been elevated to the status of an unconditioned absolute. It is to the honor of Kierkegaard that his rejection of Hegelian absolutism recalled philosophy to an awareness of its more modest beginnings and aims, by reminding philosophers that the existential self is the genuine center of man's universe. But the existential self is fraught with the consequences of its own history. It is precisely this history that philosophy must reckon with and explore in its endeavor to come to grips with reality. For the most part the 19th century was slow to answer this new summons. Husserl's effort, however, to bracket reality by means of a phenomenological reduction has led to the recent concern with the phenomenological description of reality and man termed existentialism.

This by way of an approach to Teilhard de Chardin.[1] But is it legitimate

to introduce Teilhard in a setting that presumably he refuses? In the Preface
to *The Phenomenon of Man*, he says: "If this book is to be properly under-
derstood, it must be read not as a work on metaphysics, still less as a sort
of theological essay, but purely and simply as a scientific treatise" (p. 29).
Should we not take these words as seriously as Teilhard intended us to take
them? Is not their appearance in the opening lines of the Preface a sign of
the seriousness with which they were written, and to which we must attend
if we are not to misinterpret his meaning?

Yet Teilhard himself was conscious that, since he dealt with the whole
phenomenon of man, his work could possibly look like philosophy. This is
the risk he believes he must run. With science ever extending its boundaries
in the physical universe, it becomes apparent that no fact exists in isolation,
and that every attempt at objective explanation masks a complex of assumptions. This is particularly true when an explanation is extended to include
the totality of phenomena. Science, philosophy, and religion are bound to
converge, as man approaches an explanation of totality. As Teilhard writes,

> Take any book written by one of the great modern scientists, such as
> Poincaré, Einstein or Jeans, and you will see that it is impossible to
> attempt a general scientific interpretation of the universe without *giving
> the impression* of trying to explain it through and through. But look a
> little more closely and you will see that this "hyperphysics" is still not a
> metaphysics (p. 30).*

In the case of Teilhard's own writings, notably *The Phenomenon of
Man*, the effort to describe the totality of the phenomena leads many to suspect that this is a philosophical rather than a scientific work. Nonetheless he
denies any such intention. He repeatedly warns that he is not discussing a
system of ontological and causal relations between the elements of the universe. He is, he insists, merely trying to describe an experimental law of
recurrence that would express the successive appearance in time of these
elements of the universe (p. 29). But his fears that his work might be understood as philosophy have been realized. True, certain commentators, such
as Tresmontant, though recognizing the metaphysical import and value of
the work, maintain with Teilhard that *The Phenomenon of Man* is strictly
a scientific work.[2] Other critics, for example Bosio, see in the work explicit
metaphysical commitments with respect to the nature of reality itself.[3] The
suspicion that it may be a philosophical work has apparently not been
dispelled by Teilhard's insistence to the contrary.

Teilhard's insistence on the scientific character of his work cannot be
ignored. His constant struggle with the compelling problem of plurality and

---

* Quotations from *The Phenomenon of Man* (Harper, 1959) will be identified
  simply by a page reference in the text, as here.

his efforts to resolve that struggle witness to his lifelong search for a scientific understanding of reality: "I am neither a philosopher nor a theologian, but a student of the 'phenomena' in the old Greek sense." [4] The interest he expressed in these questions was, he said, not metaphysical but physical: the presentation of an experimental law, a rule of succession within duration (p. 29). Now it was this preoccupation with succession within duration that furnished the clue to his own particular approach.

Biological evolution revealed the dynamic and mobile character of a world, realizing itself only after and because of aeons of time. Man could no longer look upon himself as a unique and isolated occurrence in the world. He had indeed primordial roots in the very stuff of the universe itself. His appearance in the world was that of a genuine historical phenomenon, whose past could be read in part in the life that surrounded him, and in part in the remains of the life that had preceded him. Since the universe had lost its sense of fixity, it, like man, was not something given, but rather something in the process of becoming. The concept of cosmogenesis replaced the concept of cosmology, because the only true account of the universe was not only as yet unwritten, but remained to be written by the evolving universe itself.

As early as the days of his theological studies at Hastings, England, Teilhard experienced the impact of the theory of evolution. He records that its effect on his intellectual formation was much less as an abstract notion than as a presence.[5] It was to become in the course of years the motive force of his scientific work: "Teilhard's entire scientific work can be characterized as an effort to read the direction of evolution in reality itself. . . ." [6] It was, then, evolution in all its biological implications, supported by meticulously gathered paleontological evidence, that formed his attitude of mind towards the phenomena of experience.

Yet it was not enough to recount the history of man written in the fossil remains from the Cambrian to the Pleistocene age; the direction of evolution in reality must be discovered. Or, as Teilhard himself puts it, "We find ourselves face to face with a problem of nature, to discover, if such exists, the direction of evolution. The question is to resolve this problem without straying from the realm of scientific facts." [7] The partly conditional character of this expression of 1936 was replaced by the following conviction expressed in *The Phenomenon of Man*: "Science in its development — and even, as I shall show, mankind in its march — is marking time at this moment, because men's minds are reluctant to recognize that evolution has a precise *orientation* and a privileged *axis*" (p. 142).

Teilhard's conviction that evolution has a direction is both a reflection of and a criticism of Bergson's doctrine of evolution. The effort to reconcile experience with the data of scientific investigation led Bergson to give a primacy to time and duration thitherto unexplored in other philosophies.

This prepossession caused Bergson to assign a philosophical significance to evolution which dictated his own unraveling of the meaning of the universe. But the Bergsonian universe tends almost inevitably to a state of divergence; it represents a continuing process of proliferation. Matter, though not impervious to the activity of the *élan vital*, necessarily fragments, dissipates and eventually terminates the activity of the *élan vital*. The goal of creation, the direction of evolution is, therefore, not an organic unity, but at best a multiplicity of persons.[8]

Bergson's novel philosophical experiment colored to some extent Teilhard's view of reality. But, unlike Bergson, Teilhard refused to identify evolution with ever-increasing divergence.[9] For him, evolution possesses a direction whose terminus is some ultimate type of convergence. An organic view of reality dominates his thinking. Creation is progressing along certain necessary lines under the aegis of evolution. The culmination of this movement will be the spiritualization of the universe as man achieves union with his true center, the Omega Point (pp. 260 ff.). In Tresmontant's paraphrase of Teilhard, the apex of creation will be a "mystical body, which remains respectful of the persons who constitute it." [10]

Clearly Teilhard's conception of evolution differs from that of Bergson's. But does Teilhard in his own way emulate Bergson's philosophical undertaking? Certainly evolution no longer seems to function simply as a scientific hypothesis. Teilhard was aware of this possible implication when he identified his work as an ultraphysics. [11] But he refused to identify his work with metaphysics, emphasizing that his was rather "an attempt to see and to show what happens to man, and what conclusions are forced upon us, when he is placed fairly and squarely within the framework of phenomena and appearances" (p. 31). And later he says, "I repeat that my only aim in these pages — and to this aim all my powers are bent — is *to see*, that is to say, to develop a *homogeneous* and *coherent* perspective of our general extended experience of man. A whole which unfolds. So please do not expect a final explanation of things here, nor a metaphysical system" (p. 35).

The refusal of Teilhard to see in his work any final explanation, a metaphysics, is understandable in light of his concern for the phenomena of experience. Whatver its value, metaphysics cannot convey the significance of the phenomena in their temporal succession and duration. What is required is a principle of explanation, derived from the phenomena themselves, which will guarantee their unity and meaning. Evolution provides just such a principle of explanation, for its proper employment affords an overall view of our general extended experience of man and the universe, in other words, an ultraphysics.

Still Teilhard's designation of his work as an ultraphysics represents more than his refusal to give a metaphysical account of the phenomena.

Ultraphysics expresses a conviction that only a "phenomenological" report can give an adequate account of the historical being man. Indeed, he shares with many of his contemporaries in philosophy a grave concern for the phenomenon that is man. His is primarily a scientific approach rather than the psychological approach of Sartre, or the moral approach of Jaspers, though Teilhard may in some sense, particularly in the latter part of *The Phenomenon of Man*, be said to take a religious approach as does Buber or Marcel.

Teilhard has even called his work a "phenomenology." [12] This is, of course, not to be understood in Husserl's sense of the term, but rather in its etymological sense.[13] For Teilhard, phenomenology locates man not only historically and in terms of observable experience, but also in so far as the "human element can be legitimately viewed by science as a prolongation and the crown, at least provisionally, of the living element." [14]

Though Teilhard's phenomenology is not Husserl's, the role that consciousness plays in Teilhard's ultraphysics aligns him closely, if somewhat ambiguously, to much of contemporary phenomenology. Consciousness is all-pervasive in his universe. It is even present incipiently in primordial matter itself. Gradually but perceptibly, consciousness emerges in the universe, until with man in the form of self-reflection the very direction of evolution becomes manifest.

The emergence of consciousness was the critical stage of transformation in the progress of the evolving universe. This was the necessary prelude to thought. With the birth of thought the noosphere came into being, and with the inception of the noosphere the ultimate term of evolution was assured. But if the apex of evolution is to be hyperpersonal, and if the fulfillment of the noosphere is to consist in a transcendent union of all men with a unique center — in which maximum personalization is to be realized without the merging of any of the participants — then there is resolved the dilemma created by the multiplicity of the phenomena which cry out for unity. [15] Evolution points the way. A transcendent and spiritual source of unity, supremely self-conscious, absolutely self-reflecting, makes ultimately intelligible an otherwise disordered plurality of phenomena.[16]

The Invitation to Criticize

The sweep of Teilhard's vision is quite astonishing. The grandeur of his imaginative expression of this vision tends to intoxicate and persuade, if not completely convince. The courage with which, in the face of so many possible misunderstandings, he proposes to unify man's experience of reality and himself is unmistakable. His is a view which echoes contemporary man's search for himself, and which finds its center in man's own growing consciousness of himself and in the destiny which that consciousness implies. But it is principally a view which demands an account of man's scientific history, and which looks to the accumulated data of the natural sciences for an understanding of that history.

Nevertheless, despite the admitted genius with which Teilhard correlates this vast variety of phenomena, *The Phenomenon of Man* invites criticism. Understandably enough, an approach so new, so different, startles anyone unaccustomed to a panoramic view of the history of the universe. The scope of its vision blurs the customary lines of demarcation. One asks, almost despairingly, to what plane of explanation such a book belongs. None of the accepted categories seems to fit. Still, as Bruno de Solages has so aptly remarked, it is vital to any appreciation of Teilhard's work to try to discover the plane of explanation on which he is operating. One cannot arbitrarily force his thought into classifications it was not designed to fit, nor can one dismiss *The Phenomenon of Man* as poetry or prophecy simply because it is difficult to classify. [17] Any criticism, therefore, must begin with an effort to appreciate what he was trying to accomplish.

We have already indicated the chief motivations and directions of Teilhard's work. We have seen that he describes it as a scientific "phenomenology," an ultraphysics. Yet *The Phenomenon of Man* is surely not science in any exact meaning of the term such as it has when applied to physics, biology or paleontology. Teilhard himself was cognizant of this when he admitted that he had written an ultraphysics. But what exactly does ultraphysics signify? If it is not science, at least in the strict sense, and if it is not metaphysics, as Teilhard so often affirms, what then is ultraphysics?

According to Teilhard, ultraphysics presents a unified view of the totality of phenomena. To achieve this, ultraphysics proposes evolution as the principle of unification for all the phenomena. Only in terms of evolution do the phenomena have meaning and direction. As Teilhard says, advancing this conception of evolution: "Is evolution a theory, a system or a hypothesis? It is much more; it is a general condition to which all theories, all systems must bow and which they must satisfy henceforward if they are to be thinkable and true. Evolution is a light illuminating all facts, a curve that all lines must follow" (p. 218).

In short, ultraphysics represents an all-embracive view of the phenomena of experience. It is a vigorous affirmation that man's scientific knowledge is not so dissimilar and segregated as it would first appear, or as many would have us believe. When seen in its totality, from the standpoint of ultraphysics, man's scientific knowledge points to a unity that the individual sciences of themselves cannot guarantee. This concern for unity, typical of Teilhard's thought, is a concern not only for the unity of knowledge of the phenomena, but also a concern for the unity of the phenomena themselves. For him, evolution furnishes the principle of unity that will resolve the problem of unity and multiplicity at the level of the phenomena.

This then is ultraphysics. But how are we to assess this new vision of experience, which wants in some manner to subsume all the sciences, to see them from a new perspective? It would perhaps be instructive to begin any such assessment with a detailed examination of the function of evolution in Teilhard's formulation. Indeed, the entire thesis of *The Phenomenon of Man* hinges on the way in which he employs this particular doctrine. Unquestionably the hypothesis of evolution is of great value for scientific investigation, but Teilhard refuses to consider evolution merely as a scientific hypothesis. As he tells us in *La vision du passé*, "Let us then put an end once and for all to the naïve conception, completely outdated today, of the hypothesis, evolution. No! in its broad outlines, evolution has ceased to be, and that long since, a hypothesis — or merely a simple method. What evolution represents in fact is a new and general dimension of the universe, affecting consequently the totality of elements and relations of the universe. Not a hypothesis, therefore, but a condition that all hypotheses must henceforward satisfy." [18]

Evolution is, accordingly, not just a simple method, but offers instead a new dimension for understanding the universe. Though Teilhard does not explicitly identify evolution with a methodology, his position vis-à-vis evolution is similar to that of Abbé Henri Breuil, who says: "The principle of evolution is only the scientific method itself, applied to all realities of any kind developing in time. It is the unique means at our disposal for trying to grasp the law of their expansion and succession, whatever their ontological substratum. Without evolution one could only erect a descriptive catalogue of things, without attempting to comprehend them." [19]

In *The Phenomenon of Man*, Teilhard certainly wishes to do more than describe the phenomena. Indeed, he aspires to grasp the law of their expansion and succession. Evolution permits him to discover the physical links of the phenomena, but more importantly to grasp the structural unity underlying the superficial juxtaposition of successions and collectivities (p. 34). Though he never directly asserts that evolution provides him with a general methodology, this is in fact the function he allots to evolution.

What led Teilhard to employ evolution in this way? The answer, of course, lies in part in his desire to present a "phenomenological" report of the universe. But does the answer also lie in part in his desire to leave ultraphysics open to metaphysics, as he so often suggests? Does evolution afford him a unified version of reality comparable to Aristotle's *Physics* or to scholastic cosmology, which will serve as a point of departure for metaphysics? [20] But then what does metaphysics mean for him? Is there any relationship between his conception of metaphysics and his use of evolution as a methodological principle of explanation of the phenomena?

There is some evidence that Teilhard conceived metaphysics in a Cartesian manner. For example, in the *Centrologie*, he indicates what metaphysics means to him: "Here is no *a priori* geometric synthesis proceeding from a definition of being, but an experimental law of recurrence, verifiable in the phenomenal sphere, and which can be properly extrapolated to the totality of space and time. Thus here is no abstract metaphysics, but a realistic ultra-physics of union." [21]

This undoubtedly suggests a Cartesian outlook on metaphysics. If indeed metaphysics is geometric and mathematical in character, then it can be nothing but a pure deductive science, abstractly explaining reality in all of its many facets from an *a priori* point of view. Viallet indirectly confirms this observation that Teilhard's conception of metaphysics was Cartesian when he remarks that Teilhard absolutely refused to engage in metaphysics, that is, to deduce the world from certain *a priori* principles.[22]

Now it is evident from *The Phenomenon of Man* that Teilhard does not wish to present an *a priori* definition of being and its implications, but rather an organic account of the observable phenomena of experience. Further, though he employs evolution as the principle of explanation and unification of the phenomena, he rejects the charge that he has made of evolution an ontological principle.[23] Ultraphysics may be open to metaphysics, but surely it is not metaphysics (p. 29, p. 169, n. 1). To counteract any tendency to explain man and reality deductively, Teilhard offers instead a more modest program. The phenomena are not susceptible of a deductive explanation without the risk of being misconstrued. Since metaphysics entails an *a priori* starting point, it has little, if any, value for the understanding of the phenomena. The point of departure for grasping the meaning of the phenomena is, therefore, not thought, but the world of experience itself. Teilhard's intention is quite clear. But does he in fact succeed? Has he perhaps succumbed to a Cartesian bias?

Does not he intimate this possibility when he says: "Blind indeed are those who do not see the sweep of a movement whose orbit infinitely transcends the natural sciences and has successively invaded and conquered the surrounding territory — chemistry, physics, sociology and even mathematics and the history of religon. One after another all the fields of human knowledge have been shaken and carried away by the same under-water current in the direction of the study of some *development*" (pp. 217 f.). No longer is evolution the best of possible hypotheses for portraying the history of the universe. Evolution has now become *the* method for the correlation, understanding, and interpretation of the totality of the phenomena. When the universe is ultimately intelligible only in terms of ultraphysics, and ultraphysics is intelligible only in terms of evolution, evolution functions as *the* methodological principle of explanation. Indeed, it is with the aid of this methodological principle, evolution, that Teilhard constructs his phenomenology, which attempts "to define this mysterious human phenomenon

s own fundamental attitudes and persuasions?
rom which he has chosen to present his "phe-
wn subjective commitments, whether scientific,

oice necessitates a certain understanding of the
rsity and its resolution, at least at the level of the
n he offers reveals the function of evolution in his
s as the principle of explanation and unification.
he hypothesis of evolution to the position of the
e of explanation a scientific procedure? [35]
phenomenology "rigorously free from any extra-
ns"? It seems unlikely. He himself admits to the sub-
f the scientific formulation. Though he may believe
in equating his subjective viewpoint with the way
the influence of his Christian faith in the formation of
t be ignored (p. 294, *see* p. 57, n. 2). Now, perhaps
some minimal guarantee, for example, of the primacy
se, but science hardly presents sufficient evidence to war-
n Teilhard describes as the Omega Point. But even more,
hypothesis of evolution to the role of a methodological
ation is an extrascientific procedure. The choice of such
rinciple as the structural principle of phenomenology may
hysics; but can an ultraphysics so constructed serve as an
departure for metaphysics?

not Teilhard has successfully avoided venturing into the
nce of being, his claim that *The Phenomenon of Man* is
ly a scientific treatise does not seem warranted (p. 29). And
arked the places in *The Phenomenon of Man* where philoso-
ue the matter further for reasons of a higher order (p. 29), his
ology itself appears likely to condition any metaphysical dis-
ight ensue. No more, then, than any other, does his phenome-
the indictment, that every phenomenology has the appearance
tification of what one has thought all along.[36]
less, whatever his reservations about the details of his phenome-
hard contends that it is fundamentally sound. Only a universe
tural principle is evolution, and whose direction is irreversible
imate convergence in the Omega Point, will suffice. Ultraphysics
st such a universe. But ultraphysics does more. It proposes to
t were, a program for thought. And it is evolution that dictates this
program. Modern man is capable of *seeing* only in terms of biologi-
time; indeed he is incapable of seeing anything otherwise — anything

experimentally by fixing its present position, structurally and historically, in relation to other forms around us which the cosmic stuff has assumed in the course of time." [24] Evolution provides unity and meaning for his phenomenology. Now it is true that Teilhard considers his phenomenology, or ultraphysics, as provisional in character, but there is nothing provisional about the ideal methodological principle of explanation, evolution.[25] What then, if any, are the implications for metaphysics of an ultraphysics whose structural principle is the methodological principle of evolution?

As we have already seen, the function of ultraphysics is to present an overall and coherent perspective of the universe (p. 35). To achieve this, ultraphysics not only registers the unity revealed by the totality of phenomena, but in fact confers upon the totality of phenomena the very unity it reveals.[26] As mathematical discovery is the bringing into existence of something new, so intellectual discovery and synthesis are no longer merely speculation but creation (pp. 248 f.). Only ultraphysics presents its own equation. Evolution equals the rise of consciousness, and the rise of consciousness equals the effect of union (p. 243). It is ultraphysics that embodies this equation and thereby confers unity upon the universe. Thus ultraphysics envisages the inclusion of man in his wholeness in a coherent picture of the world (p. 36). Its dream is the same dream "which human research obscurely fosters . . . fundamentally that of mastering, beyond all atomic or molecular affinities, the ultimate energy of which all other energies are merely servants; and thus, by grasping the very mainspring of evolution, seizing the tiller of the world" (p. 250).

No doubt ultraphysics is open to theology, for historically theology has lived more or less successfully with a variety of world views. But what are the possibilities for metaphysics? When Teilhard declares that every field of human knowledge has been shaken and carried away by some under-water current in the direction of some development (p. 218), he asserts that all human knowledge must measure up to the demands of the methodological principle of explanation, evolution. Evolution "is a general condition to which all theories, all hypotheses, all systems must bow and which they must satisfy if they are to be thinkable and true" (p. 218). Thus the ramifications of evolution reappear and go on in areas previously never imagined to be so closely linked with biology, even in the formulation and promulgation of philosophy (pp. 221 f.). Every philosophical formation, therefore, must take into account the identity of structure provided by evolution, which extends from threshold to threshold, from ultraphysics to metaphysics (p. 222).

Indeed, in Teilhard's evolving universe it is the essence of being to unify itself.[27] Such a conclusion concerning the nature of being is not surprising in view of his conception of ultraphysics. As Viallet has observed, Teilhard wished to base metaphysics on ultraphysics.[28] Clearly his ultraphysics lends itself to such a conception of being. The emphasis Teilhard places upon a delineation of the phenomena, particularly the phenomenon of man, in terms of a privileged axis whose direction is irreversible and whose terminus is union with a unique transcendent center, the Omega Point — this emphasis readily affords the basis for a metaphysics conceived primarily in terms of finality. In short, if ultraphysics is to be the basis for metaphysics, then, it seems, only this metaphysics will do. And only with such a metaphysics can being be defined in terms of its self-unification.[29]

But is Teilhard's ultraphysics equally open to a metaphysics that wants to consider reality in terms of efficient causality as well as final causality? Perhaps Teilhard's ultraphysics, like Aristotle's *Physics* to which it has been compared,[30] ignores or but scarcely accounts for those evidences of the phenomena that would give rise to an existential metaphysics — a metaphysics that can effectually account for the radical contingency of the universe. Does his ultraphysics curtail the possibility of an adequate metaphysics to the degree that his methodological principle of explanation emphasizes the unity and direction of the phenomena at the expense of their radical contingency?

Or is there inherent in this ultraphysics an even graver possibility? If, as seems possible, Teilhard understood metaphysics in a Cartesian manner, did he envision a metaphysics of the Cartesian type as the ideal complement for his ultraphysics? Perhaps the structural and methodological principle of ultraphysics entails a conception of being which is tailored to fit the contours of a universe created in the image of evolution. If this is the case, then it is not sufficient for Teilhard to insist that ultraphysics is not metaphysics, or that ultraphysics is open to metaphysics. The methodology will now dictate the nature of reality itself. Is it possible that Teilhard supplants mathematics with evolution, but retains the Cartesian dream of an ideal method? In the 19th century Comte proposed to replace metaphysics with sociology and gave us Sociologism.[31] Is Teilhard in the 20th century proposing to replace metaphysics with ultraphysics to give us Evolutionism?

Now, it may be objected that ultraphysics does not of necessity entail any particular type of metaphysics, since it aims merely to link the phenomena, not to explain them causally. Ultraphysics is but one way of explaining the phenomena. In brief, it is, as Teilhard says, a "phenomenology." But is any phenomenology free of the subjective commitments of its author? Can any phenomenology escape the charge of Cornford that "almost all philosophic arguments are invented afterwards, to recommend or defend from attack, conclusions which the philosopher was from the outset bent upon believing, before he could think of any arguments at all"?[32]

But what of Teilhard's phenomenology? Is it a scientific view free of extrascientific presuppositions, and, therefore, completely open to metaphysics? Tresmontant, for instance, speaking of *The Phenomenon of Man*,

descri
of phil
the exte
rigorousl
an accurat

Thoug
has, noneth
ing point. W
man at the ap
spiritualization
the Omega Poin
he assigns to it? L
his conception of e

For Teilhard,
142). But how chara
tion finally tends? To
is certainly none too fa
biological or paleontol
sciences lend credence to
sent a statistical record of
for determining mankind'
within the data of the natu
the organic nature of manki
the evolving universe. But wl
extrapolation to a proposed
Point?

Whatever dictates such a de
nonscientific. It reflects, instead,
tured by his Christian faith.[34] As H
to reconcile the supernatural elem
implications of science (p. 19). Thi
primacy of the human person, a con
ported, as Huxley says, by rational inqu

Further, Teilhard describes the pr
a scientific procedure. Still, as he confesse
the scientist does not escape his own subj
subject marry and mutually transform eac
and from now on man willy-nilly finds hi
looks at" (p. 32). True, he goes on to say th
proper vantage point, the subjective viewpoin
are objectively — man *sees*. This is the privileg
To see is indeed the aim of Teilhard's endeavor,

avoid the implications of hi
Will not the vantage point
nomenology" mirror his o
religious, or metaphysical?

Finally, Teilhard's ch
problem of unity and dive
phenomena. The resolutio
universe. Evolution serve
But is the elevation of
methodological principl

Is, then, Teilhard'
scientific presupposition
jective character even
that he has succeeded
things are objectively,
this conclusion cann
science may furnish
of man in the univer
rant the extrapolatio
his elevation of the
principle of expla
a methodological
result in an ultra
adequate point of

Whether or
field of the esse
purely and simp
even if he has m
phy might pur
very phenome
cussion that m
nology escape
of being a ju

Noneth
nology, Tei
whose struc
towards ul
provides j
sketch, as
projected
cal space

— even himself (p. 218). Thought is, therefore, not merely an anomaly, an epiphenomenon; in fact evolution is reducible to and identifiable with a progress towards thought (p. 220). The aim of Teilhard's ultraphysics is clear: to present a point of view from which the real will appear coherent, unified, and consequently intelligible.[37]

Ultraphysics and the Myth of Plato

This, then, is the task of ultraphysics, a phenomenology given its structure by evolution. Yet Teilhard's phenomenology is, as we have seen, neither science nor metaphysics. Teilhard himself calls it ultraphysics. Is it possible to compare Teilhard's ultraphysics with Plato's *Timaeus*? Is the function of evolution in his ultraphysics reminiscent of the role of the Demiurge in the *Timaeus*? Such a comparison is, on reflection, not so farfetched as it might initially appear. In the *Timaeus* (29 B ff.) Plato tries to supply the teleological explanation of the universe which in the *Phaedo* (96 A ff.) he intimates is necessary. For its part, Teilhard's ultraphysics is clearly teleological in character.

Further, Plato distinguishes being from becoming, the ideal from the phenomenal. To this latter category belongs the visible universe. Since the phenomenal order is not the proper subject of metaphysical investigation, and since any strictly scientific report can be only a partial account, any attempt at a unified version of the phenomenal order admits only of a likely story, a myth. Now Teilhard's ultraphysics, despite his assurances, is not, strictly speaking, science. Nor is his ultraphysics a metaphysics. If ultraphysics is neither science nor metaphysics, perhaps his ultraphysics embodies a myth, a likely account, which serves to give the unified description of reality and knowledge demanded by Teilhard's phenomenological approach.

This should not prove a surprising possibility. Man has often employed myths to give his vision of reality a unity it would otherwise not possess. After all, man's view of reality is of necessity refracted. An historical being, man's vision of the real reflects the viewpoints and the mirrors through which it appears to him. Aside from the uniquely conditioned sense experience peculiar to each man, man's vision of the real is molded in part by the social and cultural forces of his milieu. Each of these contributes to make him the historical being that he is, the observer of the real that he is, and the reporter of the real that he is. In the context of the human experience, man must sometimes resort to myth.

Even the philosopher on occasion, as Plato witnesses, must use myth. Frequently he can give only a verbal account of the real or tell a likely story of it. The refracted view of reality with which man is encumbered often reduces him to speaking of reality symbolically. The existential import of reality may be intimated; it can never be adequately conveyed. Plato's concern with the world of shadows in which man finds himself reflects man's limited ability to grasp the nature of the real. Whether or not one agrees with the Platonic resolution, everyone can learn from Plato's reticence in the presence of being.

Now, some may object that any discussion of myth in relation to Teilhard's ultraphysics is irrelevant. Teilhard, they will insist, had no such intention. True, he does not regard his ultraphysics as merely a likely account. On the contrary, he maintains that it is a true scientific description. Nonetheless, if, as many critics hold, ultraphysics is neither science nor metaphysics, then the possibility that Teilhard's ultraphysics embodies a myth suggests itself. The pieces all seem to fit, as a comparison with the *Timaeus* illustrates. As the *Timaeus* presents Plato's likely account of the rise of the cosmos from chaos through the activity of the Demiurge, so *The Phenomenon of Man* in its own way presents Teilhard's likely account of an evolving universe, an ultraphysics, in which evolution furnishes the unity of the phenomena which ultraphysics reveals. And just as Plato's cultural and scientific background provides the basis for the myth, or myths, which the *Timaeus* incorporates, so ultraphysics is rooted in Teilhard's cultural and scientific background, which we have already described.

To consider ultraphysics as myth is not necessarily to criticize Teilhard. In itself the use of myth is a legitimate procedure, provided that it remains what it purports to be, a likely probability. When, however, a likely account is presented as the unique account, criticism inevitably arises. Even considered as myth, *The Phenomenon of Man* calls for criticism on this score. Indeed, some may even suspect that, as has happened so often in philosophy, Teilhard has borrowed his myth from science only to raise once again over reality the specter of Procrustes.

Yet, however we appraise *The Phenomenon of Man*, as an ultraphysics open to metaphysics, as a phenomenology, or as myth, it is open to the same criticism. Teilhard purports to give the unique world view — a view dominated and directed by evolution — a view in which even man is defined as evolution become conscious of itself.[38] The unbounded optimism pervading *The Phenomenon of Man* confirms the expressed conviction of its author that such a world view alone achieves the inclusion of man in his wholeness in a coherent picture of the world. Still, Teilhard was aware, though belatedly, that he might be charged with naïve and exaggerated optimism (p. 309). To offset this impression he suggests that he has described, not a human idyll, but a cosmic drama (p. 309). Nevertheless, despite his recognition that the picture he presents has its negative side — the side of evil, error, disorder (p. 309) — his failure to reckon sufficiently with the negative side of the picture necessarily obscures and blurs the positive side that he does present.

Conclusion

What then is to be our assessment of *The Phenomenon of Man*? Are we to assess it as an ultraphysics whose openness to metaphysics is predetermined by its structural principle, as a phenomenology erected to justify what Teilhard has thought all along, or as a likely account gone astray? Each of these has its value as an assessment, though none of these completely measures up to the demands of this difficult work.

Whatever our own assessment, we cannot, as some have done, dismiss *The Phenomenon of Man* simply as poetry. More importantly, we cannot ignore it. We cannot, for example, ignore the willingness with which Teilhard admits all scientific data to serve the cause of a more complete understanding of man and the universe. Though we may hesitate to agree with his particular resolution, we can only admire the genius which dared to surmount the parochialism of its own discipline to seize the whole of reality in its vision. If at times Teilhard's work falters philosophically, still it stands as a symbol for all who come after. As he reminds science that it cannot ignore man, so too he reminds philosophy of its terrestrial origins.

But even more, we cannot ignore Teilhard's preoccupation with what it means to be man. He saw with clarity that a proper history of man must consider not only man's intellectual, moral and social growth, but his physical origins and development as well. Man can never truly comprehend what it means to be human until he recognizes the multitude of facets that constitute his being. To present man to himself was Teilhard's task as a man of science, but even more as a man of an age that echoes in its own unique way the Socratic aphorism: "Know thyself."

Above all, however, we cannot ignore Teilhard's love of reality. It is a love that speaks with accents of reverence and adoration. Indeed there is an almost *Hexameral* quality about his work, reminiscent of the medieval masterpieces. Teilhard wishes to convey his overwhelming love of reality to others that they might gaze on creation and see that it is good. He loves reality as a Christian man, conscious that the God of the Testaments is the Creator of the universe of being. Being must reflect His face, for He is Being.

Philosophy's perennial invitation seldom goes unheeded. Yet only a universe of surpassing wonder can explain *The Phenomenon of Man*. Teilhard was not reluctant to hazard his own response to such wonder — with what success history alone can determine. But whatever history's eventual determination, we who are fortunate to be of his time have had with Teilhard an uncommon experience. We have encountered not only a singular human being, but we have *shared* as well the drama of his own human experience as it unfolded within the context of the cosmic drama itself.

6

THE EXCELLENCE OF MAN

James M. Dorsey, M.D.

The Phenomenon of Man has a self-revering man for its base. Although intended purely and simply as a scientific treatise advancing the doctrine of evolution, it is a worthy addition to the rare literary works of science and is of interest to every well-read adult layman. In the sense that books on evolution have had an evolution of their own, Teilhard's work is a recent development of culminant importance, for it illustrates its author's evolved insight that all of his observations are self-observations. He knew and saw understandingly that his life was neither controlled nor directed by the vicissitudes of its own postulated "external environment." He knew with all the conviction of self-knowledge that every one can prove only his own existence, and that self-consciousness is the enlightenment he must use to be able to see in the direction where any and every event or experience of his life occurs. He knew in his own mind that each view is all about itself and cannot be the negation of another view.

Reverence and Self-Knowledge

My experience having demonstrated that self-insight is the criterion of mental health and strength, this standard (derived from my structural experience) is the specific one by which the following views of my understanding of Teilhard's psychology are formed.[1] * By self-insight I mean: observation of acknowledged self-evolution. Insight (inward beholding) discovers mental material with its living sensibility. My insight helps me to understand why I am ready through my sensation or perception to sense or perceive whatever I live as the "object." It reveals the self-sentience necessary to enable awareness of what is self-beneficial and what is self-detrimental. My

* Note: My considerations are restricted to Teilhard's psychology as I see it and as it may manifest itself in his essay, *The Phenomenon of Man*. Although my statements are based only upon translated self-observations, they are nevertheless an effort to record my mind's views of the way in which Teilhard used his mind.

ability to turn my mind's eye, my mind's power of observation, upon what is happening is my one possibility for being in on my own living. Quite as St. Bernard noted, "We must retire inward if we would ascend upward."

This psychological inquiry follows chiefly each of two lines of investigation of my author's intellectual activities: (1) the degree of his evident awareness of the existence of his mind, and (2) the degree of his evident awareness of the importance of his self-consciousness. Just reading the translation provided me with a wealth of data indicating that its author cherished his self-consciousness as his life's tried and true safehold.

A person's psychology is the outgrowth of the way in which he has conducted his life. His personal experiences as an individual shape his mind in characteristic ways, uniquely his own. Thus, everyone's "system of psychology" (according to which he actually works his mind) is a product of the mental activities of his very own human system. He may align himself with one "school of psychology" or another, but such an identification is a matter of convenience, his real system of psychology being the outgrowth of the shape his mind is in by virtue of the personal experiences he has undergone.

It appears that there have always been, at least potentially, two schools of psychology. The one claims that the "many" exists for, and in, the "one"; the other claims that the "one" exists for, and in, the "many." Democratic government, defined specifically as conscious self-government, attempts to recognize the allness of individuality and carries with it the ensouling view that the state exists for the individual. Every other kind of government in one way or another and in one degree or another carries with it the enslaving view that the individual exists for and in the state, that man was made for the Sabbath.

Every person's "system of education" is similarly reducible to the development of self-knowledge occurring in his human system. The educational principles to which he subscribes are decided by the nature and needs of his psychological being. Teilhard noted, "Man, the knowing subject, will perceive at last that man, 'the object of knowledge,' is the key to the whole science of nature." And, "Following Greek thought — following all thought in fact — are not 'to be' and 'to be one' identical?" It is evident that Teilhard sensed the learning process and all learning as consisting of nothing but the living process and the student's living. As he said, the researcher's goal is no longer to find gold, but life.

In his fitting Introduction, Sir Julian Huxley attributes to his Teilhard's mind "concern with establishing a global unification of human awareness," adding, "He has both clarified and unified our vision of reality." Thus, Huxley distills the meaning of Teilhard's book, "We, mankind, contain the possibilities of the earth's immense future, and can realize more of them on condition that we increase our knowledge and love. That it seems to me, is the distillation of *The Phenomenon of Man*."

I have helped myself freely also to Claude Tresmontant's excellent study, *Pierre Teilhard de Chardin: His Thought*.[2] This is an able translation, containing powerful excerpts from various of Teilhard's works. Of particular interest to one attempting a task like mine, it records Teilhard's accounting for physical evil as being a *"statistical necessity."* [3] Certainly, but only, by viewing the individual alone, the pejorative connotation of evil gradually vanishes as one sees the lessons of helpfulness discoverable in each event deprecated.

My greatest overall mental finding indicates Teilhard's genius, namely, his spirited appreciation of the importance of having his consciousness report his underived and unrelational selfhood. He was a peacemaker by virtue of the comprehensiveness of his mind-dependent insight. He used three expressions for the same thing: "within," "consciousness," and "spontaneity." Of sharp significance for my pointing up his application to developing his insight is the importance he assigned to human sensibility: "Throughout this book, the term 'consciousness' is taken in its widest sense to indicate every kind of psychicism, from the most rudimentary forms of interior preception imaginable to the human phenomenon of reflective thought" (p. 57).

Teilhard was capable of sovereign psychology. Majestically and minutely his writing reflects self-reverence and originality. The translation implies that his use of language was spontaneous rather than practiced: as if he had freed himself from the shackles of his "received" vocabulary. His use of words is that of the inventor of them. His word-pictures reflect free functioning of his ability to see that he was not only subject but also object. His grammar, as translated, indicates him to have been a mind-conscious man devoted to the equilibrium and unity of his inner life. Observations of his semantics, vocabulary, and grammar based upon the reading of his original writing bear out the estimate that he consistently knew what he was talking about, namely, himself. Said he, "I have not erected any inner partition in my mind." [4] And again, "nothing is profane here below on earth to him who knows how to see." [5]

For the purpose of writing *The Phenomenon of Man* it appears that Teilhard often deliberately suspended reference to his self-insight (self-consciousness) in order to be able to speak his "scientist's" language of "external data": "objectivity," "materiality," "impersonal," "dispassionate," "mechanization," "space," "time," "plurality," "statistics," and so on. He offered a quantity of technical knowledge tooled by this "scientific" kind of naming in his fine effort to meet the scientist on his own ground. In great measure he succeeded in attaining a language inoffensively free of the remarkable truth that he had already learned to talk Teilhard, learned to christen his all "Teilhard."

His fundamental thesis, "that life displays an organically articulated unity which manifestly indicates the phenomenon of growth" (p. 139), reflects his devotion to the truth of individuality. Said he, "From the biosphere to the species is nothing but an immense ramification of psychism seeking for itself by means of different forms (p. 151). . . . Life is the rise of consciousness (p. 153). . . . The ego only persists, by becoming ever more itself, in the measure in which it makes everything else itself. *So man becomes a person in and through personalization*" (p. 172).

Everyone's way of taking care of his world is a direct expression of the way he takes care of his own mind. Without my sense of personal identity I cannot care whether I live or die. It appears evident that Teilhard consciously initiated, venerated, and cultivated his mental properties as such. In 1916 he wrote, "It is my fondest conviction that any kind of disinterestedness about that which constitutes the most noble charm and interest of our natural life is not the basis of our supernatural growth." [6] His mind's consciousness, his mind's eye, saw negation, denial, ignoration as protective devices in no sense undermining life's true orientation of affirmation. Yea-sayer that he was, he spared himself argument.

Ever since Freud created a technique for cultivating self-consciousness, equating psychotherapy with the growth of self-insight (by discovering the mind-strengthening and mind-healing possibilities in the study and practice of free-association), the religious orientation, "the sacred integrity of the soul," has found analogy in the scientific orientation, "the conscious integrity of the mind."

A mind disciplining itself by the study and practice of free association arouses its basic manpower: perception of self-living. Teilhard's awareness that his personal experiences were his own mental events enabled him, 1) to observe that his mental material was his own, and 2) to feel sure who he was. In speaking of the course of evolution, he recorded: "The more often I come across this problem and the longer I pore over it, the more firmly it is impressed upon me that in fact we are confronted with an effect not of external forces but of psychology" (p. 150).

The heeded fact that there can be no consciousness other than self-consciousness (consciousness being constituted only of selfness), has life-saving meaning, for attention to this fact constitutes being fully awake. By means of my consciousness I can live the observation that I am alive, for it is the very sense of being alive. Its exercise develops the true (full) meaning of personal identity. Teilhard repeatedly observed that no perspective other than that of self-consciousness can provide biologically adequate apprehension of life or justify full measurement of individual human being.

Seeing the Whole of Life

Teilhard used key words that indicated his reliance upon "seeing," identifying himself definitely as a seer rather than as a reasoner. For him consciousness was a word of rich meaning seeming to include even "knowing." "The animal 'only knows' while man 'knows that he knows.' " [7] Consistently he featured the sensibility of individuality. To illustrate: "Discover the universe in the exceptional, . . . The meaning of human phenomenon in the eyes of the scientist, . . . Modern man has a great need to be able to see this direction [in evolution], . . . The consciousness of each one of us is evolution perceiving itself and reflecting." In his Foreword he stated: "This work may be summed up as an attempt *to see* and *to show* what happens to man, . . . *Seeing.* We might say that the whole of life lies in that verb — if not in end, at least in essence" (p. 31). "*To see or to perish* is the very condition laid upon everything that makes up the universe: . . . The more one looks, the more one sees. And the more one sees, the better one knows where to look" (pp. 31 and 280).

He delivered himself from dissension by his clearly independent realization that one person, or thing, can have nothing to do with another. In his chapter "The Within of Things" he made it clear that dispute is most often traceable to the fact that each disputant is arguing about something different from that which his opponent is arguing about. In his law of recurrence, his law of complexity/consciousness [8] featuring the element of mental development as all development, he showed his recognition of the synthesizing power of mind. He described the *within* of man as "the object of a direct intuition and the substance of all knowledge" (p. 300). He referred to the process of mental development as "increase in interiorisation." [9]

Throughout his writing he consciously tried to avoid dualism, consistently achieving this goal by his conscious use of his mind, that is, by recognizing that each of his observations (whether nominated "external" or "internal") was a mental event (personal experience) taking place only where mental events must take place.

Every person has an integrated mind. It is the consciously integrated mind that is the rare possession of the genius which permits him to enjoy all the advantages of the seer. Only the seer can spare himself the addiction of living as if he can be out of his mind. It is the consciously integrated mind which experiences knowledge as conscious self-knowledge, which calls its soul its own and its all its soul.

As did Teilhard, each consciously integrated person identifies himself as an orthogenetic evolutionist, as a vitalist. It was obvious to him that experimentally by fixing its present position, structurally and historically, in relation to other forms around us which the cosmic stuff has assumed in the course of time." [24] Evolution provides unity and meaning for his phenomenology. Now it is true that Teilhard considers his phenomenology, or ultraphysics, as provisional in character, but there is nothing provisional about the ideal methodological principle of explanation, evolution.[25] What then, if any, are the implications for metaphysics of an ultraphysics whose structural principle is the methodological principle of evolution?

As we have already seen, the function of ultraphysics is to present an overall and coherent perspective of the universe (p. 35). To achieve this, ultraphysics not only registers the unity revealed by the totality of phenomena, but in fact confers upon the totality of phenomena the very unity it reveals.[26] As mathematical discovery is the bringing into existence of something new, so intellectual discovery and synthesis are no longer merely speculation but creation (pp. 248 f.). Only ultraphysics presents its own equation. Evolution equals the rise of consciousness, and the rise of consciousness equals the effect of union (p. 243). It is ultraphysics that embodies this equation and thereby confers unity upon the universe. Thus ultraphysics envisages the inclusion of man in his wholeness in a coherent picture of the world (p. 36). Its dream is the same dream "which human research obscurely fosters . . . fundamentally that of mastering, beyond all atomic or molecular affinities, the ultimate energy of which all other energies are merely servants; and thus, by grasping the very mainspring of evolution, seizing the tiller of the world" (p. 250).

No doubt ultraphysics is open to theology, for historically theology has lived more or less successfully with a variety of world views. But what are the possibilities for metaphysics? When Teilhard declares that every field of human knowledge has been shaken and carried away by some under-water current in the direction of some development (p. 218), he asserts that all human knowledge must measure up to the demands of the methodological principle of explanation, evolution. Evolution "is a general condition to which all theories, all hypotheses, all systems must bow and which they must satisfy if they are to be thinkable and true" (p. 218). Thus the ramifications of evolution reappear and go on in areas previously never imagined to be so closely linked with biology, even in the formulation and promulgation of philosophy (pp. 221 f.). Every philosophical formation, therefore, must take into account the identity of structure provided by evolution, which extends from threshold to threshold, from ultraphysics to metaphysics (p. 222).

Indeed, in Teilhard's evolving universe it is the essence of being to unify itself.[27] Such a conclusion concerning the nature of being is not surprising in view of his conception of ultraphysics. As Viallet has observed, Teilhard wished to base metaphysics on ultraphysics.[28] Clearly his ultraphysics lends itself to such a conception of being. The emphasis Teilhard places upon a delineation of the phenomena, particularly the phenomenon of man, in terms of a privileged axis whose direction is irreversible and whose terminus is union with a unique transcendent center, the Omega Point — this emphasis readily affords the basis for a metaphysics conceived primarily in terms of finality. In short, if ultraphysics is to be the basis for metaphysics, then, it seems, only this metaphysics will do. And only with such a metaphysics can being be defined in terms of its self-unification.[29]

But is Teilhard's ultraphysics equally open to a metaphysics that wants to consider reality in terms of efficient causality as well as final causality? Perhaps Teilhard's ultraphysics, like Aristotle's *Physics* to which it has been compared,[30] ignores or but scarcely accounts for those evidences of the phenomena that would give rise to an existential metaphysics — a metaphysics that can effectually account for the radical contingency of the universe. Does his ultraphysics curtail the possibility of an adequate metaphysics to the degree that his methodological principle of explanation emphasizes the unity and direction of the phenomena at the expense of their radical contingency?

Or is there inherent in this ultraphysics an even graver possibility? If, as seems possible, Teilhard understood metaphysics in a Cartesian manner, did he envision a metaphysics of the Cartesian type as the ideal complement for his ultraphysics? Perhaps the structural and methodological principle of ultraphysics entails a conception of being which is tailored to fit the contours of a universe created in the image of evolution. If this is the case, then it is not sufficient for Teilhard to insist that ultraphysics is not metaphysics, or that ultraphysics is open to metaphysics. The methodology will now dictate the nature of reality itself. Is it possible that Teilhard supplants mathematics with evolution, but retains the Cartesian dream of an ideal method? In the 19th century Comte proposed to replace metaphysics with sociology and gave us Sociologism.[31] Is Teilhard in the 20th century proposing to replace metaphysics with ultraphysics to give us Evolutionism?

Now, it may be objected that ultraphysics does not of necessity entail any particular type of metaphysics, since it aims merely to link the phenomena, not to explain them causally. Ultraphysics is but one way of explaining the phenomena. In brief, it is, as Teilhard says, a "phenomenology." But is any phenomenology free of the subjective commitments of its author? Can any phenomenology escape the charge of Cornford that "almost all philosophic arguments are invented afterwards, to recommend or defend from attack, conclusions which the philosopher was from the outset bent upon believing, before he could think of any arguments at all"?[32]

But what of Teilhard's phenomenology? Is it a scientific view free of extrascientific presuppositions, and, therefore, completely open to metaphysics? Tresmontant, for instance, speaking of *The Phenomenon of Man,* describes it in this way: "To be sure, the vision of the world thus disclosed is of philosophical import and value, but it commits the philosopher only to the extent that it has been formulated by means, and according to methods, rigorously free from any extrascientific presuppositions." [33] Is this, however, an accurate assessment of Teilhard's vision?

Though Teilhard undertakes the presentation of a phenomenology, he has, nonetheless, chosen to take his stand on a certain preconditioned starting point. What does his choice involve? Initially, it involves the location of man at the apex of evolutionary convergence, whose ultimate term is the spiritualization of the universe as man achieves union with his true center, the Omega Point (pp. 260 ff.). But why does he see in evolution the direction he assigns to it? Did his commitment to Christian faith influence in any way his conception of evolution?

For Teilhard, evolution has a direction, an orientation and an axis (p. 142). But how characterize the ultimate stage of convergence to which evolution finally tends? To describe this point of convergence as a "mystical body" is certainly none too fanciful. Does, however, the scientific evidence, whether biological or paleontological, yield such a conclusion? Even if the social sciences lend credence to a convergent view of evolution, do they not represent a statistical record of man and his activity, rather than present a criterion for determining mankind's destiny? There are, it is true, concrete evidences within the data of the natural sciences which give rise to such conceptions as the organic nature of mankind and the significance of man's appearance in the evolving universe. But what warrant is there for a seemingly gratuitous extrapolation to a proposed goal such as Teilhard presents — the Omega Point?

Whatever dictates such a development is certainly extrascientific, indeed nonscientific. It reflects, instead, a set of assumptions engendered and nurtured by his Christian faith.[34] As Huxley has observed, Teilhard's intention is to reconcile the supernatural elements in Christianity with the facts and implications of science (p. 19). This, however, implies a conviction of the primacy of the human person, a conviction grounded in faith, albeit supported, as Huxley says, by rational inquiry and scientific knowledge (p. 19).

Further, Teilhard describes the presentation of his phenomenology as a scientific procedure. Still, as he confesses, even in his scientific investigations the scientist does not escape his own subjective commitments: "Object and subject marry and mutually transform each other in the act of knowledge; and from now on man willy-nilly finds his own image stamped on all he looks at" (p. 32). True, he goes on to say that, when man has attained the proper vantage point, the subjective viewpoint coincides with the way things are objectively — man *sees*. This is the privilege of man's knowledge (p. 32). *To see* is indeed the aim of Teilhard's endeavor, but can his own act of *seeing* avoid the implications of his own fundamental attitudes and persuasions? Will not the vantage point from which he has chosen to present his "phenomenology" mirror his own subjective commitments, whether scientific, religious, or metaphysical?

Finally, Teilhard's choice necessitates a certain understanding of the problem of unity and diversity and its resolution, at least at the level of the phenomena. The resolution he offers reveals the function of evolution in his universe. Evolution serves as the principle of explanation and unification. But is the elevation of the hypothesis of evolution to the position of the methodological principle of explanation a scientific procedure? [35]

Is, then, Teilhard's phenomenology "rigorously free from any extra-scientific presuppositions"? It seems unlikely. He himself admits to the subjective character even of the scientific formulation. Though he may believe that he has succeeded in equating his subjective viewpoint with the way things are objectively, the influence of his Christian faith in the formation of this conclusion cannot be ignored (p. 294, *see* p. 57, n. 2). Now, perhaps science may furnish some minimal guarantee, for example, of the primacy of man in the universe, but science hardly presents sufficient evidence to warrant the extrapolation Teilhard describes as the Omega Point. But even more, his elevation of the hypothesis of evolution to the role of a methodological principle of explanation is an extrascientific procedure. The choice of such a methodological principle as the structural principle of phenomenology may result in an ultraphysics; but can an ultraphysics so constructed serve as an adequate point of departure for metaphysics?

Whether or not Teilhard has successfully avoided venturing into the field of the essence of being, his claim that *The Phenomenon of Man* is purely and simply a scientific treatise does not seem warranted (p. 29). And even if he has marked the places in *The Phenomenon of Man* where philosophy might pursue the matter further for reasons of a higher order (p. 29), his very phenomenology itself appears likely to condition any metaphysical discussion that might ensue. No more, then, than any other, does his phenomenology escape the indictment, that every phenomenology has the appearance of being a justification of what one has thought all along.[36]

Nonetheless, whatever his reservations about the details of his phenomenology, Teilhard contends that it is fundamentally sound. Only a universe whose structural principle is evolution, and whose direction is irreversible towards ultimate convergence in the Omega Point, will suffice. Ultraphysics provides just such a universe. But ultraphysics does more. It proposes to sketch, as it were, a program for thought. And it is evolution that dictates this projected program. Modern man is capable of *seeing* only in terms of biological space-time; indeed he is incapable of seeing anything otherwise — anything

— even himself (p. 218). Thought is, therefore, not merely an anomaly, an epiphenomenon; in fact evolution is reducible to and identifiable with a progress towards thought (p. 220). The aim of Teilhard's ultraphysics is clear: to present a point of view from which the real will appear coherent, unified, and consequently intelligible.[37]

Ultraphysics and the Myth of Plato

This, then, is the task of ultraphysics, a phenomenology given its structure by evolution. Yet Teilhard's phenomenology is, as we have seen, neither science nor metaphysics. Teilhard himself calls it ultraphysics. Is it possible to compare Teilhard's ultraphysics with Plato's *Timaeus?* Is the function of evolution in his ultraphysics reminiscent of the role of the Demiurge in the *Timaeus?* Such a comparison is, on reflection, not so farfetched as it might initially appear. In the *Timaeus* (29 B ff.) Plato tries to supply the teleological explanation of the universe which in the *Phaedo* (96 A ff.) he intimates is necessary. For its part, Teilhard's ultraphysics is clearly teleological in character.

Further, Plato distinguishes being from becoming, the ideal from the phenomenal. To this latter category belongs the visible universe. Since the phenomenal order is not the proper subject of metaphysical investigation, and since any strictly scientific report can be only a partial account, any attempt at a unified version of the phenomenal order admits only of a likely story, a myth. Now Teilhard's ultraphysics, despite his assurances, is not, strictly speaking, science. Nor is his ultraphysics a metaphysics. If ultraphysics is neither science nor metaphysics, perhaps his ultraphysics embodies a myth, a likely account, which serves to give the unified description of reality and knowledge demanded by Teilhard's phenomenological approach.

This should not prove a surprising possibility. Man has often employed myths to give his vision of reality a unity it would otherwise not possess. After all, man's view of reality is of necessity refracted. An historical being, man's vision of the real reflects the viewpoints and the mirrors through which it appears to him. Aside from the uniquely conditioned sense experience peculiar to each man, man's vision of the real is molded in part by the social and cultural forces of his milieu. Each of these contributes to make him the historical being that he is, the observer of the real that he is, and the reporter of the real that he is. In the context of the human experience, man must sometimes resort to myth.

Even the philosopher on occasion, as Plato witnesses, must use myth. Frequently he can give only a verbal account of the real or tell a likely story of it. The refracted view of reality with which man is encumbered often reduces him to speaking of reality symbolically. The existential import of reality may be intimated; it can never be adequately conveyed. Plato's concern with the world of shadows in which man finds himself reflects man's limited ability to grasp the nature of the real. Whether or not one agrees with the Platonic resolution, everyone can learn from Plato's reticence in the presence of being.

Now, some may object that any discussion of myth in relation to Teilhard's ultraphysics is irrelevant. Teilhard, they will insist, had no such intention. True, he does not regard his ultraphysics as merely a likely account. On the contrary, he maintains that it is a true scientific description. Nonetheless, if, as many critics hold, ultraphysics is neither science nor metaphysics, then the possibility that Teilhard's ultraphysics embodies a myth suggests itself. The pieces all seem to fit, as a comparison with the *Timaeus* illustrates. As the *Timaeus* presents Plato's likely account of the rise of the cosmos from chaos through the activity of the Demiurge, so *The Phenomenon of Man* in its own way presents Teilhard's likely account of an evolving universe, an ultraphysics, in which evolution furnishes the unity of the phenomena which ultraphysics reveals. And just as Plato's cultural and scientific background provides the basis for the myth, or myths, which the *Timaeus* incorporates, so ultraphysics is rooted in Teilhard's cultural and scientific background, which we have already described.

To consider ultraphysics as myth is not necessarily to criticize Teilhard. In itself the use of myth is a legitimate procedure, provided that it remains what it purports to be, a likely probability. When, however, a likely account is presented as the unique account, criticism inevitably arises. Even considered as myth, *The Phenomenon of Man* calls for criticism on this score. Indeed, some may even suspect that, as has happened so often in philosophy, Teilhard has borrowed his myth from science only to raise once again over reality the specter of Procrustes.

Yet, however we appraise *The Phenomenon of Man*, as an ultraphysics open to metaphysics, as a phenomenology, or as myth, it is open to the same criticism. Teilhard purports to give the unique world view — a view dominated and directed by evolution — a view in which even man is defined as evolution become conscious of itself.[38] The unbounded optimism pervading *The Phenomenon of Man* confirms the expressed conviction of its author that such a world view alone achieves the inclusion of man in his wholeness in a coherent picture of the world. Still, Teilhard was aware, though belatedly, that he might be charged with naïve and exaggerated optimism (p. 309). To offset this impression he suggests that he has described, not a human idyll, but a cosmic drama (p. 309). Nevertheless, despite his recognition that the picture he presents has its negative side — the side of evil, error, disorder (p. 309) — his failure to reckon sufficiently with the negative side of the picture necessarily obscures and blurs the positive side that he does present.

Conclusion

What then is to be our assessment of *The Phenomenon of Man*? Are we to assess it as an ultraphysics whose openness to metaphysics is predetermined by its structural principle, as a phenomenology erected to justify what Teilhard has thought all along, or as a likely account gone astray? Each of these has its value as an assessment, though none of these completely measures up to the demands of this difficult work.

Whatever our own assessment, we cannot, as some have done, dismiss *The Phenomenon of Man* simply as poetry. More importantly, we cannot ignore it. We cannot, for example, ignore the willingness with which Teilhard admits all scientific data to serve the cause of a more complete understanding of man and the universe. Though we may hesitate to agree with his particular resolution, we can only admire the genius which dared to surmount the parochialism of its own discipline to seize the whole of reality in its vision. If at times Teilhard's work falters philosophically, still it stands as a symbol for all who come after. As he reminds science that it cannot ignore man, so too he reminds philosophy of its terrestrial origins.

But even more, we cannot ignore Teilhard's preoccupation with what it means to be man. He saw with clarity that a proper history of man must consider not only man's intellectual, moral and social growth, but his physical origins and development as well. Man can never truly comprehend what it means to be human until he recognizes the multitude of facets that constitute his being. To present man to himself was Teilhard's task as a man of science, but even more as a man of an age that echoes in its own unique way the Socratic aphorism: "Know thyself."

Above all, however, we cannot ignore Teilhard's love of reality. It is a love that speaks with accents of reverence and adoration. Indeed there is an almost *Hexameral* quality about his work, reminiscent of the medieval masterpieces. Teilhard wishes to convey his overwhelming love of reality to others that they might gaze on creation and see that it is good. He loves reality as a Christian man, conscious that the God of the Testaments is the Creator of the universe of being. Being must reflect His face, for He is Being.

Philosophy's perennial invitation seldom goes unheeded. Yet only a universe of surpassing wonder can explain *The Phenomenon of Man*. Teilhard was not reluctant to hazard his own response to such wonder — with what success history alone can determine. But whatever history's eventual determination, we who are fortunate to be of his time have had with Teilhard an uncommon experience. We have encountered not only a singular human being, but we have *shared* as well the drama of his own human experience as it unfolded within the context of the cosmic drama itself.

6

THE EXCELLENCE OF MAN

James M. Dorsey, M.D.

The Phenomenon of Man has a self-revering man for its base. Although intended purely and simply as a scientific treatise advancing the doctrine of evolution, it is a worthy addition to the rare literary works of science and is of interest to every well-read adult layman. In the sense that books on evolution have had an evolution of their own, Teilhard's work is a recent development of culminant importance, for it illustrates its author's evolved insight that all of his observations are self-observations. He knew and saw understandingly that his life was neither controlled nor directed by the vicissitudes of its own postulated "external environment." He knew with all the conviction of self-knowledge that every one can prove only his own existence, and that self-consciousness is the enlightenment he must use to be able to see in the direction where any and every event or experience of his life occurs. He knew in his own mind that each view is all about itself and cannot be the negation of another view.

Reverence and Self-Knowledge

My experience having demonstrated that self-insight is the criterion of mental health and strength, this standard (derived from my structural experience) is the specific one by which the following views of my understanding of Teilhard's psychology are formed.[1] * By self-insight I mean: observation of acknowledged self-evolution. Insight (inward beholding) discovers mental material with its living sensibility. My insight helps me to understand why I am ready through my sensation or perception to sense or perceive whatever I live as the "object." It reveals the self-sentience necessary to enable awareness of what is self-beneficial and what is self-detrimental. My

* Note: My considerations are restricted to Teilhard's psychology as I see it and as it may manifest itself in his essay, *The Phenomenon of Man*. Although my statements are based only upon translated self-observations, they are nevertheless an effort to record my mind's views of the way in which Teilhard used his mind.

ability to turn my mind's eye, my mind's power of observation, upon what is happening is my one possibility for being in on my own living. Quite as St. Bernard noted, "We must retire inward if we would ascend upward."

This psychological inquiry follows chiefly each of two lines of investigation of my author's intellectual activities: (1) the degree of his evident awareness of the existence of his mind, and (2) the degree of his evident awareness of the importance of his self-consciousness. Just reading the translation provided me with a wealth of data indicating that its author cherished his self-consciousness as his life's tried and true safehold.

A person's psychology is the outgrowth of the way in which he has conducted his life. His personal experiences as an individual shape his mind in characteristic ways, uniquely his own. Thus, everyone's "system of psychology" (according to which he actually works his mind) is a product of the mental activities of his very own human system. He may align himself with one "school of psychology" or another, but such an identification is a matter of convenience, his real system of psychology being the outgrowth of the shape his mind is in by virtue of the personal experiences he has undergone.

It appears that there have always been, at least potentially, two schools of psychology. The one claims that the "many" exists for, and in, the "one"; the other claims that the "one" exists for, and in, the "many." Democratic government, defined specifically as conscious self-government, attempts to recognize the allness of individuality and carries with it the ensouling view that the state exists for the individual. Every other kind of government in one way or another and in one degree or another carries with it the enslaving view that the individual exists for and in the state, that man was made for the Sabbath.

Every person's "system of education" is similarly reducible to the development of self-knowledge occurring in his human system. The educational principles to which he subscribes are decided by the nature and needs of his psychological being. Teilhard noted, "Man, the knowing subject, will perceive at last that man, 'the object of knowledge,' is the key to the whole science of nature." And, "Following Greek thought — following all thought in fact — are not 'to be' and 'to be one' identical?" It is evident that Teilhard sensed the learning process and all learning as consisting of nothing but the living process and the student's living. As he said, the researcher's goal is no longer to find gold, but life.

In his fitting Introduction, Sir Julian Huxley attributes to his Teilhard's mind "concern with establishing a global unification of human awareness," adding, "He has both clarified and unified our vision of reality." Thus, Huxley distills the meaning of Teilhard's book, "We, mankind, contain the possibilities of the earth's immense future, and can realize more of them on condition that we increase our knowledge and love. That it seems to me, is the distillation of *The Phenomenon of Man*."

I have helped myself freely also to Claude Tresmontant's excellent study, *Pierre Teilhard de Chardin: His Thought*.[2] This is an able translation, containing powerful excerpts from various of Teilhard's works. Of particular interest to one attempting a task like mine, it records Teilhard's accounting for physical evil as being a *"statistical necessity."* [3] Certainly, but only, by viewing the individual alone, the pejorative connotation of evil gradually vanishes as one sees the lessons of helpfulness discoverable in each event deprecated.

My greatest overall mental finding indicates Teilhard's genius, namely, his spirited appreciation of the importance of having his consciousness report his underived and unrelational selfhood. He was a peacemaker by virtue of the comprehensiveness of his mind-dependent insight. He used three expressions for the same thing: "within," "consciousness," and "spontaneity." Of sharp significance for my pointing up his application to developing his insight is the importance he assigned to human sensibility: "Throughout this book, the term 'consciousness' is taken in its widest sense to indicate every kind of psychicism, from the most rudimentary forms of interior preception imaginable to the human phenomenon of reflective thought" (p. 57).

Teilhard was capable of sovereign psychology. Majestically and minutely his writing reflects self-reverence and originality. The translation implies that his use of language was spontaneous rather than practiced: as if he had freed himself from the shackles of his "received" vocabulary. His use of words is that of the inventor of them. His word-pictures reflect free functioning of his ability to see that he was not only subject but also object. His grammar, as translated, indicates him to have been a mind-conscious man devoted to the equilibrium and unity of his inner life. Observations of his semantics, vocabulary, and grammar based upon the reading of his original writing bear out the estimate that he consistently knew what he was talking about, namely, himself. Said he, "I have not erected any inner partition in my mind." [4] And again, "nothing is profane here below on earth to him who knows how to see." [5]

For the purpose of writing *The Phenomenon of Man* it appears that Teilhard often deliberately suspended reference to his self-insight (self-consciousness) in order to be able to speak his "scientist's" language of "external data": "objectivity," "materiality," "impersonal," "dispassionate," "mechanization," "space," "time," "plurality," "statistics," and so on. He offered a quantity of technical knowledge tooled by this "scientific" kind of naming in his fine effort to meet the scientist on his own ground. In great measure he succeeded in attaining a language inoffensively free of the remarkable truth that he had already learned to talk Teilhard, learned to christen his all "Teilhard."

His fundamental thesis, "that life displays an organically articulated unity which manifestly indicates the phenomenon of growth" (p. 139), reflects his devotion to the truth of individuality. Said he, "From the biosphere to the species is nothing but an immense ramification of psychism seeking for itself by means of different forms (p. 151). . . . Life is the rise of consciousness (p. 153). . . . The ego only persists, by becoming ever more itself, in the measure in which it makes everything else itself. *So man becomes a person in and through personalization*" (p. 172).

Everyone's way of taking care of his world is a direct expression of the way he takes care of his own mind. Without my sense of personal identity I cannot care whether I live or die. It appears evident that Teilhard consciously initiated, venerated, and cultivated his mental properties as such. In 1916 he wrote, "It is my fondest conviction that any kind of disinterestedness about that which constitutes the most noble charm and interest of our natural life is not the basis of our supernatural growth." [6] His mind's consciousness, his mind's eye, saw negation, denial, ignoration as protective devices in no sense undermining life's true orientation of affirmation. Yea-sayer that he was, he spared himself argument.

Ever since Freud created a technique for cultivating self-consciousness, equating psychotherapy with the growth of self-insight (by discovering the mind-strengthening and mind-healing possibilities in the study and practice of free-association), the religious orientation, "the sacred integrity of the soul," has found analogy in the scientific orientation, "the conscious integrity of the mind."

A mind disciplining itself by the study and practice of free association arouses its basic manpower: perception of self-living. Teilhard's awareness that his personal experiences were his own mental events enabled him, 1) to observe that his mental material was his own, and 2) to feel sure who he was. In speaking of the course of evolution, he recorded: "The more often I come across this problem and the longer I pore over it, the more firmly it is impressed upon me that in fact we are confronted with an effect not of external forces but of psychology" (p. 150).

The heeded fact that there can be no consciousness other than self-consciousness (consciousness being constituted only of selfness), has life-saving meaning, for attention to this fact constitutes being fully awake. By means of my consciousness I can live the observation that I am alive, for it is the very sense of being alive. Its exercise develops the true (full) meaning of personal identity. Teilhard repeatedly observed that no perspective other than that of self-consciousness can provide biologically adequate apprehension of life or justify full measurement of individual human being.

Seeing the Whole of Life

Teilhard used key words that indicated his reliance upon "seeing," identifying himself definitely as a seer rather than as a reasoner. For him consciousness was a word of rich meaning seeming to include even "knowing." "The animal 'only knows' while man 'knows that he knows.' " [7] Consistently he featured the sensibility of individuality. To illustrate: "Discover the universe in the exceptional, . . . The meaning of human phenomenon in the eyes of the scientist, . . . Modern man has a great need to be able to see this direction [in evolution], . . . The consciousness of each one of us is evolution perceiving itself and reflecting." In his Foreword he stated: "This work may be summed up as an attempt *to see* and *to show* what happens to man, . . . *Seeing.* We might say that the whole of life lies in that verb — if not in end, at least in essence" (p. 31). "*To see or to perish* is the very condition laid upon everything that makes up the universe: . . . The more one looks, the more one sees. And the more one sees, the better one knows where to look" (pp. 31 and 280).

He delivered himself from dissension by his clearly independent realization that one person, or thing, can have nothing to do with another. In his chapter "The Within of Things" he made it clear that dispute is most often traceable to the fact that each disputant is arguing about something different from that which his opponent is arguing about. In his law of recurrence, his law of complexity/consciousness [8] featuring the element of mental development as all development, he showed his recognition of the synthesizing power of mind. He described the *within* of man as "the object of a direct intuition and the substance of all knowledge" (p. 300). He referred to the process of mental development as "increase in interiorisation." [9]

Throughout his writing he consciously tried to avoid dualism, consistently achieving this goal by his conscious use of his mind, that is, by recognizing that each of his observations (whether nominated "external" or "internal") was a mental event (personal experience) taking place only where mental events must take place.

Every person has an integrated mind. It is the consciously integrated mind that is the rare possession of the genius which permits him to enjoy all the advantages of the seer. Only the seer can spare himself the addiction of living as if he can be out of his mind. It is the consciously integrated mind which experiences knowledge as conscious self-knowledge, which calls its soul its own and its all its soul.

As did Teilhard, each consciously integrated person identifies himself as an orthogenetic evolutionist, as a vitalist. It was obvious to him that evolution can only be autogenetic (or autonomic). He recognized ectogenetic evolution as an illusion creating a phantom problem traceable to the fact that it implies that every individual "lives in an environment" rather than that every individual has his environment living within him. The consciously integrated mind recognizes that every problem subsumed by the word "materialism" is a phantom problem traceable to the lack of insight that "materialism" can be nothing but rejected or ignored (repressed) idealism. Only the consciously integrated mind can heed the following literary bull which confounds illusional "materiality" with psychic (individual) reality. "I assume that an external material universe exists and that it corresponds with my perceptions *of it*."

Teilhard's view of evolution was that it is an ascent towards consciousness. "Is it not possible that in our theories and in our acts we have neglected to give due place to the person, and the forces of personalization?" (p. 257). "Are we not at every instant living the experience of a universe whose immensity, by the play of our senses and our reason, is gathered up more and more simply in each one of us?" (p. 259). He made the point very strongly that "the concentration of a conscious universe" would be unthinkable, except that "each particular consciousness" becomes "still more itself and thus more clearly distinct from others the closer it gets to them in Omega" (p. 261). He spoke of the "depth and incommunicability of the ego" (p. 262). He distinguished narrow and broad self-love:

> Egoism, whether personal or racial, is quite rightly excited by the idea of the element ascending through faithfulness to life, to the extremes of the incommunicable and the exclusive that it holds within it. It *feels* right. Its only mistake, but a fatal one, is *to confuse individuality with personality*. In trying to separate itself as much as possible from others, the element individualises itself; but in doing so it becomes retrograde and seeks to drag the world backwards towards plurality and into matter. In fact it diminishes itself and loses itself. To be fully ourselves it is in the opposite direction, in the direction of convergence with all the rest, that we must advance — towards the 'other.' The goal of ourselves, the acme of our originality, is not our individuality but our person; and according to the evolutionary structure of the world, we can only find our person by uniting together. There is no mind without synthesis. The same law holds good from top to bottom. The true ego grows in inverse proportion to 'egoism.' Like the Omega which attracts it, the element only becomes personal when it universalises itself (p. 263).

Quite as Occam observed, Teilhard saw that everything real is individual. "Particular" is (its own) "universal"; "universal" is (its own) "particular." Each judgment posits all that can be: one is one. Whatever is, completely and only is. Whatever is, is its own everything. Reality (whatever is) is all and only existence.

There are many adjectives that have been used for describing the quality properly signifying healthful individuality, to wit, "courageous," "noble," "outstanding," "strong," "powerful," "rugged," and so on. I submit the one adjective adequate for the purpose to be "conscious." Conscious individuality exercises man's true nature, personal identity. Only a conscious individual can use his mind's culminant power, i.e., his power of identifying himself in his every experience, his every life reach. Teilhard knowingly exercised his indomitable freedom, conscious function of mind, imagination. To use Henry M. Wriston's choice phrase, he had "stars in his eyes." [10]

As is true of every individual, man *is* his own everything — it is only his awareness regarding his comprehensiveness which can be lacking. But it is necessary that he be able to see himself as his own all, in order to be able to see himself as his own end rather than as a means, or way, to an end. Seeing himself as his own end, he becomes a conscious evolutionary finalist, the direction of his development being ever selfward. His constitutional necessity to be conscious only with regard to a minute portion of his living on any given occasion of his whole living tends to conceal the truth of his allness. As Teilhard might put it, his world is disclosed (veiled) in his selfhood: man must consciously think for himself in order to see only personal meaning in all his words.

The Dynamic Mind

Every mind is a dynamic whole consisting of that mind's unique meanings. Hence it is that self-consciousness (living selfness with awareness) is essential for self-realization. Conscious self-fulfillment is required in order that man see himself as the end that he is rather than as the means that his necessary practice of self-unconsciousness would appear to make of him. I define that ambiguous term "meaning" most broadly yet specifically as: Importance for human living. All that is mental (mind, the manifold of meaning) exists *an sich*, unrelationally. Meaning, the only stuff or reality of mental existence, is a synonym for being. Meaningless is a synonym for non-existence. Meaning is all that there is to mental power. Mind is a realm of ends, a universe existing in its every particular. Teilhard harmonized his mind by his sensing the meaning of his underlying personal sameness in it: "Religion and science are the two conjugated faces or phases of one and the same act of complete knowledge" (p. 284 f.).

Any and all living is successful living. Any sense of personal identity, but nothing else, constitutes the person's appreciation of his living. Living is always novel. Most helpful for life is the liver's realization that he is the who-what-why and all the rest of it. In his Preface Teilhard wrote of the subjectivity in what appears to be objectivity: "While this aura of subjective interpretation may remain imperceptible where the field of observation is limited, it is bound to become practically dominant as soon as the field of vision extends to the whole" (p. 30). My tendency to confuse the way (pleasurefully or painfully) I live an experience with that experience itself, my ability to distract my own attention, my inclination to seek repose rather than to undergo hardship and, above all, my ability to disregard the truth of my personal identity in all of my living — mental resources such as these obscure my personal responsibility for making myself what I am. Thus I may live on, trapped in my semantic snares.

What a difference in the appreciation of personal dignity if a person says, "I traveled around the world" or, "I lived myself as traveling around the world I was living." Teilhard protected himself against this sure cultivation of self-disesteem deriving from regarding oneself as a part only of a whole that one has created himself. Note the self-esteem distinguishing, "I do not exist in a medium that influences me — my individuality is inviolable." Only a human individual mind is capable of living all that can be meant by "totalitarian ideology," "social evolution," "collective action," or "mass media." It is a fundamental and indisputable truth that any and all of such meaning is to be found only in an individual's mind. Illusions such as "authoritarianism," "coercion," "policing" are traceable to bare spots in an individual's conscious integrity and dignity. May it be repeated and repeated, every individual's mind is integrated, all in one piece. It is only the consciousness associated with that integration which may be either present or absent. In his Preface Teilhard first wrote of his Essay's "two basic assumptions" (his mind's conscious unifications), and only then proceeded, "The first is the primacy accorded to the psychic and to thought in the stuff of the universe, and the second is to the 'biological' value attributed to the social fact around us" (p. 30).

Teilhard recognized his organismic theory of the society of humanity ("noosphere") as being a creation of his own individual mind. Each of these and many another conception advanced in the interest of self-benefit test the strength and freedom of the reader's imagination. His plea for a *science of human energetics* as well as for the reconciliation of the disciplines of religion and science was a courageous living of his Catholicity (p. 283). His hyperzoan or epi-individual conception of all of mankind as having an individual mega-synthesis of its own, which includes life of its own, was a conscious personification offered for consideration of its benefit for human individuality. He saw that Utopia can exist only within the utopian, that heaven exists in its God. His emphasis upon the helpfulness of consciousness, in the sense of self-awareness, indicated his recognition of the propriety in attributing to human individuality its divine independence, initiative, and creativity. He beheld his human ethic as a development comparable to the kind of ability for self-care a man gives himself upon having a part of himself (or all of himself) clear up from an anesthetic (thus restoring natural powers of sensibility for living of pain and pleasure).

From his studies of evolution, Teilhard developed not only his conception of the unity of all life, but also his conception of the life of all existence. He did not exclude life even from his descriptions of life. His world orientation went beyond the primitive view that he belonged to an external universe as a brother to his fellowman and each animal, plant and mineral. His awareness of his authentic personal individuality, like that of the early Christians, awakened his sense of personal identity in all of his self-begotten creations. His self-view transcended that of belonging to any thing that he relegated as "external" to him (including the human race). Rather he saw everything as being what it was, namely, a part of himself. He loved his neighbor *as* (not "as if") himself. He loved his "enemy" as a difficult but helpful way of loving himself. Seeing the truth about his self, the one reality of his life, made him appreciate his wholeness. He trained his mental eye to see that his same life animated his ego and alter. He found that to describe anything of his world fully was to extol it. He liked to present for consideration views, not reasoning. He seemed to recognize argument as ever an intellectual dodge. One cannot help noting his tenderness in his living of his unseeing observers, "They do not know how to see, how to make the necessary adjustments in their vision" (p. 114). Of a trying observation he said, "We must 'make our eyes see'" (p. 122). His own experience had taught him that every bit of self-insight is attained only by hard work made possible only by an indomitable will to evolve that life consciousness: "The mysterious law which, from the humblest chemism to the highest synthesis of the spirit, makes all progress in the direction of increased unity express itself in terms of work and effort" (p. 310).[11]

Being and Becoming

For everyone who cannot recognize a problem as a disguised solution, there is ever associated with the evolutionary conception the troublesome problem of the concept of "progress." In his discussion of this meaning, it is as if Teilhard recognized how dear an illusion it is to the heart of everyone who is unable to recognize comprehensively that his God is always, all in all. The consciously integrated mind observed, "Whatever is, perfectly is." I trace my concept of perfectibility to my inability to be aware of existing perfection. Such meanings as "increasing self-insight," "improvement," "increasing ability to live fittingly," and so on, are based upon my dear illusions of past and future "change." "Amelioration" depends for its meaning upon the impossibility that the given existent can be the same and different. Sameness is itself, and cannot differ from itself. The creative power of the life process accounts perfectly for every moment of being, thoroughly, completely. Becoming, is becoming aware. If I am unable to see that truth, I am perfectly unable to do so, and this inability properly troubles me.

The consciously integrated mind recognizes every kind of experience as therapeutic, as helpful, as perfectly ideally practical. As Teilhard put it,

"Suffering is above all the consequence and the price of the travail of development." [12] Perfection is always present; it is the awareness of perfection only that can be described as "attainable." St. Paul clarified, "Nothing is of itself unclean, but to him who regards anything as unclean, to him it is unclean." [13]

Teilhard located his Kingdom of God, as he did his all, in his divine individuality: "Subjectively, first of all, we are inevitably the focus of our own observation. In its early, naïve stage, science, perhaps inevitably, imagined that we could observe things in themselves, as they would behave in our absence" (p. 32). To "fuse into a unity that is conscious of its organization" (as Teilhard described the act of becoming conscious of mental integration) is the ideal way of living every experience — excepting the instances when self-unconsciousness, as in sleep or self-ignoration while awake, serves a restorative, recuperative, or otherwise life-saving purpose.[14] Innumerable phantom problems are traceable to the fact that one assumes that he as subject can somehow be conscious of all of himself as subject and can as object be conscious of all of himself as object.

The truth of the matter is that one can speak only for a very minute portion of oneself at any given moment, and similarly, that he can live himself as object only to a minute extent at any given moment. To illustrate, when I focus my consciousness to be able to say "I am my own everything," the fraction of me which lives this experience as subject and object is infinitely small compared with my whole being. Realization of this truth would enable me to see the sense in living my neighbor's observation as, also, my very own experience that I create in my own mind and designate "my neighbor."

Teilhard recognized his own individuations: "For a mind that has awakened to a full meaning of evolution, mere inexplicable similitude is resolved in identity" (p. 222). He referred to each fundamentally new self-view as involving "the inner terrors of a metamorphosis. The child is terrified when it opens its eyes for the first time. Similarly, for our mind to adjust itself to lines and horizons enlarged beyond measure, it must renounce the comfort of familiar narrowness. It must create a new equilibrium for everything that had formerly been so neatly arranged in its small inner world" (p. 225). And again, "A new domain of psychical expansion — that is what we lack. And it is staring us in the face if we would only raise our heads to look at it" (p. 253). In all this material it is evident that Teilhard recognized the fact that personal unity, the sacred integrity of the human soul, is always present. "Uniting" really means only seeing unity that already existed.[15]

By his fidelity to his truth of individuality, Teilhard safeguarded himself against all the phantom problems traceable to his illusions of "betweenness" and of "communication." With the same comprehensive self-insight he could renounce the gladiatorial theory of existence, the tooth and claw ethic, and the police ethic. His clear view that the individual is made up of nothing but individuality disclosed to him the true ethic of self-help.

Teilhard's *Phenomenon of Man* constitutes an appeal to the consent of man to see to his self-government. As is every existent, man is moral. He may or may not be aware that he is moral. To the extent that he is capable of living himself consciously, his morality is beyond criticism. Anyone who can see his world as his own creation thereby takes upon himself a corresponding ethic. The only foolproof morality is one based upon the realization that a gain to anyone in my world is a gain to me, and that a loss to anyone in my world is a loss to me. A serious complication for the operation of this true human system of morals is the fact that no one is capable of viewing all of himself at any given moment. Similarly, he is incapable of viewing all of his world at any given moment. Nevertheless, self-consciousness provides a wholesomely workable "conscience."

For instance, I wish to have my every man treat his everyone and everything consciously as living elements of himself. This wish is based upon the realization of the loving care with which I proceed when I am conscious that my self-benefit is all that is involved in my act.

Teilhard saw that living consciously is living willingly, and indulged the natural need of his mind for revering its oneness. Concretely, he sensed his knowledge as being self-knowledge, as having its source in his own self-growth, in his own incarnant personal experience. For instance, with regard to his conception of divinity, it is as though he said to himself, "If I cannot see and operate my own dignity, any claim I might make regarding divinity must lack its most convincing force." And, "If I cannot trust myself, how trustworthy is any declaration or observation I may make?"

It seems that man represses (alienates from his sense of his personal identity) his divinity more than any other truth of his being. Thus, he lives his "conscience" unconsciously. His godliness-ignoration is accomplished largely as a product of his designating much of his own mental life as "extramental" "nonmental" or "impersonal" existence. Without his sense of personal identity (which includes "thinking subject" and "object of thought") what meaning has his *personal* observation? And yet, as Teilhard indicated, the scope of his divine look decided the measure of his divine realization. His life, a process of self-creation, originated from itself its meaning of divinity. Teilhard saw that the plural constitutive forces of eclecticism could not serve as the generative power of conscious individuality. Man, whose essence is unity, is a "one-man" human being. He can grow the insight to see the idea of "plurality" as being a product of his indifference. His experiences of nostalgia and of *unio mystica* may be expressions of his need to renounce his own habit of mental dissociation.

To ignore that my consciousness is made up of my selfness is to deprive myself of my sense of personal identity just where I need that sense of being, in order to appreciate the wonderfulness of my living. How well Teilhard portrayed this view: "Union can only increase through an increase in consciousness, that is to say, in vision (p. 31). . . . If to see more is really to become more, if deeper vision is really fuller being, then we should look closely at man in order to increase our capacity to live. . . . It often happens that what stares us in the face is the most difficult to perceive (p. 33). . . . I repeat that my only aim in these pages — and to this aim all my powers are bent — is to *see*; that is to say, to develop a *homogeneous* and *coherent* perspective of our general extended experience of man. A *whole* which unfolds (p. 35). . . . Up to now has science every troubled to look at the world other than from *without*?" (p. 52). Teilhard looked at his world and found it good. God being all, whatever is, is adorable. Whatever is, is divine. The process of "deification" is all and only the discovery of already existing divinity. Existence *is* godhood; it is only divinity-*awareness* which can be accurately described as "attainable" or "yet to be discovered." [16]

Teilhard observed clearly the self-disesteem an individual practices when he dissociates his temporal and spatial from his personal orientation. The earth is estimated to be approximately as many years old as the number of its human inhabitants. Considering its cosmic background, the earth is a speck. One must measure distances astronomically in terms of light years, and so on. See how Teilhard treated this illusion: "The consciousness of each of us is evolution looking at itself and reflecting (p. 220). . . . In the first and most widespread degree, 'the malady of space-time' manifests itself as a rule by a feeling of futility, of being crushed by the enormities of the cosmos" (p. 226). . . . Fundamentally, asks Teilhard, is not everything, apart from the present, mere conjecture? "I know of no more moving story nor any more revealing of a biological reality of a noogenesis than that of intelligence struggling step by step from the beginning to overcome the encircling illusion of proximity" (p. 215).

The succedaneum for self-consciousness is the wish to be "the center of attention," that is, the subject of "somebody else's consciousness." To the extent that I am incapable of living self-consciously — or, as Teilhard put it, "God all *in everyone*" (p. 308). I must depend upon the applause and the jeering of my own created "others" for the conduct of my life. Lacking self-consciousness, my way of life must be that of the actor or actress. If I am not capable of living my environment as existing within me, I must regulate my life as if I can be under the control of "environmental conditions." Teilhard envisaged his world as one where "one gives one's life to be and to know, rather than to possess" (p. 280).

Lacking self-consciousness, I panic if I do not have "company" with whom I can assure myself of my continuing existence. Without the proper sense of my personal identity I feel unable to take care of myself "alone." The fact is that I do face self-annihilation to the degree that I cannot see that I have myself to take care of. "In the course of the coming centuries it is indispensable that a nobly human form of eugenics, on a standard worthy of our personalities, should be discovered and developed" (p. 282).

This kind of longheaded comprehensiveness characterizes Teilhard's psychology. In so far as I can grow the strength of mind to be able to see that my life is all and only about me, my interest in eugenics finds expression as a natural self-interest. Sufficient self-consciousness conceives every individual as beginning his own inviolable living at the moment of his biological conception. The individual is always the issue of his own life process and has nothing but himself (narrowly or broadly conceived) "in mind." With St. Augustine he may say of his God, "Thou, O Lord, . . . didst turn me towards myself, taking me from behind my back, where I had placed myself." Teilhard indicated that all that life is capable of goes into the making of each man. His life is always employing all its resourcefulness. He is his own purpose, plan, direction, and final end. As Teilhard commented, "Carrel referred to man as 'the unknown.' But man, we should add, is the solution of everything that we can know" (p. 281).

In his chapter, "The Christian Phenomenon," under the section, Power of Growth, Teilhard reported his Christogenesis. Here he expressed the insight that the discipline of universal love is both daring and demanding. "Alone, [Christianity] can bend our hearts not only to the service of that tremendous movement of the world which bears us along, but beyond, to embrace that movement in love" (p. 297). It is particularly in this area that Teilhard saw his Christianity-experiences as having sustained his power of substantiating his own views of his life.

In his Appendix, Teilhard insightfully accounted for the fact that he had not spoken of pain or wrong, on the bases that his aim in this book had "been limited to bringing out the positive essence of the biological process of hominisation," and that, in the interests of clarity and simplicity, he had not "considered it necessary to provide the negative of the photograph."

In review, Teilhard's psychology was that of consciously keeping himself in his effort to describe his views of evolution: "I have tried to show that we can hope for no progress on earth without the primacy and triumph of the *personal* at the summit of *mind*" (p. 297). He worked his mind in a life-affirming way — "energy," "existence," "unity," "identity," "person," and "synthesis" being central ideas of his. He found, rather than lost, his mind in his "objectivity," in his "phenomenon," and in his God. He cherished evidently the helpfulness of his life's powers of consciousness, love, freedom, work, training, and adventure. He saw that it was divine to be human and that his human being did not compel his overlooking his divinity.

A "GENTILE'S" VIEW

Arthur J. Knodel

Teilhard de Chardin had an immense sympathy for outsiders of all sorts, among whom must be counted those outside the Church — the "Gentiles," as he called them; and those outside the ranks of professional science — let us simply call them "laymen." I, the writer of this essay, am both a "Gentile" and a layman. I speak only for myself, but it is my hope that what I have to say will reflect at least some of the thoughts and reactions of other "Gentiles" and laymen who have been drawn to Teilhard's works.

What first attracted me was simply the rather uncommon spectacle of a Jesuit priest proclaiming the necessity of accepting evolution unreservedly and *in toto*. But simple curiosity was not long in changing to deep interest and frequent admiration. I was struck, more or less simultaneously but in varying degrees, by three things in particular, namely, (1) Teilhard's gifts as a science popularizer, (2) certain aspects of his evolutionary synthesis which, I feel, are of special interest to a nonbeliever, and (3) Teilhard himself, considered as a *phénomène humain*. The second item is certainly the most important of the three; yet it can only be arbitrarily separated from the other two, as anyone familiar with Teilhard's writings would be quick to point out.

The Popularizer

France is not alone in having produced eminent scientists who were also highly successful at explaining the intricacies of their special field of knowledge to the uninitiated; yet it would be hard to find a succession of *vulgarisateurs* equal to the one that stretches uninterruptedly from Fontenelle through Henri Poincaré and beyond. Teilhard de Chardin unquestionably takes his place in that distinguished lineage.

Much of what Teilhard wrote concerning evolution and kindred topics simply reinforces what other scientists have said. To lay a solid groundwork for his theories and speculations, Teilhard had to repeat facts and arguments that are the common property of men of science; but in so doing he already betrays the organizing and synthetical faculty that was peculiarly his. One has only to read a page or two of even his most arid technical paper to realize that he possessed the inestimable gift of simplifying without grossly distorting and of finding the configurative device that transmits complex information efficiently to his reader. In this latter regard he is a master of expository metaphor. And in saying that, I am thinking, not of Teilhard's flights into the rarefied regions of the Omega Point, Christification, and the like, but simply of his formulation of already well-known scientific facts in a figurative language that is both economical and striking. By way of example:

> . . . Every distance in space, every morphological deviation, presupposes and expresses a duration.
>
> Let us take the very simple case of existing vertebrates. In the time of Linnaeus the classification of these animals had advanced sufficiently for them to be arranged in a definite structure of orders, families, genera, etc. Yet the naturalists of the day were unable to provide any scientific explanation of this system. We know now that the system of Linnaeus merely represents a present-day cross-section of a genealogical *tree* whose principal branches were the *phyla* coming down through the centuries. Accordingly the zoological separation of living creatures into different types reveals and measures in each case a difference in age. In the constellation of species, everything which exists and the place which it occupies implies a certain past, a certain genesis. In particular every time the zoologist meets a more primitive type than those he is familiar with (take the amphioxus, for example) the result is not merely to extend by one more unit the range of animal forms: no, a discovery of that sort *ipso facto* implies a stage, a verticil, another ring on the tree-trunk of evolution. For the amphioxus we can only find a place in the present animal kingdom by supposing a whole "proto-vertebrate" stage of life in the past, coming somewhere beneath the fishes (pp. 83–84).

This passage, quite truthfully chosen at random, tells us nothing that is in any way new or startling; and on the literary level it merely exploits the tried-and-true metaphor of the evolutionary tree of life — but with an unusual condensation and exploitation of all the possibilities of the metaphor. As Teilhard here develops the figure, some of the most far-reaching implications of the whole evolutionary picture are clearly prepared for: the inevitability of the concept of organic process and the imperative need of depth-projection in time — to name two. Nor is that all, for the metaphor is further and illuminatingly developed in subsequent pages.

Supporting this use of expository metaphor is the richness of Teilhard's vocabulary. Some critics have complained that even his nonscientific works bristle uncomfortably with technical terms and cacophonous neologisms. I am much more impressed by the peculiar felicity of most of Teilhard's terminology. When his neologisms are finally sprung on us, they usually have about them an air of inevitability which indicates that a very real need has been filled. Teilhard was anything but a pedant. What we know of his letters would prove the point, even if we did not possess the copious testimony of the persons with whom he constantly lived and worked. His vocabulary is, in fact, of a piece with his metaphorical gift and is dictated by the same need of clarity and economy of expression.

In all this, of course, I have left aside the lyrical pieces — for they are surely that — that punctuate the steady flow of Teilhard's technical communications and philosophical speculations. In those lyrical pieces, such as *La Messe sur le monde*, language is used to communicate an affective state, in short, for poetic ends. And while his language in these pieces is replete with the terms of Christian mysticism side by side with those of the natural and physical sciences, the sureness with which both kinds of terms are handled and the effectiveness with which they communicate his fervor certainly merit Teilhard the title of "poet," though it is one that he surely did not seek.

These lyrical asides, however, are an organic part of his total production, and not simply alien igneous intrusions thrusting up through the slowly accumulated scientific data. The same qualities of fervor and tension, albeit in less concentrated form, are discernible as well in the work of Teilhard the scientific expositor. There is in the very nature of his evolutionary synthesis a tremendous sweep and dramatic forward movement; but quite apart from that, in his most straightforward exposition of a technical scientific problem we sense a tension and expectancy that can only come from a complete absorption in the material that is being presented. After all, the question of whether *Homo sapiens* first appeared in Africa or Asia does not seem as if it would be particularly interesting to a layman. Yet, when we read Teilhard's speculations on the subject and follow his piecing together of evidence, gathered from a wide scientific experience in remote corners of the globe, the unraveling speculation creates something akin to suspense.

And the same can be said for the various other presentations of specialized subjects which Teilhard puts within the layman's grasp. It is as if we were reading a first-rate mystery story — first-rate, perhaps, because the particular mystery to be solved is one that for Teilhard inevitably opened out, so to speak, on the ultimate Mystery. His investigation of the most specialized technical details is always carried on in full consciousness of the total picture. And whether we do or do not agree with the various solutions offered by Teilhard, I think it is beyond doubt that the constant awareness of the total phenomenon and a passionate desire to penetrate that phenomenon account for the exceptionally dramatic quality of so much of Teilhard's purely scientific work. This concern with the total phenomenon is also, I believe, what gives his interpretation of the inescapable fact of evolution its greatest attraction for the "Gentile."

Aspects of the Evolutionary Synthesis

This is not the place to review the main lines of Teilhard's integral evolutionism, with its culmination in a startling reinterpretation of the Christian

mysteries. That is the purpose of other essays in this collection. It will, however, be impossible to avoid some repetition as we try to make clear why
certain aspects of Teilhard's evolutionism are of special interest to the nonbeliever. I shall focus attention on two aspects in particular. First there is
the arresting way in which Teilhard integrates man into the evolutionary
scheme — in short, his elaboration of the drama of hominization. And second,
there is an element that is less easy to formulate because it is, ultimately,
more an attitude arising from intellectual premises than it is an actual intellectual concept. I refer to Teilhard's deep persuasion that we are now living
in the midst of a tremendous evolutionary breakthrough. Since man's role in
that breakthrough is crucial for Teilhard, it is easy to see how closely the two
aspects are connected. Both merit discussion; but it is only fitting that we
first mention those points in the Teilhardian evolutionary scheme that the
"Gentile" will find hard to accept, even though he may find them interesting
and provocative.

The inclusiveness of Teilhard's synthesis is certainly one of its greatest
attractions, but sometimes things are subsumed in too arbitrary a fashion.
On the intellectual plane, this is true of the identification of the famous
Omega Point with a personalized deity who at one instant in the history of
our planet took on human guise and promulgated the Christian mysteries.
And the identification of certain of those mysteries with specific cosmological
phenomena — an identification that has worried the orthodox — is intellec-
tually arbitrary quite apart from any question of orthodoxy. On a more affective plane, another aspect of Teilhard's views that many a "Gentile" will
probably reject, albeit *à contrecœur*, is his long-term optimism. But let us
delay the discussion of his personalism and optimism until after we have
commented on the first great point of interest: the overriding importance
assigned to the phenomenon of man.

For all its central importance, the primacy of the human was not Teilhard's actual starting point or even his preconceived goal. As more and more
of his writings are published, it becomes clear that he started out with a dual
but compartmentalized interest. At a very early stage he felt his religious
calling, and almost simultaneously he discovered within himself a passion for
"matter" — more specifically for rocks, for geology. In this latter connection,
he became steadily more interested in paleontology; and then, within that
field he was to become a mammalian specialist, and finally — but by no means
exclusively — he concentrated on the primates, notably the hominids. This
slow and gradual focussing on the problem of hominization is, I feel, important and reassuring, for it minimized the possibility of an arrangement of
data to suit a preconceived end.

It did not take Teilhard long to realize that biological evolution is an
irrefutable fact. That realization alone, considering his background and con-

nections, was fraught with danger. But he went even further. So much impressed was he by the ordering of data made possible by biological evolution that he began seeking ways to extend this configurative principle both backward and forward: backward into prebiological domains and forward into domains where biology is forced to assimilate psychology and human history. And that, of course, is how he came to regard evolution as the cosmic process *par excellence*, with biological evolution as only one segment of that process.

Developments in the physical sciences in the last fifty years have certainly helped to make Teilhard's two-way extrapolation more plausible, for we are now told that matter is still being "created" in the universe and that the demarcation between organic and so-called inorganic matter becomes increasingly blurred. Chemical "missing links" are daily being discovered, bringing molecules, megamolecules, and self-reproducing viruses progressively closer to each other.

As for the missing links at the other end of the biological segment of evolution, it is common knowledge that Teilhard played a particularly active part in discoveries that supplied some of the most famous "missing links" (*Sinanthropus, Homo solensis, Australopithecus*) — even though the "missing link" metaphor is here misleading, since the picture of the actual relation between anthropoids and hominids becomes ever more complicated, with certain of the strains leading apparently to dead ends and with certain "links" in the main line still lacking.

Up to this point, however, Teilhard's conceptions, though they are expressed in particularly striking terms, are not too different from those of some other biologists and paleontologists. More original, perhaps, is his formulation of the forward movement of evolution in terms of what he called evolutionary "thresholds" and "leaps," along with the associated ideas of the progressive "complexification" and "centration" of the world-stuff. We know that Teilhard believed that the weight of empirical evidence imposed the view of an irreversible evolution, but we also know that he did not believe there was a discernible constant rate of evolutionary change. Instead, he thought that a kind of boiling point is reached, and at that moment (and it may be reached at widely varying points in cosmic space and time) evolution leaps across the threshold. The leap from megamolecules to self-reproducing viruses, for example, takes us across the threshold that separates the lithosphere from the biosphere. But where Teilhard becomes especially interesting is in the further extension of the principle of thresholds. Through his intensive study of mammals, and especially the primates, he concluded that with the emergence of *Homo sapiens*, of man the user of fire, tools and speech, another critical threshold has been and is still being crossed. We are passing from the biosphere into the noosphere, from the envelope of self-reproducing life into the envelope of self-consciousness and symbolic thought.

This notion of the threshold between the biosphere and the noosphere, which Teilhard backs up with a wealth of data, gives special importance to the human species. Man does not become, as he was in the Middle Ages, the creature for whom the universe was specially created and at whose center he found himself — in short, anthropocentrism of the Ptolemaic-Dantesque sort remains entirely out of the question. But man does take on an importance in the evolutionary process considerably greater than "the paragon of animals" which he was in the older Darwinian scheme. He is indeed the paragon of animals, but even biologically he is something more and something different. And that fact is crucial for Teilhard. It is hopelessly unscientific to regard the fact of self-consciousness as a mere sport, as a kind of "epiphenomenon." (Indeed, the very idea of "epiphenomena" seems most unscientific to me, as I suspect it did to Teilhard, though I do not know that he says so in so many words.) To be scientifically consistent, self-consciousness must take its place in the total phenomenon, in the entire scheme of things. The scientist above everyone else must see life steadily *and* see it whole; in fact, for him wholeness of vision should probably take priority. And Teilhard's attempt to find the true place of self-consciousness in the total phenomenon, no matter how provisional and partial that attempt may turn out to be, is to me the most striking and significant aspect of his scientific speculation.

But before considering some of the consequences of the view that a new threshold is being crossed with the appearance of *Homo sapiens*, we must review at least some of the reasons that led Teilhard to adopt this view. These reasons are quite numerous, but it will suffice here to mention only the two crucial ones, the two that have to do with certain irreducible peculiarities of the human species. First, there is the peculiarity of reflective thought. The use of fire and the fabrication of utensils are the earliest expression of this, and, from these rudimentary beginnings, symbolic speech and conceptual thought seem to have sprung, or, at least, to have simultaneously developed. The plasticity of man's behavior, his ability to adjust it to constantly varying and sometimes entirely new situations, is one of man's great distinguishing characteristics. This plasticity of behavior seems to be the biological outcome of the second great human peculiarity, namely, the phyletic convergence of *Homo sapiens*.

In all the major phyla, including those of the vertebrates, speciation goes on more and more intensely, giving rise to an ever-increasing number of mutually infertile species. The phyla "fan out" or "ramify" into ever more divergent and noninterbreeding species that finally atrophy at a point of maximum specialized adaptation. Teilhard presents very interesting evidence to indicate that this was the case even for the prehominids. But on arriving at man the artificer, the fanning-out process seems to be suddenly reversed. Instead of the subspecies evolving into full-blown and mutually infertile species, they coalesce. All the ethnic groups known to exist today, no matter how great their physical and mental divergence, are mutually fertile. The shuffling of genes into more and more combinations, with consequent enrichment of traits, goes on to produce an ever more adaptable human being. And the success of *Homo sapiens* on the biological level is today attested by the way he has invaded every nook and cranny of the earth's surface and, still more, by the incredible breeding-storm that, sociologists tell us, is producing a population explosion heretofore undreamed of.

This pooling of genetic potentialities, this immensely increased biological adaptability, is translated, according to Teilhard, into the fact of ever-increasing socialization. Human ties become ever more immediate and inescapable. The human network grows tighter over the surface of the whole planet. Here again the evidence seems to me conclusive. But instead of the dread and anxiety that most of us feel at the spectacle of population explosions and an ever-tightening web of human relations, Teilhard felt reassured and, at moments at least, actually exhilarated by the spectacle. He considered such phenomena as nuclear fission and thermonuclear fusion, or the creation of electronic "brains" that can come up with mathematical functions the human mind has not yet happened upon, as a logical part of the evolutionary process. They were for him proof of the intuition that he had had at quite an early date that the boiling point has once more been reached, that we are here on earth in the very midst of one of those leaps into a new evolutionary stage fraught with novelties as yet unimaginable.

One of the characteristics of this next stage will be the counterpart on the intellectual level of the process of phyletic convergence on the human-biological level. Teilhard foresaw vast poolings of data and knowledge and a co-operation of men of learning in all fields such as have never before been undertaken. He regarded his own participation in such enterprises as the Chinese Geological Survey and the African research made possible by the Wenner-Gren Foundation as only the timidest beginnings of such international co-operation. And we know how fascinated he was by such scientific associations as those that made possible the realization of the various giant particle-accelerators. His co-operation with Sir Julian Huxley in the halcyon days of UNESCO is a matter of record. It is here that Teilhard's profound but far from naïve internationalism fits in.

All this leads to the view that the evolutionary process on earth is at the point where it can begin to control its own movement. It cannot, according to Teilhard, be reversed; but it can be knowingly directed and canalized. And indeed, he says, it must be.

It is striking to see how close this view is to that of scientists in other fields and particularly of scientists who are outside the religious fold. It was my good fortune to spend an evening recently in conversation with — or, more accurately, listening to — a leading French atomic scientist. His enthusiasm for the research he was directing was so overwhelming that, momentarily at least, its sheer joyousness made one forget the destructive potential that such research holds. He is a militant and uncompromising agnostic, yet his consciousness of an imminent breakthrough and of his participating in a world-wide phenomenon of overwhelming importance made him sound at times as if he were reading some of Teilhard's pages to me. What made the similarity even more striking was the man's insistence, not merely on the necessity of, but on the immense exhilaration of global scientific research and teamwork. "We are," he kept reiterating, "on the verge of the most incredible age in all human history; the releasing of nuclear forces can be compared only with man's discovery of the use of fire."

The prospect of what this scientist called "the plastification of the earth's surface" (it occurred to me that "plastification" was the kind of word that the inventor of "complexification" and "cephalization" might well have used) that is, the possibility of operating such radical changes as, let us say, the creation of a range of mountains in the Sahara to provide rain and hence fertility for a vast waste land — did not frighten him. And this was the sort of prospect that did not frighten Teilhard either. When some of us timidly reminded the scientist of the misgivings that even some of his most eminent co-workers had about the destructive potential of their discoveries, the reaction was surprising. Yes, of course, there had already been terrible destruction, but not more terrible than other kinds of destruction in the past. After all, whole civilizations had died out. But as for the total destruction of mankind, no, that was quite out of the question. It was not in the scheme of things. *"Car, comme presque tout homme de science, je suis, au fond, profondément optimiste."*

It came as no great surprise to learn that this militant agnostic was thoroughly familiar with Teilhard's writings and deeply impressed by the extraordinary lucidity with which Teilhard had been able to express many of the views that he himself had been expounding. His declaration about being "at heart, profoundly optimistic" brings us once more to the same aspect of Teilhard's thought. There is, of course, no question of Teilhard's optimism being bland or complacent. He had seen the excruciating suffering of trench warfare in World War I, he had traveled the world over and undoubtedly seen the extremes of poverty and disease that only the Orient can exhibit; he was acutely aware of physical suffering, as his heartbreaking tribute to his invalid sister so eloquently shows.[1] But, in spite of all this, he remained profoundly optimistic.

It is easy to assume that we are faced with a traditional Christian optimism. Because of his religious faith he was convinced *a priori* that everything would come out right in the end. But it need hardly be pointed out that Christian pessimism — represented today by all shades of Christian existentialism — is, if anything, a more flourishing tradition than Christian optimism. The central doctrines of the Fall and of man's abjection before God lend themselves much more easily to a pessimistic view. And besides, as the agnostic scientist showed, a profound optimism can exist apart from any belief in Christian finalism. That Teilhard's Catholicism abetted his optimism is undeniable; but the optimism was there in the first place. The conviction that man is genuinely at the forefront of a great evolutionary adventure likewise contributed to Teilhard's optimism. But I suspect that it stemmed most of all from his own unflagging decency and admirable naïveté. Again and again we hear how incapable he was of imputing ulterior motives to the persons with whom he had to deal. On the whole, he was fortunate in his human contacts, for many a person as fundamentally decent as Teilhard has been brutally taken advantage of and persecuted. But even if all of this makes Teilhard a particularly congenial figure, it does not make his optimism (nor that of the agnostic scientist) more easily acceptable.

Even if we assume that the spearhead of the evolutionary process — what Teilhard calls "la flèche" — will move inexorably forward to levels of more complexity and fuller realization, this assumption still does not explain or justify the incredible waste and pain and destruction that, from the human point of view, run all through biological evolution. And what may be blind antagonism and struggle for survival on a lower level become in the noosphere man's terrifying inhumanity to man. I am, of course, not the first to put forth this objection to Teilhard's optimism (it is interesting to note that a fellow Christian of Teilhard's, Gabriel Marcel, also raised the objection). To be told that this strain of suffering and self-conscious evil is part of a vast *via dolorosa* that eventually leads to liberation and fulfillment seems not merely gratuitous and autistic; in the face of the terrible protracted and lonely suffering that surrounds us everywhere, it is, in human terms, almost an insult.

This brings us to another and allied aspect of Teilhard's thought that I mentioned as hard to accept: his personalism. Teilhard very reasonably regarded as quite untenable the view of man as the terminus of evolution. There is nothing to indicate that the process stops with man. All the weight of probability is on the side of further projection of the cosmic evolutionary process. But, as we know, Teilhard foresees an increasing coalescence of the noosphere until another critical threshold is reached, which he designated as the Omega Point. This point Teilhard quite arbitrarily identifies with

Parousia, the second coming of Christ. But even leaving aside this orthodox religious interpretation, there is a concordant element that is not necessarily Christian in character — namely, the necessity of thinking of the Omega Point, and what is beyond, in anthropomorphic terms. An adoration of abstract forces is impossible, says Teilhard. These forces must take on a head and a heart, a human visage, to be genuinely adorable. That contention *per se* is probably true; the kind of loving surrender that is the ultimate in adoration can only be to something that, somehow, remains human. The overwhelming difficulty is that concrete evidence of the existence of such a personalized God is lacking.

Moreover, is such a God really desirable? Humanizing the forces beyond us may conceivably be repellent to the human heart and mind, for in human terms there can be no justification for the meaningless suffering and gratuitous cruelty that run all through the development of life and extend throughout history. To tell us that the suffering and cruelty seem meaningless to us only because we cannot view them under the aspect of eternity is to beg the question. In the face of Teilhard's personalism, many a "Gentile," including myself, will be constrained to say that beyond our human horizon there is indeed Mystery, but that "It has no face; it is not faceless; it is not conscious; it is not unconsciousness: it is Mystery" (Edna St. Vincent Millay). No, neither the actual existence, nor perhaps even the desirability of the existence of a personalized God, is likely to be readily acceptable to many "Gentiles."

But what is unquestionably impressive is Teilhard's marshaling of paleontological data to prove that man occupies a special place in the vast evolutionary process that constitutes the cosmos. That contention seems about as close to a certainty as we are likely to come across in this life. While it renders untenable the extreme forms of existentialism in which man really has no place in the scheme of things and must therefore pit himself against the web of absurdity that enmeshes him, it does not by any means dissipate our feelings of extreme loneliness and helplessness as we face day-by-day concrete situations. It does seem to indicate that we are playing a strangely important role, but we cannot be sure just what that role involves. Our dignity, then, resides not in blind faith and a surrender to the forces that are manifest in the evolutionary forward movement, but in a dogged effort to understand that movement as best we can and to diminish suffering and gratuitous cruelty in the noosphere in every way we can, in full recognition of the fact that the outcome of even the most carefully conceived and executed act is problematic and that there is every chance of failure.

There are, of course, many other *aperçus*, many other speculations in Teilhard's work which I have not even touched upon; and almost all of them, whether ultimately acceptable or not, are of interest. And then we must recall that all the data are not yet in. We laymen must await the verdict of Teilhard's fellow scientists on many a crucial point and promising suggestion. Teilhard himself not only accepted such criticism, he invited it; for he was a person of great stature, an exceptional *phénomène humain*.

Teilhard the Man

The dozens of testimonials that have come from the friends and associates of Teilhard in all walks of life attest the unusual human qualities of the man. But such proof is really not needed, for it must be obvious to even casual readers of his works (and for the moment I am not speaking of his personal letters) that they are in the presence of a human being who suffered and exulted deeply, who lived with uncommon awareness and intensity. Here is one place where we need not feel uneasy in repeating the cliché that the man "lived his thought." That thought was set in motion by certain aptitudes he was quick to discover within himself when he was still quite young; but reciprocally, his conduct as he became ever more involved in the "paleontological adventure" was dictated by the system of thought that he progressively elaborated. The "Gentile" especially cannot fail to be impressed by the profound cohesion and unity of Teilhard's life, while at the same time he cannot fail to wonder at the number of strange paradoxes presented by that life.

Surely one of the most curious of those paradoxes is the fact that Teilhard's membership in the Society of Jesus accounts for certain of the most important circumstances that made possible his paleontological research, which in its turn produced most of the ideas that his Jesuit superiors found too daring for comfort and for the printed page. Had Teilhard not been a Jesuit, would he have been able to penetrate those remote regions of China, such as the Ordos, where, alone among Occidentals, the Jesuits had a legal foothold? That circumstance undoubtedly made possible the pioneer work in mapping the fossiliferous areas of China — an achievement that is one of Teilhard's earlier claims to scientific fame. And later, when it was made clear that his religious community would rather have him in China, and still later in the United States, rather than in France, did not these "exiles" make possible Teilhard's participation in the Choukoutien project, which resulted in the discovery of Peking Man, and in the treks that resulted in the work on the African origins of *Homo sapiens*?

And then, in more general terms, Teilhard's ecclesiastical status surely made it possible for him to devote himself to science in a way that the usual scientist *dans le siècle* seldom can. He was spared the responsibility of marital ties and bringing up a family; his movements were therefore relatively unhampered, and his membership in the Society of Jesus provided him with a *pied-à-terre* almost everywhere he went.

These paradoxes inevitably arouse the outsider's curiosity about the exact nature of Teilhard's relations with the Society of Jesus. The matter is a delicate one, and though much has already been written about it, vast blanks and many a question mark still remain. But beyond this lies the even more fascinating question of the exact quality of Teilhard's religious faith.

When we read of Teilhard's puritanical Catholic Auvergnat background and of his early and wholehearted acceptance of this heritage, we realize that a Catholic *ambiance* was as natural to him as the air he breathed. One has no difficulty believing that there was never the slightest question of his breaking with the Society of Jesus, let alone with the Church as a whole. Moreover, his submission to the will of his superiors and his unswerving loyalty to the Society are both matters of record. Yet it does seem to me that the complete and uninterrupted serenity of Teilhard's faith, on which his apologists somewhat stridently insist, is open to serious question.

There are, for example, those published fragments of letters relative to the death of Teilhard's beloved friend and scientific collaborator, Davidson Black. I may be pardoned, I hope, for quoting three very similar passages, for the very fact of reiteration is important here. First, from two letters, both dated March 18, 1934:

> . . . Davidson Black died suddenly two nights ago (heart failure). . . . Black was feeling better (or so it seemed). He had just been chatting animatedly with some friends, full of plans, as usual. A moment later he was found dead, near the table in the Lab you are familiar with, between the *Sinanthropus* and the skull from the Upper Cave. A fine death, in full career. But leaving a terrible void. We shall have to close ranks in order to go on with the work.
> . . . But what an absurd thing this life appears to be! So absurd that one feels thrown back upon a stubborn and desperate faith in the reality and continuing presence of the spirit. Otherwise (if there is no Spirit, I mean), we would really be imbeciles not to walk out on the human struggle.[2]

And that same day:

> Today I feel deeply the need for saving the world from its material darkness. You already know that Dr. Black passed away. The apparent absurdity of this premature end, the Stoic but blind acceptance of this fatal blow by all our friends here, the complete absence of "light" over the poor dead body lying in the cold room of the P.U.M.C. — it all deepened my grief and revolted my spirit. Either there is, somewhere, an outlet for thought and personality — or else the World is a hideous mistake. And then we should *have* to stop. But since no one will admit we must stop — well, we

must *believe*. To awaken that faith must be, more than ever, my duty. I swore it to myself, over the remains of Davy — who was more than a brother to me.[3]

Finally, some three weeks later:

> . . . It was with Black that I thought out, loved and planned my work. All that, but something more, too. I mean a concrete and acute "realization" of the immense vanity of the "human struggle" if there is no natural, as well as supernatural, outlet of the universe into some sort of deathless consciousness. In the disarray that followed Black's death, in the stifling atmosphere of "agnostic" regrets that surrounded him, I swore over the dead body of my friend to fight harder than ever to give hope to mankind's working and searching.[4]

Surely these poignant lines have in them an element of purely human and nondoctrinal revolt. The sense of the absurd that has become the overworked shibboleth of existentialism, but that assails all of us at times in one form or another, is patently present here. M. Cuénot felt compelled to add a footnote to the passage quoted in his book (the second passage above): "It is well to emphasize that Father Teilhard did not at all believe in immortality out of desperation. His conviction, both Christian and philosophical, was in no way the result of an emotional shock. The emotional shock simply intensified the conviction."[5] Perhaps so. But Teilhard should be allowed to speak for himself. M. Cuénot's assurance had, for me at least, precisely the reverse effect it was intended to have.

There is another especially interesting — and tantalizingly incomplete — fragment (presumably of a letter) concerning Teilhard's fellow Catholic, Paul Claudel. Teilhard is quoted as saying:

> Claudel finds no difficulty in the multiplicity of worlds: they juggle for our amusement. Nor any difficulty in the historical interpretation of the Bible; isn't it quite enough that the Bible provides such prodigious food for thought? There is no adversary in sight, at the present time, to Christianity — isn't Christianity the only real influence on men of good will? The idea of a man undergoing an intellectual crisis at the present moment strikes him as an anachronism.[6]

Does this not clearly imply that, while there was no difficulty in these questions for Claudel, there certainly must have been for the speaker? And if the whole passage in which the above sentences occur is read, it is quite clear that its not-so-gentle irony (whether conscious or unconscious) indicates Teilhard's acute discomfort at the kind of airy intellectual sleight-of-hand implied in Claudel's attitude. And this and the other passages I have quoted are not the only ones of their kind.

Obviously, all the data are not yet available. Too many of the persons intimately connected with Teilhard's life are still alive for a complete "deposition" to be feasible. Yet biographical memoirs and reminiscences about Teilhard are already legion; and at least one immense biographical mosaic, by Claude Cuénot, has already been published. But all of them leave us unsatisfied. The best key to Teilhard's extraordinary life remains his own "lyrical" pieces and above all the two absorbing, but unfailingly irritating, collections of epistolary fragments (*Lettres de voyage* and *Nouvelles lettres de voyage*). They are unfailingly irritating because the letters are almost never quoted *in toto*, and the reader has no real clue as to the nature of the materials omitted. But these fragments, along with the equally copious fragments quoted by M. Cuénot in his book (almost invariably without indicating the recipient of the letter quoted) suffice to make it perfectly clear that Teilhard was one of the great French letter writers of modern times.

I can only hope that a truly critical edition, without any apologetic intent, of as many of Teilhard's letters as can be collected will be forthcoming as soon as possible. Such a document would be of the greatest interest to "Gentile" and believer, to scientist and layman alike. Not only would it shed light on the specific question of the exact quality of Teilhard's religious belief and other equally important personal matters; it would also be a travel-diary of an uncommonly vivid sort and an astonishing chronicle of one of the great scientific adventures of the first half of the 20th century. Perhaps even more important is the fact that much of the material that ultimately went into Teilhard's formal essays is to be found in the letters in a nascent state, so to speak; and nowhere is it more evident that the thought and the man are one.

I do not think that even the most uncritical of Teilhard's admirers have anything to fear from the publication of such a document. If it by chance revealed more acute crises of momentary disbelief and doubt than have yet been revealed, then the interest would be all the greater, for we would undoubtedly have a far clearer notion of the way in which those doubts were resolved — as we know they were — in Teilhard's own thinking.

He remained in and belongs to the Church, whatever may be the reservations in this regard that the Church may put forward. But in a most uncommon way he speaks to all men. It was he who wrote, after listening to a paper by one of his "Gentile" fellow scientists:

> . . . There is, outside the Church, an immense fund of goodness and beauty, which will undoubtedly achieve full realization only in Christ, but which meanwhile does exist and with which we must sympathize if we would be fully Christian ourselves and if we would annex this goodness and beauty to God.[7]

He belonged to all men, and his prayer was to be, not extrahuman or super-human, but fully human:

> . . . I still see only one way out: to keep going forward, believing ever more firmly. May the Lord only keep alive within me a passionate delight in the world and a great gentleness, and may He help me to be, to the very end, fully human.[8]

8

THE BIRTH OF LIFE AND CONSCIOUSNESS

Richard W. Balek

The thought of Teilhard concerning the origin of life and consciousness can be essentially summarized by the following excerpt:

> On the scientific plane, the quarrel between materialists and the upholders of a spiritual interpretation, between finalists and determinists, still endures . . . each only sees half the problem. . . . I am convinced that the two points of view require to be brought into union, and that they soon will unite in a kind of phenomenology or generalized physics in which the *internal aspect* of things as well as the *external aspect* of the world will be taken into account (p. 53).

He sees clearly the incompatibility of the points of view of the mechanist and the neovitalist. He suggests in addition that this incompatibility will remain as long as the upholders of the respective notions refuse to acknowledge each other.

For the vitalist, even the final mechanical explanation will not completely account for any given phenomenon. What the mechanist calls causal explanation is really only a description — a recounting of the sequence of events that constitute a given situation. The mechanist begins with the existence of a material, operative system and simply describes the behavior of matter under given conditions without accounting for the ability of the inert matter to react or behave as it does.

The vitalist requires that a fundamental directing force be added to inorganic matter to account for its ability to organize into the system which we call life. This force is a spiritual entity and is not amenable to scientific investigation.

Neither of these schools of thought can ever completely triumph over the other, since both represent an aspect of the truth. It is only via the correlation of what is true in both points of view that a coherent picture of the universe is possible.

Teilhard conceives of a purely mechanical description of the development of the universe — a continuous evolution from inorganic matter to life and even to consciousness without the intervention of a vitalistic force. His requirement is that this spiritual force exist from the onset in simple, unorganized matter.

His call is a grandiloquent appeal to dispel the closed-mindedness of our current scientific view of the world, to reformulate our fundamental notions concerning the nature of our universe. Just as the introduction of the theory of relativity forced us to readjust our basic concepts of the duality of matter and energy, so also, says Teilhard, must we re-examine our present concept of the duality of the material and the spiritual. So also must we come to recognize that materiality and spirituality, which we have habitually considered only in isolation from each other, actually represent the same reality and are only different manifestations of that reality.

The "internal aspect of things" to which Teilhard refers is an inner striving, a minuscule consciousness, which is as much a part of atomic matter as the material stuff of which it is made. Obviously this notion is not a conclusion drawn from observation of simple matter. It is rather a result of the extrapolation from the characteristics of man and animals to the necessary potential existence of these characteristics in simple matter. It is the result of an attempt to add unity and continuity to a total view of reality. This particular total view of reality begins, however, with the *observation* of the existence of consciousness in the human animal. It begins with the *observation* that life is an organized system. It begins with the acceptance of the notions that love and beauty at the human level and regulation at the biotic level are kinds of reality which are different from the completely passive existence of a totally inert matter.

Teilhard does not ask the question, How does dull, mechanical matter give rise to this entity which I call consciousness? This is not a valid question for him because it eliminates from consideration too large a segment of observable reality. More significant for him is the question, What must be the nature of matter in order for it to be able to give rise to consciousness? This question is more significant because it includes more of the real world of experience. If one begins his inquiry with physical matter only, then he can legitimately neglect the role of consciousness in his subject — not that consciousness is absent but that it is present in such meager degree as to escape notice. But the object of Teilhard's science is the explanation of all things in nature; and this, for Teilhard, includes the realm of life and consciousness as necessarily as it does the realm of inorganic matter:

> In the eyes of the physicist, nothing exists legitimately, at least up to now, except the *without* [external aspect] of things. The same intellectual attitude is still permissible in the bacteriologist, whose cultures (apart from some substantial difficulties) are treated as laboratory reagents. But it is still more difficult in the realm of plants. It tends to become a gamble in

the case of the biologist studying the behaviour of insects or coelenterates. It seems merely futile with regard to the vertebrates. Finally, it breaks down completely with man, in whom the existence of a within [internal aspect] can no longer be evaded, because it is the object of a direct intuition and the substance of all knowledge (p. 55).

The mechanism, then, by which Teilhard unifies these various levels of reality is evolution. It follows, therefore, that for consciousness to have evolved from matter, it necessarily had to exist in some rudimentary form in what we have heretofore considered to be unconscious matter:

. . . consciousness, in order to be integrated into a world-system, necessitates consideration of the existence of a new aspect or dimension in the stuff of the universe (p. 55).

This view is certainly not unique to the thought of Teilhard. In holding to this interpretation Teilhard allies himself with a mode of thought which is common to many thinkers, both scientists and nonscientists.

We find that Teilhard's views reflect the thought of men like J. C. Smuts, who has written:

In spite of the great advances which have been made in knowledge, some fundamental gaps still remain; matter, life and mind still remain utterly disparate phenomena. Yet the concepts of all three arise in experience, and in the human all three meet and apparently intermingle, so that the last word about them has not yet been said. Reformed concepts of all three are wanted. . . . The acceptance of evolution as a fact, the origin of life-structures from the inorganic, must mean a complete revolution in our idea of matter. If matter holds the promise and potency of life and mind it is no longer the old matter of the physical materialists. . . . a re-survey will be made in the sequel of our ideas relating to matter, life and mind, and an attempt will be made to reach the fundamental unity and continuity which underlie and connect all three.[1]

Teilhard's critics have been scathing on the point that his is not a scientifically based thesis. The point is well taken in that Teilhard himself claims to be scientific, but it should be remembered that he meant that he would use as his foundation that which is known with scientific certitude. Consider the points on which he is "nonscientific."

a) That spiritual energy does exist — which is tantamount to an anti-mechanistic stand.
b) That via some evolutionary process this spiritual energy, working within and through matter, gave rise to life and consciousness.

The first point we have already discussed, pointing out that this is an attitude of many contemporary scholars. It is true that in Teilhard's work one is aware that this attitude appears to represent gross assumption. This is due to a great extent, I am sure, to the fact that he does not provide argument or defense for his stand against pure mechanism. This particular point is less disturbing if one recalls that Teilhard is writing against a background of such defense, and for him to repeat these is needless. Quite recently Sinnott has presented an excellent review of such arguments in which he states that

> The mechanistic hypothesis as applied to man gets itself tangled in such a web of paradoxes and contradictions that to accept it requires a degree of metaphysical agility most of us do not possess. Common sense cries out against it, and although we have ample warning today that common sense is often fallible, the practical fact is that we cannot think and act as if we were machines. The very conduct of scientific research presupposes that there are many courses among which we can choose and find our way, many purposes that we can entertain. *The empirical basis of this conclusion is as firm as that of any the scientist can reach.*[2]

It appears then that what Teilhard refers to as spiritual energy has real meaning to the people of the scientific world even though the true nature of that entity is not fully known. *Apropos* of the same notion it is interesting to note that in a study of the problem of causality in the realm of physics, Cassirer concludes,

> Modern physics had to abandon the hope of exhaustively presenting the whole of natural happening by means of a single strictly determined system of symbols. It finds itself faced with the necessity of applying various types of symbols, of schematic explanations to the same event. It has to describe one and the same entity as a particle and a wave, and must not be deterred in this use by the fact that the intuitive combination of the two pictures proves impossible. . . . When, even in science, such a superposition of dissimilar aspects is necessary, it will be the more easily understandable that we shall meet such a superposition again as soon as we go outside its realm — as soon as we seek to realize the full concept of reality, which requires the co-operation of all functions of the spirit and can only be reached through all of them together.[3]

On the second point — that the proposed mechanism of evolution is non-scientific — this is granted. But it should be noted that Teilhard himself suggests as much in his first elaboration of spiritual energy:

> Naturally the following considerations do not pretend to be a truly satisfactory solution of the problem of spiritual energy. Their aim is merely to show by means of one example what, in my opinion, an integral science of nature should adopt as its line of research and the kind of interpretation it should follow (p. 62).

Also, it is in this area in which he becomes most fanciful. It is here that one has most difficulty in separating Teilhard the scientist from Teilhard the poet. For example, Teilhard is quite explicit in that ". . . to see . . . and not to explain . . . is the sole aim of this study" (p. 58). Almost immediately thereupon he states the "law of complexity and consciousness: a law that implies a psychically convergent structure and curvature of the world" (p. 61), which is a requirement for his *explanation* of the evolutionary process. Again, he claims that his subsequent arguments will derive from the "without" of things, from their external aspect, and so come under the heading of scientific observation. He follows in the succeeding pages with an enumeration of several phenomena occurring in biological organisms, e.g., differentiation, accumulation of variations; and then proceeds to explain the occurrence of these phenomena on the basis of the conscious, selective activity of bionts. "The organism . . . is able to find room inside itself to lodge the countless mechanisms added successively in the course of its differentiation" (p. 107), obviously in reference to the *within* of the organism. In the same vein Teilhard considers the role of natural selection in his proposed system of heredity and evolutionary development. Yet Forsthoefel concludes that Teilhard's genetics reflects a Lamarckian point of view which biologists in general consider to be unproven.[4]

When Teilhard discusses his new concepts of radial and tangential energy, one recognizes the similarity between his "closed, curved system" and the systems of classical thermodynamics. Yet his account of the mechanism of the necessary interrelatedness and interconversion of these energies reduces to simply "They are constantly associated and in some way pass into one another" (p. 64), an explanation that is certainly not related to thermodynamics.

The above criticism is not meant to deny all factual foundation to Teilhard for, indeed, all of his work begins with observed reality. Its purpose is merely to point out that the accumulation of scientific fact is, to date, inadequate to Teilhard's purpose — that of "presenting a unified picture of the world in a space-time continuum," and, further, that where there are gaps in our scientific knowledge, Teilhard fills in with fertile imagination. It is his ability to admix fact and speculation which, in my mind, accounts for Teilhard's popularity, for the unwary reader may easily be seduced into accepting the entire work as scientifically valid.

In summary I should like to restate the major points I have tried to bring out. First, that while Teilhard claims to be writing a scientific tract, his main purpose is to present his personal viewpoint of the total universe. Since there is no such unified whole that is known with scientific certitude, his task is to erect a cohesive superstructure using as a foundation the incomplete set of scientific facts which is available (e.g., thermodynamics, evolution) and the views which are acceptable to other members of the scientific community (e.g., the theory of organism, the nonmateriality of human values).

Secondly, that the major weakness in Teilhard's work derives from his attempt to substantiate his poetic vision of the world with an incomplete science. In so doing he is forced to stretch known facts and to invent new concepts that have only a superficial resemblance to accepted fact.

Thirdly, that much of the attention Teilhard receives is due to the apparent correlation of his thesis with accepted scientific fact. His work, already appealing in an aesthetic sense, and satisfying to the phenomenologically oriented mind, takes on added significance by virtue of this tenuous connection with the facts of natural science.

Finally, that, while it is true that some of Teilhard's presentation does have scientific foundation, much of the book justifies the feeling of many of his critics that he was, in the words of Simpson, ". . . primarily a Christian mystic and only secondarily, although importantly, a scientist." [5]

9

BENEATH THE MICROSCOPE

Paulinus F. Forsthoefel, S. J.

Before we begin our consideration of some biological aspects of Teilhard de Chardin's book *The Phenomenon of Man*, we may ask ourselves a more general question: Is this work a scientific treatise? At the beginning of his masterpiece, Teilhard insists repeatedly that he is considering the universe and man's place in it from a purely phenomenological viewpoint, and he distinguishes this approach from that of a philosopher or a theologian. Plainly he wishes his conclusions to stand on their scientific bases alone. As we read his work, we find much that is based on established scientific facts or on very probable inductions from these facts. When, however, he introduces his postulate of Omega to provide a goal for human evolution of the future, he has left the domain of pure science for that of philosophy and even theology. However much we admire and understand the need for such a postulate, we must admit that this postulate goes beyond the field of natural science as such. Strict natural science as such can neither assert nor deny the existence of Omega, since natural science deals by definition only with experimental data and the relations among such data.

There is of course a fundamental difficulty in the task Teilhard set for himself. Is it possible to consider man only from a purely phenomenological or scientific viewpoint and at the same time in any adequate degree to unveil the mystery of man? It seems inevitable that one will enter the domain of philosophy and even theology in such a quest. The paleontologist George Gaylord Simpson could not treat the phenomenon of human evolution without entering into the question of the impact this has on human morals.[1] The geneticist Theodosius Dobzhansky[2] and the scientific popularizer Julian Huxley[3] have both had similar experiences. Granted this fundamental difficulty, it remains true that Teilhard's work in its entirety cannot be called simply a scientific treatise in the ordinary sense. In his search for the fundamental reasons for the origin of the stars and planets, the atoms, the molecules, living things, man himself, in various laws of nature such as that of "complexification," Teilhard appears to have created more a philosophy than a science. One is tempted to call his work a cosmology. Some may be tempted to go even farther and call it a poetic hymn written by one inspired in praise of the creative work of evolution, rather than a sober work of science. Whatever we may think of the result, however, it is certain that Teilhard himself meant to base his work on the most assured facts of science and that he conceived his originality to be in the discovery of certain general scientific laws. The purpose of the present essay is to examine the scientific validity of some of his work having a rather direct biological bearing. In the course of the essay, from time to time we shall deliberately stray into the field of philosophy to consider important philosophical implications.

The Origin of Life

The first problem with a biological bearing which Teilhard confronts is the origin of life. In recent years biologists have considered this problem and have examined the conditions under which life could have come into existence on the earth. Pasteur, it was realized, never proved that life could not come into existence spontaneously but only that, under conditions now existing on the earth, life always arises from pre-existing life. The question remains untouched whether, under conditions prevailing on the early earth, life could come into existence spontaneously. Naturally the leaders in the theoretical and experimental attack on the problem have been not strictly biologists but biochemists, notably the Russian Oparin.[4] One proposal is that the borderline of life was reached by a series of chemical processes, beginning with the formation of ammonia, methane, and water under the reducing conditions present in the primitive atmosphere, continuing with formation of simple sugars, fatty acids, amino acids, purines, and pyrimidines, and ending with the development of self-reproducing giant molecules, the nucleoproteins. Further progress would result in viruses and simple cells.[5]

Teilhard's description of the origin of life resembles the speculations of the biochemists without being so elaborate. He describes how, after crystallization on the primitive earth led to formation of our minerals, polymerization followed and formed a sea of protein molecules on the surface of the earth. Among these, complexity reached so high a degree that eventually living cells were formed. Thus the origin of living things is explained as a result of the law of "complexification": when organization passed a certain level of complexity, a living center, the cell, was born, endowed with the power to multiply, diversify, and associate into multicellular organisms. Teilhard attacks the problem of the origin of life on a level of generality far removed from the elaborate and detailed calculations of the biochemists in terms of chemical affinities, energy requirements, and chemical equilibria. His solution does not lend itself to verification by any definite experiment, and in that sense is not helpful to the experimental scientist.

In this question of the spontaneous origin of life, it will be helpful to distinguish two problems. First, is it possible for the complex organization of materials found in all living things to arise as the result of chance? Farther on in this essay the nature of chance will be examined in some detail. For the present it may suffice to define very briefly a chance effect as an effect produced by efficient causes but not as the proper end of their activity. The efficient causes producing life's complex organization as a chance effect would be the atoms and molecules of physics and chemistry. The second problem concerns precisely the relation between life and the complex organization of materials. Is life only the resultant of the complex arrangement of materials, and are all its properties completely reducible to the physical and chemical properties of the various materials in the complex? Or is life something over and above this complex organization of materials? If it is something beyond the complex organization, is it necessary to postulate the intervention of some extrinsic cause to endow the complex with "life"?

In regard to the first problem, the question may be asked: Did not the biophysicist Lecomte du Noüy demonstrate the extreme improbability of a protein molecule's forming from the chance collisions of its constituent atoms? [6] True, but Lecomte du Noüy's argument does not disprove the possibility of the spontaneous origin of protein and other organic molecules, and this for at least two reasons. First, it ignores the chemical affinities of the constituent atoms which cause them to join preferentially in certain definite ways. Second, biochemists do not imagine that the protein molecule originated as a whole at once, but first its constituent parts, the amino acids. Only then are these thought to have linked together to form the protein molecule itself. The American biochemist Miller has already shown that when methane, ammonia, water, and hydrogen are subjected to a high-frequency electric spark (equivalent to the effect of atmospheric lightning), amino acids such as glycine, alanine, and other organic compounds are formed.[7]

Further, as soon as self-reproducing molecules (nucleoproteins) arose, the anti-chance factor of natural selection could enter the picture. Chance alterations in the structure of these molecules would bring about differences in the efficiency with which they would utilize raw materials for self-reproduction. Those most efficient would out-reproduce the others and gradually dominate the world of prelife. Similarly, natural selection would favor the development of those combinations of the materials found in a cell best adapted to maintain themselves and to reproduce. Despite the important part played by the anti-chance factor of natural selection in this view of the origin of life, the role of chance remains very important. That the part played by chance does not remove the origin of life from the scope of God's causality and providence will be made clear at the end of this essay when the related problem of the role of chance in the evolutionary origin of progressively better adapted organisms will be considered.

As for the second problem, those who think of life as only the resultant of the complex arrangement of materials would not require the intervention of any extrinsic cause to raise the complex to the level of vital activity. These would hold that the distinction between nonliving and living things is only accidental. Those who are struck by the essential unity and goal-seeking tendency of every living thing maintain that life involves more than just a complex organization. They hold that there is an essential distinction between nonliving and living things. Teilhard agrees that there is a difference between living and nonliving things, but the difference he describes seems more accidental than essential. He ascribes rudimentary inner consciousness and spontaneity to the atoms and to their constituents, the protons, neutrons, and electrons, proportioned to their comparatively simple structure. The level of consciousness and spontaneity rises as the organization of the material bodies grows more complex, as in the megamolecules, the proteins. The degree of organization characteristic of the cell represents a critical change in the intimate arrangement of many substances of all degrees of particulate magnitude. This critical change in organization shown by the cell is accompanied by a critical change in the level and nature of its state of consciousness and spontaneity. The living cell exhibits now all the unique properties characteristic of life: reproduction, diversification, association into multicellular organisms, and evolution into higher forms of life.

Since Teilhard already ascribes a rudimentary form of life to what we would call nonliving matter, it is not surprising that he does not concern himself with the need for the intervention of an extrinsic cause to bridge the chasm between nonliving and living things. To him, the origin of life is not the origin of something absolutely new, but rather a metamorphosis of what is already present. In his Preface, he notes that he has marked in his work the places where philosophers and theologians in pursuing the matter further would be entitled for reasons of a higher order to look for breaks in continuity. Significantly, he makes no such remark here, while he does so when he treats later on of the decisive transit of man from the status of the nonreflecting animal to the reflecting human being.

The reason Teilhard assigns consciousness and spontaneity to all particles in the universe is that in his view the fundamental unity of the world demands it. In other words, without this postulate it is impossible for science to cover the totality of the cosmic phenomenon by one coherent explanation. Some modern scientists such as Julian Huxley[8] have also ascribed rudimentary mind to inert matter, but the trend of most biologists has been to look upon consciousness and spontaneity as originating only when the level of organization of matter reaches the complexity characteristic of living things. Therefore Teilhard stands almost alone among modern experimental scientists in his wide extension of consciousness throughout matter. It seems likely that modern biologists will not follow him in this conclusion, especially since Teilhard admits that the existence of consciousness and spontaneity in so-called inert matter cannot be verified, since it is below the level of observation.

Scholastic philosophers will reject Teilhard's view that inert matter possesses a rudimentary life ("prelife") because they hold that the essential characteristic of life, the power of self-movement, in any true sense, is missing in inert matter.[9] Further, they hold that life is more than the resultant of the complex organization of matter. They would seem then to have to demand the intervention of an extrinsic cause to raise the complex to vital activity and thus be unable to hold that the origin of this vital activity is entirely spontaneous. Historically, it is interesting to recall that the greatest philosopher of the Middle Ages, Thomas Aquinas, saw no philosophical difficulty in spontaneous generation of rather complex living forms from inanimate material.[10]

Teilhard insists that the special properties of what we ordinarily call life emerge only when a critical point is reached in the complex arrangement of macromolecules and associated materials. He is silent on any need to postulate the intervention of an extrinsic cause, partly because such an intervention goes outside the phenomena with which he is exclusively concerning himself, and partly because to him the transit to life is a metamorphosis of a rudimentary molecular life already present. He could not, however, object if a philosopher operating on a supraphenomenological level of explanation feels obliged to invoke the intervention of an extrinsic cause (God) to bridge the gap between inert and living matter. This action could be considered as part of God's ordinary providence and activity in the world. As God in His ordinary providence infuses a human soul in the matter prepared when a human egg is fecundated, similarly here when matter has reached the degree of organization requisite to support the activities of life, God in His ordinary providence would transform the complex of materials into a single being (an organism) with a true unity of structure and function operating on the level of life. Such an explanation would deny the possibility of the entirely spontaneous origin of life.

Another approach seems philosophically defensible.[11] In this view, no special intervention of an extrinsic cause would be postulated. When matter has reached the degree of complex and unified organization characteristic of life, it would show the properties of life. The ability of matter to show these vital properties when organized into a unified complex would be due to powers received originally from the Creator of matter, but latent until the level of organization characteristic of life is reached. Thus the Creator of matter is the ultimate efficient cause of the origin of life, while the causes bringing about the complex arrangement of materials as their effects would be the proximate efficient causes of its origin. Once a certain amount of matter has reached the level of organization requisite for vital activity, a living being would arise without any special intervention of the Creator. This living being would have an essential unity and be the true center of its vital activity.

The situation is comparable to the case of natural generation. Here the parent organisms are the proximate efficient causes of the arrangement of materials capable of supporting life similar to their own. As soon as the parents have prepared such an arrangement of materials, these materials show vital activity characteristic of the particular arrangement. A new form (in philosophical terminology) has arisen. Regarding the first origin of life, no previous activity of parent organisms is possible. Yet supposing development of the organization of materials requisite for vital activity, the same result as in natural generation would follow: a living being would arise. Thus, supposing the origin of this complex and unified organization as the chance effect of natural causes, the possibility of the entirely spontaneous origin of living things as far as science is concerned would be admitted, viz., no *special* intervention of any extrinsic cause would be postulated.

Before concluding this section of the essay dealing with the origin of life, it may be of interest to discuss briefly the question of where Teilhard stands in relation to the two opposing camps of vitalists and mechanists. The extreme vitalists hold that there is a special entity in a living organism which directs all its manifold activities to definite goals. The extreme mechanists hold that a living thing consists only of a complex arrangement of atoms and molecules whose physical and chemical interactions explain all its vital phenomena, including consciousness and spontaneity. Teilhard takes a view between these extremes. True, for him life emerges with the attainment of a new critical level of complexity in the arrangement of many particles of matter — an idea resembling the mechanistic position. The resemblance, however, is only superficial. Teilhard conceives of all matter as possessing both a *"within"* (its inner consciousness and spontaneity) and a *"without"* (the external aspects of matter studied by physics and chemistry). Although these are connected parts of one and the same phenomenon so that a high level of one is correlated with a high level of the other, Teilhard gives the primacy and the initiative to the *within* of things. Thus the *within* acts to increase its own level of consciousness and spontaneity by bringing about an increase in the complexity of its *without*.

This novel concept of Teilhard's as applied to the origin and nature of life is far removed from the mechanistic idea, which makes consciousness and spontaneity only epiphenomena of the chemical and physical interactions of highly organized matter. On the other hand, Teilhard's idea of life is also different from the vitalistic conception. There is no room in his idea for an entity residing in the midst of matter which is alive, essentially separate from this matter, for Teilhard stresses the "centreity," the unity of a living thing. Modern biologists have repudiated extreme vitalism and have adopted extreme mechanism as a working hypothesis in their researches. Some, however, have championed views similar to those of Teilhard when they discuss the intimate nature of life. Thus Sinnott has pointed out that extreme mechanism ignores the fundamental scientific reality of self-regulation towards goals found in all living things. The living thing is an organism, an organized whole, with an inherent tendency to develop and maintain a characteristic bodily structure and behavior pattern. This inherent tendency is the essential quality of life. Like Teilhard, Sinnott identifies mind with life.[12]

Genes and the Game of Chance

The guiding theme of *The Phenomenon of Man* is certainly evolution. Teilhard says that nothing escapes the scope of this process, which pervades and underlies all natural phenomena. One of the great advances of modern biological science has been to work out the mechanisms by which biological or organic evolution proceeds. These mechanisms involve alterations in the hereditary characteristics passed down from one generation to the next. Modern genetics has traced these alterations in hereditary characteristics to changes in the chromosomes found in the nuclei of cells. These changes in chromosomes may be changes in the individual genes themselves or may be larger changes such as those involving inversion of a segment of one chromosome, the translocation of a segment of one chromosome to another, or even the multiplication of the entire set of chromosomes to various degrees (polyploidy). Usually geneticists use the term "mutation" for changes in the individual genes and reserve the general term "chromosomal aberrations" for the larger changes. Both the small and large alterations of the chromosomes are of decisive importance in the mechanism of evolution since they provide the raw material for changes from one generation to the next. Evolution would be impossible if the chromosomes were immutable.

An immense amount of work has been done by geneticists on the nature, origin, and properties of gene mutations. Of importance here is the conclusion rather decisively established that gene mutations are random in the sense that they do not occur as an adaptive response to a particular environmental situation. For instance, it is possible to screen out streptomycin-resistant mutants in bacteria from those sensitive to this antibiotic by adding streptomycin to the culture medium. One might say that a mutation to streptomycin-resistance is of obvious adaptive significance to a particular bacterium under these conditions and that some of the bacteria in the culture are able to undergo this mutation on being challenged by the drug. Experiments have shown, however, that whether or not streptomycin is added to the culture medium, a certain small number of bacteria are mutating to streptomycin-resistance.[13] The mutation, therefore, is not evoked as an adaptive response to the streptomycin. Experiments such as these have convinced almost all modern geneticists that mutations and chromosomal alterations in general are not of themselves adaptive in the sense described. How then explain the existence of adaptation?

All modern biologists accept the obvious fact that living things show adaptation to their particular environments. A study of the anatomy and physiology of living organisms proves this conclusively. Although ordinarily only the hard parts (bones, shells, etc.) remain of extinct forms of life, it is evident that these forms were also adapted to their environments. Whence the origin of these adaptations? It seems safe to say that the practically unanimous opinion of modern biologists is that the only natural observable "force" explaining these adaptations is natural selection. Granted the random origin of the raw material of hereditary variation by mutations and chromosomal aberrations, it is by natural selection that organisms accumulate the particular chromosomal alterations with effects favorable to their survival in their environment.

Natural selection is not conceived of as merely a sieve that lets adapted organisms pass through to survive and to propagate their kind and holds back unadapted organisms to become extinct. This would ascribe to it a completely passive role. Modern biology thinks of natural selection as a creative process in the sense that it brings about the development of new organisms embodying specific and individual combinations of hereditary traits adaptive to the particular environment in which these organisms are living. Contemporary biologists find the essence of natural selection to be "differential reproduction." [14]

Those organisms that leave more descendants to the next generation are more favored by natural selection. On the average and in the long run, the organisms embodying the most adapted combinations of hereditary traits will leave more descendants to the next generation than those less well adapted. Thus progressively greater adaptation is favored by natural selection and in a sense is produced by natural selection.

It is obvious that from the viewpoint of a biologist working as an experimental scientist, natural selection is a natural phenomenon not to be personalized and given forevision of the results of its operations. To him, it is a blind process dependent for its direction on the particular environmental circumstances in which it is operating. Thus it can favor equally well regression of organs or their progressive perfection. The functionless vestigial eyes of the fish living in the perpetual darkness of caves are explained by a relaxation of the selection process under circumstances where eyes have no adaptive significance. Under other circumstances, animal eyes have had high adaptive significance, and those involving mutations producing better-functioning eyes were favored.

The origin of entirely new types of organisms, e.g., mammals from reptiles, is explained by modern evolutionary theory in essentially the same way as the origin of better-adapted forms of the same type. There is a difference of opinion as to the kind of change in the chromosomes providing the hereditary basis for the changes in type. Most geneticists favor gene mutations each of small effect but whose interactions when combined in one organism by natural selection lead to decisive changes in type. Thus the formation of new types would be a gradual process. Goldschmidt has favored single gene mutations of large effect which by altering embryonic development at an early stage bring about a new and divergent pattern of organization equivalent to a new type. He has even proposed that a rather drastic remodeling of the entire chromosomal architecture might occasionally give rise to a new type of organism.[15] Both schools of thought agree that natural selection governs the survival and perfecting of the new types.

Teilhard does not favor the modern genetical theory of evolution described in the paragraphs above. He explains evolution as a drive of life to expand into all available environments. Life is inventive and tries all possible solutions for the problems of existence posed by these environments. Once it has found a workable solution, it perfects it. Teilhard ascribes to life, then, a fundamental inner impetus that drives it on to higher and higher levels. Evolution to him is fundamentally a psychic phenomenon, the ascent of every living thing to a higher degree of immanent spontaneity. The gradual external changes, as in type of teeth and feet, in the various lines of evolution are secondary to the basic internal changes in the *within* of living things.

Teilhard is aware that his explanation of evolution will seem Lamarckian. Lamarck's second law of evolution enunciated in the introduction to the first volume of his *Invertebrate Zoology* is translated by Cannon as follows: "The production of a new organ in an animal body results from a new need which continues to make itself felt, and from a new movement that this need brings about and maintains." His fourth law is: "Everything acquired or changed during an individual's lifetime is preserved by heredity and transmitted to that individual's progeny." [16] Teilhard's psychic evolution is certainly similar to these ideas of Lamarck, and in particular one seems justified in saying that Teilhard assumes the reality of Lamarck's second law, the inheritance of acquired characteristics. Recently Martin Jarrett-Kerr in the Preface to his translation of *Teilhard de Chardin, His Life and Spirit* by Nicolas Corte, has denied that Teilhard assumed the inheritance of acquired characteristics.[17] True Teilhard is aware of the lack of evidence for this view, yet his theory of evolution seems to assume it as valid. In later works he does not repudiate his assumption of its validity.[18]

Lamarck, as already noted, made the inheritance of acquired characteristics the basis of his theory of evolution. Darwin, who ascribed the predominant and important role in evolution to natural selection, assigned a secondary role to this presumed phenomenon. Toward the close of the 19th century, the neo-Lamarckians, with the distinguished zoologists Von Nägeli and Hertwig among their number, made against the inheritance of acquired characteristics the main explanation of evolution. In our own times, Lysenko and his followers in Russia have claimed to have demonstrated the reality of the inheritance of acquired characteristics. Lysenko has asserted that an essential property of living things is their power to modify themselves in terms of the changed conditions of their environment and to pass on their changed nature to their descendants.[19] Very recently, the British biologist Cannon has championed Lamarck's views and has attacked the modern genetical explanation of evolution in terms of gene mutations and natural selection.[20]

However, allowing for a few discordant views such as those mentioned, biologists today generally agree that the inheritance of acquired characteristics has never been demonstrated. The experiments of Lysenko and his followers can all be explained without recourse to Lamarck's ideas. Cannon's criticisms of the modern genetical theory of evolution seem to rest on a misunderstanding of the theory. The inheritance of acquired characteristics is naturally attractive, since it simplifies enormously our understanding of the mechanism of evolution; but biologists today think these mechanisms in large part can best be understood in terms of the experimental facts of gene mutations and natural selection. It comes then as a surprise to a modern biologist reading Teilhard's work to find that his explanation of evolution assumes the reality of the inheritance of acquired characteristics.

Intimately related to Teilhard's conviction that life rises to higher levels by virtue of an inner impetus is his concept that its progressive evolution proceeds along definite lines predetermined in direction by this inner impetus or drive. The tendency of life to evolve along preferred lines or axes leading to greater consciousness and spontaneity Teilhard calls "orthogenesis." Teilhard extends orthogenesis to the entire world of things. Thus the protons, neutrons, and electrons tend to form the atoms of the periodic table, the atoms tend to form first the micromolecules of the minerals, then the macromolecules of the organic compounds, the macromolecules tend to form living centers (cells), the cells tend to arrange themselves into organisms, organisms seek ever greater and greater "centreity" which amounts to greater and greater consciousness and spontaneity. The process culminates in the emergence of man, where consciousness has passed over into the realm of reflection. Teilhard asserts that orthogenesis is the dynamic and only complete form of heredity, and that heredity conceived of as involving only the recombination and shuffling of characters according to Mendel's laws brings about nothing really new.

Modern biologists agree with Teilhard that the record of past evolution as preserved in the rocks often shows steady changes in definite directions. Thus the various groups of mammals show a general tendency to increase in body size. The evolution of the horse proceeds from a multiple-toed small form with teeth adapted to browsing on twigs (*Eohippus*) through intermediate stages to the modern horse with one functional toe on each foot, large in size, and with teeth adapted to grazing on grass (*Equus*). In this case, as in similar ones, however, the actual picture is rather of a number of continuously branching lines, one of which we rather arbitrarily single out as the main line. Granted that evolution often has proceeded along fairly definite lines some of which have resulted in an increase of "spontaneity and consciousness," the upward trend in the lines of evolution is by no means universal. The coelocanth fish *Latimeria* discovered in recent years off the coasts of Madagascar in apparently essentially unaltered form from its Cretaceous ancestor of 135,000,000 years ago, is one example of evolution standing still.

Modern biologists as a group reject Teilhard's orthogenesis as an explanation of evolution for several reasons.[21] First, if a reality, then evolution along definite lines should be much more evident than appears to be the fact. Second, Teilhard's orthogenesis itself is not a scientific explanation in the sense that it explains the causes of the phenomena of evolution in terms of simpler, experimentally verifiable factors. Third, the progressive trends in evolution can be explained in terms of the known factors of gene mutation and natural selection. When environmental conditions change slowly over many millions of years, adaptation to these changing conditions will be favored. The effect will be evolution in certain definite directions. Thus selection under these conditions will be "orthoselection." When a new environmental opportunity arises, organisms carrying mutations endowing them with adaptability to these new conditions will be favored, and evolution will proceed along a new line which may result in the appearance eventually of an organism of a different type. The branching appearance of the actual record of evolution comes from the simultaneous expansion of organisms into the several environments available at the time. If an organism is well adapted to a relatively static environment, retention of its adaptive features will be favored by natural selection. This is an explanation of evolutionary static organisms such as *Latimeria*.

Teilhard is well aware that modern biologists as a group do not favor his orthogenesis as an explanation of evolution moving along certain favored lines. He believes that natural selection involves pure chance as an explanation of the progressive changes in evolution, whereas pure chance cannot explain anything progressive. The modern synthetic theory of evolution conceives the origin of mutations as a chance process but regards natural selection as an anti-chance factor. By it, the raw material of hereditary variation furnished by mutation is molded into a progressively better adapted organism. Teilhard does not appear to understand the role of natural selection as an anti-chance factor in progressive evolution, since he feels obliged to assign this role to an internal principle in living organisms actively seeking to perfect themselves and utilizing for this end whatever the fortuitous play of external circumstances and of gene mutations provides in the way of raw materials.

Teilhard completed *The Phenomenon of Man* at Peking, China, in June, 1940. Eleven years later, 1951, in Paris, in an essay unpublished at the time, he again contrasted the two opposing explanations of the fact that evolution moves along certain privileged directions: orthoselection ("*orthogénèse passive*") and orthoelection ("*orthogénèse active*").[22] In this short work, he concedes that orthoselection appears to play the main role in evolutionary progress in organisms below the level of man. Once the level of man is reached, however, then orthoselection begins to play the main role, Man, the researcher and inventor, is able to plan his own future on the earth. Yet, Teilhard argues, if one admits that the social and intellectual evolution of man is but a prolongation of zoological evolution, then one must concede that, even on the level of prehuman evolution, orthoelection was at work, although on that level submerged by the play of blind chance forces. Modern biologists will admit the power of man to direct his own cultural evolution and even to some extent his own biological evolution, but they will still deny that evolution below man depends for its progress on the inventive efforts of living things to raise themselves higher on the scale of life. To repeat, there is no evidence for the inheritance of acquired characteristics which would provide the basis for such self-directed evolution.

The Christian biologist is left with an apparent dilemma. He is convinced by the convergence of many lines of evidence that evolution is a fact, and may even, as has Wasmann, have provided a part of that evidence. The theoretical and experimental researches of modern biologists, however, have shown that biological evolution mainly involves random mutations of the genes and the action of natural selection, with the fortuitous circumstances of the particular environments in which the organisms exist providing the direction along which selection proceeds. The biochemists also, as we have seen, have furnished us with an explanation of the beginning of evolution in the spontaneous origin of life in which chance plays an important role. How reconcile all this with the providential activity of God, the Creator and Conserver of all things in the universe? The Christian biologist may say that God creates by evolution; but is the mechanism of evolution with its heavy emphasis on chance reconcilable with the Christian idea of God's activity in the world? This problem has not escaped the attention of Christian biologists. It certainly was prominent in the mind of Teilhard de Chardin and in part explains his aversion toward the theory of natural selection. To him it gave too much play to the blind forces of chance. Moreover, he saw evolution moving in certain definite directions, and this orientation could be explained, he thought, only by postulating inner strivings of organisms for greater and greater consciousness and spontaneity. The outward sign of this impulse was the increasing "cerebralization" discernible in the evolutionary history of the chordates. Teilhard's contemporary, Lecomte du Noüy, made no attempt to stay on the strictly phenomenological or scientific level in his discussion of the problem of evolution. To him evolution was the unfolding of God's plan to bring man into existence. The chance play of physical, chemical, and biological factors was oriented by God toward that goal ("telefinalism").[23]

Any solution of the apparent dilemma should be consistent both with sound biology and with sound philosophy. It is unfortunate that Teilhard assumed in his theory of evolution the unproved hypothesis of the inheritance of acquired characteristics. Lecomte du Noüy greatly weakened the impact of his book on the scientific world by a number of incorrect statements, e.g., that amphibians developed in evolutionary history before the fishes. He also assumed the inheritance of acquired characteristics to be a fact. The solution of the dilemma should recognize the role of random gene mutations in providing the source of hereditary variation and the role of natural selection in developing organisms with the particular combinations of hereditary traits adaptive to their environments. As a first step in a solution, it should be observed that the physical and chemical properties of matter in living organisms are factors in evolution which are determined and do not vary in a random way. Thus, to this extent at least, chance does not play an exclusive role in evolution. Secondly, mutations cannot be random in an absolute, unrestricted sense. The basic physical structure and chemical properties of the genic material impose definite limitations on what changes it can undergo and still act as a functional unit of heredity. The same observation applies to the fluctuations in the environment: there are limits to what variations can occur, given previous conditions. Third, to ascribe phenomena to chance is not to deny any causality to them.

Certainly there have to be efficient causes of the mutations and fluctuations in the environment. The biologist has long been studying the possible efficient causes of spontaneous random mutations and has speculated that the ionizing action of cosmic rays resulting in permanent chemical alterations of the genes may be the cause of some of these. The geologist also has attempted to unravel the causes of the long-term fluctuations in the global environment, which have involved periods of invasion by the seas of portions of the continents, folding of the rock mantle of the earth into ranges of lofty mountains, etc. It is only when the question of final causality arises, i.e., ascribing a purpose or goal to the workings of evolution, that a difference of opinion arises. Many biologists deny any purpose to evolution and its mechanisms, and they base their denial in part on the final residual role that must be left to chance in its operation. They assume that chance and purpose are contradictory concepts.

At this point we should ask: What is chance? The philosopher Klubertanz answers that chance is "the concurrence or interference of several causal chains such that the concurrence is outside the goal of any of the causes taken singly." [24] This rather abstruse definition can be clarified by an example. Engineer Jones is operating a freight train from Chicago to Detroit to deliver steel for a manufacturing plant. Farmer Brown is driving his automobile from Toledo to Flint to visit his parents. The paths of the two cross at a little town. Here Brown fails to see the train and is killed while attempting to cross in front of it. We would say that his death is a chance event, since it resulted from the mutual interference of the courses of action of two agents each of which had his own goals, neither of which goals involved the death of Brown. In this example, chance does not result in a new being, but in the destruction of one. What about our cases where through chance new beings are brought into existence, viz., living things from nonliving matter and better-adapted organisms from less-adapted ones?

Philosophy proves that any process by which a new being comes into existence must have an end or purpose. This end or purpose can escape the ends of all secondary causes involved in the producton of the new being, but cannot escape the end of the First Cause. Applied to our cases, this principle means that it is possible to conceive of the origin of life or of evolutionary novelties as the results (in part) of the chance operation of countless secondary causes, but that it is not possible to conceive of these results as undirected by God to their determinate ends.

Solving the Dilemma

Here then we have the solution of our dilemma. The role of chance is saved in the world of phenomena studied by science while the role of purpose is also saved in the world of ultimate meaning studied by philosophy and theology. Therefore, when a biologist denies any purpose to the chance phenomena that resulted in life and evolutionary progress, he is not speaking as a scientist but as a philosopher, and his conclusion must be rejected as lacking philosophical truth. Certainly the biologist as a scientist need not have recourse to teleology in explaining these phenomena, but he cannot arrive at a philosophical — i.e., ultimate — explanation of them, without invoking teleology.

The fact that the course of evolution has resulted in the emergence of man, a unique being, akin to the animal world in his body, but raised above it in his power to reason and to reflect, undoubtedly was the source of Teilhard's inspiration as to the significance of the entire process of cosmic and organic evolution. He saw the entire course of evolution as leading to man. It is no wonder then that he saw in all the stages of evolution a constant seeking after greater consciousness and spontaneity which was to culminate in the reflective ability and freedom of man himself. He interpreted the course of evolution according to the light thrown on it by considering man as the goal of evolution, the reverse of the procedure of many other biologists who attempt to understand man as only an accidental product of the course of evolution. The biologist who is convinced that an Intelligent First Cause exists as the explanation of the ultimate origin of the universe finds it inconceivable that this Intelligent Being would be unconcerned with the progressive development (evolution) of His creation. He will agree therefore with Teilhard that the course of evolution had a plan which included the emergence of man as its goal and in this sense was truly orthogenetic. He will still disagree with Teilhard as to the mechanism of evolution. To him, in light of modern genetical research, the actual mechanism used by God in His plan appears to be based on random gene mutation and natural selection, and not on an inner drive of organisms to perfect themselves. He will, however, agree with Teilhard that this mechanism of itself cannot explain the plan behind the course of evolution. He finds the explanation of the plan in the action of God directing the foreseen results of the play of immense numbers of factors toward higher and higher goals, culminating eventually in man.

A few remarks in conclusion. As a scientist, Teilhard de Chardin was primarily a paleontologist, not a geneticist. But the problem of the mechanisms of evolution is essentially a problem of genetics. Teilhard's lack of firsthand familiarity with genetics may explain his failure to integrate the roles of gene mutation and natural selection into his theory of evolution. Does this failure completely vitiate his general treatment of evolution? Certainly the important role that the *fact* of evolution plays in his work remains intact. It has just been explained in what sense his view of evolution as orthogenetic is correct. No one will quarrel with Teilhard's concept that the course of evolution is directed by the evolving organisms themselves when evolution has reached the level of man's social evolution. The inheritance of acquired characteristics when considered in the form of the accumulation and transmission of human culture is also a fact. Hence the main weakness of Teilhard's work, so far as biology is involved, concerns the mechanisms of evolution below the level of man. Even here it is perhaps possible to work out a solution that will be true to modern genetics and yet salvage Teilhard's ideas in modified form — in particular, his view that acquired characteristics are inherited. For instance, Waddington has conceived of an explanation called "genetic assimilation" for the conversion of acquired characteristics into inherited ones.[25] To Teilhard, *The Phenomenon of Man* was his own definitive treatment of his subject: the place and future of man as a phenomenon of nature. He would, however, be the first to welcome other attempts which, while true to his fundamental vision of the transcendent importance of man in nature, will be more in accord with the findings of modern biology. His great work has facilitated any such attempts made in the future.

Editor's Note: When Lamarck offered the first scientific explanation of the evolutionary mechanism he stressed the inheritance of acquired characteristics as the sole causal mechanism of the evolutionary process. Fifty years later Darwin and Wallace relegated the Lamarckian explanation to temporary obscurity and raised aloft the banner for natural selection. Both theories, it seems, may be trying to oversimplify a very complex net of causal relations. The original theories have already undergone several revisions: the neo-Darwinian school of Simpson, Huxley, and Dobzhansky, the macro-evolutionary thought of Goldschmidt, the neo-Lamarckian view, etc.

A parallel situation in the recent developments in the field of biochemistry and genetics indicates that a "solution" to the age-old battle between the vitalists and mechanists may be found in a *via media* which will find a partial answer and some validity in both these seemingly opposed schools. The present truce of the physicists on the wave/corpuscular nature of light falls in the same trend. May it not be that Teilhard's view, when fully appreciated and studied, will be another *via media* solution? As anthropologist J. Franklin Ewing points out, "Teilhard attempts to reconcile what other men consider irreconcilable opposites. The within of things shows a Lamarckian inner principle; the without is Darwinian" (*Theological Studies*, 22:1 (March 1961), p. 94).

We might compare the pure Lamarckian view with its philosophical context to the vitalist position, and the more materialistically inclined Darwinian outlook to the mechanistic interpretation of life. In such a comparison the value of both views becomes clearer. "In the case of the evolution of animals, a direction is registered in the increasing complexity and effectiveness of the nervous system. After the great change-over from reptiles to mammals, this direction is most noticeable in the development of the brain. Here is evidence of the within of things, an orthogenesis; nor does this within negate the evidence of the without of things, which is Darwinian in nature (i.e., mutations, natural selection, etc.)" (Ewing, *ibid.*). The discussion of "The Role of the

Gene in Evolution," by Carl C. Lindegren seems to indicate only one example of a growing appreciation of this *via media* solution. Certainly his explanation of adaptive enzyme synthesis and the plasticity of the gene seems to point in this direction (*Annals of the New York Academy of Science,* LXIX (August 30, 1957), pp. 338–51).

This editorial comment is made without any note of criticism or contradiction of the views expressed in this or other essays in the symposium. The author's views and critiques still stand. However because of the tentative nature of all these studies, I have felt free to add a comment made very recently by J. Franklin Ewing, since it seems to offer a new insight and clarification on a point in Teilhard's thought which is somewhat nebulous and confusing. Ewing's interpretation was made after the essays in this book were completed and hence none of the authors were able to make use of it. All of this will remind the student that much in Teilhard's thought remains indefinite or undefinable at this moment; only much study will bring some of these points into sharp focus.

10

MAN AND THE BEHAVIORAL SCIENCES

James L. Foy, M.D.

This essay will attempt to expose the idea of man to be found in the work of Pierre Teilhard de Chardin, principally, of course, in his long essay, *The Phenomenon of Man*. The relevance of Teilhard's ideas to neurology, neurophysiology, psychology, and psychiatry will be examined; and some recent findings and theories in these fields of behavioral science, which bear on Teilhard's evolutionist view of man, will be explored. Only a tentative approach to these aims will be possible in this essay.

"Science?"

The controversy that surrounds the legitimate question concerning the exact nature of the thought and contribution of Teilhard has tended to obscure the work itself. Before making any summary exposition of his anthropology, it would be best to consider Teilhard's avowed point of view stipulated at the beginning of *The Phenomenon of Man*. Confronted with the originality and boldness of the author's ideas, reviewers have labored under much confusion in attempts to pigeonhole and label the thought expressed in the book. Teilhard has been called a scientist, a phenomenologist, a natural philosopher, a cosmologist, a metaphysician, a visionary poet and a mystic, by as many different critics. In his Preface the author asks that his book be understood as a scientific treatise dealing with man solely as a phenomenon but also with the whole phenomenon of man.

Like all highly original and audacious systematizers, Teilhard in his *Weltanschauung* insists upon new words and new word combinations to signify new concepts. For me his book is a scientific formulation of a theory of biogenesis and anthropogenesis. Neither the ambitious scope of his theory nor its synthetic aims detracts from the scientific quality of the work, based as it is on a few identified assumptions, laws of nature, and empirical data. The theoretical superstructure is closely reasoned and comprehensive, with definitions of terms, internal consistency and logic of elaborated principles, and an admirable economy of construction. Like other well-made scientific theories, Teilhard's theory startles us by its formal elegance and creativeness.

Because of the scope and breadth of the theory of matter and man proposed in *The Phenomenon of Man*, some of its stated and unstated hypotheses are not readily capable of validation by experimental investigation. Other hypotheses generated from the theoretical system are open to experimental inquiry and validation. The positivist is immediately on guard, as he must be when faced with theory in psychology and the behavioral sciences. Freud's theory of a dynamic unconscious is a further case in point. Of the many hypotheses derived from Freud's theory, some are accessible to validation by experimental methods, others are not.

The last portion of *The Phenomenon of Man*, in which Teilhard argues his concept of convergence, human unification and the Omega Point, seems to go distinctly beyond scientific extrapolation. Here the theory of anthropogenesis is superseded by a *mystique*. I prefer to read this chapter as an additional appendix to the full body of theory, which remains a scientific treatise. My reading of the book is at variance with an opinion expressed recently by G. G. Simpson, who rejects its scientific value flatly but admires its "mystical evolutionism." [1]

The appendices to *The Phenomenon of Man* and many of his other writings indicate the Christian and the mystical preoccupations of Teilhard de Chardin. Any knowledge of his biography leaves the impression of a whole man in a single passionate quest for truth. His role as Christian-priest-mystic was wholly compatible with and complementary to his role as paleontologist-scientist. His work of a lifetime points as a witness to a new era in the relations between Christianity and science, unhampered by the old false antagonisms, prejudices and dualisms.

Complexity/Consciousness

In examining Teilhard's idea of man I shall intentionally neglect that part of his theory dealing with problems of cosmogenesis and biogenesis. The key concept of his theory of anthropogenesis — indeed the nuclear idea in his system — is a postulate he calls the law of complexity/consciousness. Starting from "the general and fundamental fact that organic evolution exists, applicable equally to life as a whole or to any given living creature in particular" (p. 140 n.), the law of complexity/consciousness is applied to answer questions raised after acceptance of this fact. Evolution then is accepted as a process at work in organic reality. Actually Teilhard argues for an evolutive process taking place in the whole of reality. Evolution is thought of as a dimension, the temporal dimension, of reality.

Complexity is defined as that quality possessed by an organism because of its being formed by a greater number of elements and because of the elements themselves being more closely organized among themselves.

Aggregation, crystallization, and polymerization of atomic and molecular particles might be seen as tentative steps toward complexification. Even before the threshold of life has been crossed, complexity manifests itself, not only by increase in the number and variety of elements in a particle, but also by a truly organized heterogeneity, a particular form of grouping which binds certain elements to itself in a closed whole having a determined radius. Examples of complexity are readily available in the atom, the molecule, the unicellular organism, or the animal.

Consciousness is defined in its widest sense, indicating every kind of psychism, from the most rudimentary forms of interior perception imaginable to the human phenomenon of reflective thought (p. 57 n.). The term _within_ or the _within of things_ is also introduced to signify consciousness. Consciousness is seen as hand in glove with complexity. This radical idea goes beyond the increasing complexity of external and internal structure of organisms on the tree of life, to posit, as another aspect to that structure, an expanding interiorization or consciousness turning more and more back upon itself. To avoid treating consciousness as an epiphenomenon, restricted to the higher forms of living things, Teilhard suggests that all members of the biosphere share a form of consciousness as a corollary to their complexity. In his theory of cosmogenesis Teilhard argues that the stuff of the universe itself must be taken as having a double aspect to its structure. _"In a coherent perspective of the world: life inevitably assumes a 'pre-life' for as far back before it as the eye can see"_ (p. 57). Together with the exterior _without_ of prelife, there would be the _within_ of preconsciousness.

From the phenomenal and more strictly scientific point of view an analysis is offered to support the hypothesis of consciousness as a recurrent law of nature. This analysis follows from observations on the properties of two classes of matter. First, there is the appearance of preliving matter as a distracting multitude of microscopic particles perfectly alike among themselves, each coextensive with the cosmic realm, connected among themselves by a comprehensive energy, and revealing themselves by overall effects, subject to the laws of statistics. Second, there is the appearance of living matter as mega- or ultra-molecules, less numerous, whose highly individualized elements escape from the slavery of large numbers and behave with a basic spontaneity. In the first condition atomicity would be a common property of the _within_ and the _without_ of inorganic particles. The second condition of a smaller number of very complex groupings could be defined as a richer _within_ or concentration of consciousness, lining a more highly organized material edifice. A qualitative law of development could be elaborated which would "be capable of explaining, first of all the invisibility, then the appearance, and then the gradual dominance of the _within_ in comparison to the _without_ of things" (p. 61).

The phylogenetic scale can be seen as an evolutionary stream drifting towards more and more complexity/consciousness. The emergence of consciousness and its enrichment is called in Teilhard's terminology interiorization or corpusculization. An organism is said to be more strongly centered, or possessing greater centricity, as it exhibits a more extensive complexification and corpusculization.

Energy

The problem of energy is too formidable for any one scientific theory to apprehend entirely in its physical, biological, and psychological dimensions. Teilhard attempts to hold within his theory all forms of energy and their known governing thermodynamic principles. His thought is difficult to follow, but he begins simply: "We shall assume that, essentially, all energy is psychic* in nature; but add that in each particular element this fundamental energy is divided into two distinct components: a *tangential energy* which links the element with all others of the same order (that is to say of the same complexity and the same centricity) as itself in the universe; and a *radial energy* which draws it towards ever greater complexity and centricity — in other words forward" (p. 64 f.).

An important concept introduced under the discussion of energy is arrangement. Arrangement refers to particles, elements, and, I assume, organic parts ordering themselves in new positions of internal complexity. Tangential energy is either an energy of radiation, subject to the laws of conservation and entropy; or an energy of arrangement, which is antientropic but only appreciable in living creatures, especially in the human.

This idea of a tangential energy of arrangement coincides with contemporary neurophysiological theory, which discards energy consumption, transformation, and liberation as important variables in brain studies to emphasize the amount and type of order achieved in the neurons comprising brain elements. Neurophysiologists consider this fundamentally a problem of negative entropy.

Radial energy would be augmented when tangential energy effects an arrangement in the direction of complexity, since centricity is automatically increased. Here Teilhard's thinking becomes decisively tautological. In another passage he is ready to admit that an unanswered question exists in regard to this special energy, radial energy, carrying all nature and organic life in the direction of higher forms of complexity and centricity (p. 66).

Cephalization and the Threshold of Reflection

Leaving aside at this point the development of Teilhard's theory of biogenesis, permit me to concentrate more thoroughly on the theory of anthro-

*Erroneously rendered as "physical" in the official English translation. (*Editor's note*)

pogenesis. An examination of the tree of life reveals, both in the chordate branch and the arthropod branch, an evolution of the nervous system. There is a simultaneous growth in volume and arrangement of nervous tissue. An essential drift can be detected in the direction of concentration of the nervous system in the cephalic region of the organism. Cephalization is a process within evolution toward more voluminous brains. Cephalization can be applied as a yardstick to measure the degree of interiorization or the level of consciousness attained by an organism.

Cephalization is a measure for reading the drift of complexity/consciousness. "Since . . . the natural history of living creatures amounts on the *exterior* to the gradual establishment of a vast nervous system, it therefore corresponds on the *interior* to the installation of a psychic state on the very dimensions of the earth. On the surface, we find the nerve fibers and ganglions; deep down, consciousness" (p. 146).

Turning briefly to the higher forms of insect life on the arthropod branch, we find apparent a psychology reflecting their cephalization. This is, however, a psychology highly precisioned, relentlessly patterned, and absorbed in function. In some species a social phenomenon is observed, but consciousness is frozen in habitual acts and organic reflexes (p. 154).

Among the vertebrates, especially the mammals, we feel "at home." Their animation, exuberance, and curiosity betray an interiorization and consciousness quite different from that observed in the hive and the anthill. Finally the primates "represent a phylum of *pure and direct cerebralization*." Their brains are massive and convoluted; the cerebral hemispheres come into dominance. With this remarkable complexification, consciousness is brought to a critical point.

The crux of Teilhard's theory of anthropogenesis is the emergence of reflective thought within the temporal dimension which is evolution. This emergence takes place according to the law of complexity/consciousness and leads immediately to the question of man.

The definition of the term "reflection" is important enough to warrant further quotation. "From our experimental point of view, reflection is, as the word indicates, the power acquired by a consciousness to turn in upon itself, to take possession of itself *as of an object* endowed with its own particular consistence and value: no longer merely to know, but to know oneself; no longer merely to know, but to know that one knows" (p. 165).

Teilhard points to the primates, in which brain and consequently animal consciousness were fashioned to such a supple and rich degree that the evolutionary step immediately following could not take place without that whole animal consciousness being recast and consolidated upon itself. He indicates that such a critical leap forward might be explained by a slight expenditure of tangential energy effecting a new ordering or arrangement of organic parts, and consequently a radical advance along the axis of complexity/consciousness, served by radial energy. This theoretical anthropogenetic mechanism, if it does not demolish a spirit/matter dualism, at least brings transcendentalism and materialism to a wholly new level of discussion.

Having passed the threshold of reflection the human stem appears, and human phylogenesis continues under the influence of natural selection. But reflection, once established, increases, and a continuing and transmissible tradition of reflection emerges. Within the human layer neo-Lamarckian ideas are valid. Acquired characteristics are "transmitted" in the historical and cultural traditions made possible by reflection.

More important than Teilhard's assent to neo-Lamarckian views is his concept of a noosphere (p. 182). The engendering and subsequent development of all the stages of reflective thought establish a complex membrane over and above the biosphere, that envelope of living forms. The noosphere is a new "thinking layer," more coherent and just as extensive as any preceding layer.

Hominization is yet another term introduced to elucidate the processes and events taking place in the world of nature as a consequence of human reflection. The impact of a noosphere on the other layers of the earth effects this hominization. In a narrower sense it is used to define the leap across the threshold from instinct to thought.[2] Hominization might also be seen as a process taking place within and between individual reflective intelligences, helping to define the matrix of socialization and interrelatedness in which mankind finds itself. There is an idea of interpersonalism in Teilhard's theory, but before examining that question, which is more highly speculative, we must take up the phenomenology of personalization.

Personalization

"The reflective psychic center, once turned in upon itself, can only subsist by means of a double movement which is in reality one and the same. It centers itself further on itself by penetration into a new space, and at the same time it centers the rest of the world around itself by the establishment of an ever more coherent and better organized perspective in the realities which surround it" (p. 172). Teilhard's phylogenetic view of the person making his appearance in human history corresponds closely with the ontogenesis of ego as conceived of in psychoanalytic theory. I refer especially to Erikson's concept of ego identity [3] and Hartmann's discussion of adaptation in ego psychology.[4]

Personalization is an evolutive manifestation of another degree, another order of complexity. Each reflective center has become "someone." A new unfolding of consciousness is apparent, and its ascent must be defined and regulated harmoniously by the persons themselves. "We thus reach the personalization of the individual by the 'hominization' of the whole group" (p. 174).

Teilhard's theory of man and his evolution takes on a much more speculative cast when he deals with the problem of the person in the social phenomenon. While remaining biologically oriented, his thought has many parallels with social psychological theory. The isolation of the individual and the isolation of the group are both rejected after careful demonstration that the evolutionary future of man lies in a confluence of thought, which is both an inevitable outcome of man's multiplying on the spherical earth, and the intervention of a superarrangement or megasynthesis of all the thinking elements of the earth.

The opposition between the collective and the person poses the kinds of questions that discourage us and cause the greatest apprehension. Applying a psychobiological axiom without recourse to a *mystique*, one can say that union differentiates:

> In any domain — whether it be the cells of a body, the members of a society or the elements of a spiritual synthesis — *union differentiates*. In every organized whole, the parts perfect themselves. . . . Through neglect of this universal rule many a system of pantheism has led us astray to the cult of a great All in which individuals are supposed to be merged like a drop in the ocean or like a dissolving grain of salt. Applied to the case of the summation of consciousnesses, the law of union rids us of this perilous and recurrent illusion. No, following the confluent orbits of their centers, the grains of consciousness do not tend to lose their outlines and blend, but, on the contrary, to accentuate the depth and incommunicability of their egos (p. 262).

Insisting emphatically on a distinction between individuality and personality, Teilhard extrapolates a human convergence with "each" advancing towards the "other." The goal is not a fragmented collection of individualities but a union of personalities or a synthesis of centered consciousnesses. "Since it is a question of achieving a synthesis of centers, it is center to center that they must make contact and *not otherwise*. Thus, amongst the various forms of psychic inter-activity animating the noosphere, the energies we must identify, harness and develop before all others are those of an 'intercentric' nature, if we want to give effective help to the progress of evolution in ourselves" (p. 263).

At this point it is clear that implicit in Teilhard's theory there is a profound psychology of interpersonalism and intersubjectivity. He uses the term "hyperpersonalization" to delineate that trend toward a grouping of centers. As regards the energies available for a human convergence, there are the powers in human knowledge at work in the organization of research and there are the varieties of human love. Both knowledge and love must themselves be examined *sub specie evolutionis*. The direction taken in their future development would be along the lines of a highly personalized complexity/consciousness. Teilhard elaborates his biologically oriented *mystique* of human energy and unification in other texts.[5]

Brain, Energy, and Mind

Teilhard's scientific phenomenology of man undercuts a mind/matter dualism in an effective, if ambiguous manner. The following quotation helps make clear his point of view in *The Phenomenon of Man*: ". . . matter and spirit do not present themselves as 'things' or 'natures' but as simple related *variables*, of which it behooves us to determine not the secret essence but the curve in function of space and time. And I recall that at this level of reflection [i.e., the phenomenal point of view] 'consciousness' presents itself and demands to be treated, not as a sort of particular and subsistent entity, but as an 'effect,' as the 'specific effect' of complexity" (p. 307).

The ambiguity lies, of course, in the energizing of the spiral of complexity/consciousness as it figures in Teilhard's theory of biogenesis and anthropogenesis. This has already been commented upon in the exposition of his energy hypotheses. In spite of this ambiguity, Teilhard's anthropology is elaborated in such a way that consciousness and/or mind remains something more than an abstraction interposed between brain and behavior.

Sir Charles Sherrington, writing in his famous Gifford Lectures, seems to me to be a striking forerunner of Teilhard de Chardin. Evolution is central to his speculation. He comments upon increasing complexity of organization and ampler integration of the nervous system as providing a direction to organic evolution. He observes evolution treating and handling body and mind together as one affair. He writes of an energy-system and a mental-system, conjoined into one bivalent individual. Sherrington, the physiologist, holds to a dualism, because he cannot identify brain with mind: yet he sees nature avoiding any body-mind or energy-psyche dichotomy:

> We have, it may seem, to admit that energy and mind are phenomena of two categories. Mind as attaching to any unicellular life would seem to me to be unrecognizable to observation; but I would not feel that permits me to affirm it is not there. Indeed, I would think, that since mind appears in the developing soma that amounts to showing that it is potential in the ovum (and sperm) from which the soma sprang. The appearance of recognizable mind in the soma would then be not a creation *de novo* but a development of mind from unrecognizable into recognizable.[6]

Here Sherrington seems to anticipate the Teilhardian concepts of the *within* and the *without* of things.

Julian Huxley, a contemporary of Teilhard de Chardin, while recognizing the mental capacities of the human brain for perception, emotion, and preparation for action, as not identical with its material properties, still maintains that mental and psychological events are also material events, "but experienced from the inside instead of studied from the outside." [7] His stated materialist position does not keep him from sharing much of Teilhard's optimism and humanism, as well as the basic idea of a human convergence. It is undeniable that both men, in their productivity as writers, in their evolutionist preoccupations, and in their extrapolations about the future of mankind, share also the role of prophet.

Once over the threshold of reflective thought, emergent man is quite different from his immediate nonreflective predecessor. The threshold is a critical one. Teilhard would seem to invite the philosopher and theologian to examine this critical zone from their points of view. A recent book by Stephan Strasser proposes a phenomenological analysis of a fundamental question of philosophical anthropology regarding the metaphysical basis of the identity, unity, and substantiality of the ego.[8] Such a study suggests a metaphysical inquiry into the existence of a personalized reflective center, as understood in Teilhardian terms.

Complexity in the Behavioral Sciences

The sciences of human behavior pose obvious problems of multidisciplinary and interdisciplinary research. Consider that the sociologist, anthropologist, psychologist, neurophysiologist, and neurochemist all contribute something to the pursuit of scientific knowledge about man. Rohrer is one of many writers who have called attention to the cultural pattern of science and the observation that valid scientific statements concerning human activity can be made at several distinct descriptive levels.[9] Behavioral science, for example, can be a multidisciplinary operation at four descriptive levels: biophysical, biochemical, neurophysiological, and psychological. The difficulties of scientific methodology and investigation at any one level are staggering, especially when addressed to complex mental processes of behavior. The problems of integrating the knowledge obtained at different descriptive levels by use of co-ordinating definitions are even more formidable, with few successful achievements of any rigorous order. When one must further consider that much of our science of human behavior, at any of the above levels, is highly exploratory and in some instances primitive in approach, the expected total complexity will be magnified to an astonishing degree.

Nevertheless, in spite of this edifice of complexity, the work of research and investigation proceeds along all levels with some beginnings in the direction of integration and cross-fertilization of various disciplines. The following list of areas of research into human behavior provides a guide to much current scientific work: enzymatic and hormonal activity in the central nervous system, vegetative nervous system responses, sensory-motor functions, perceptual-motor functions and cognition. It can be seen that such a grouping furnishes a crude model of human behavior along phylogenetic lines.

Teilhard's law of complexity/consciousness can be seen as operating in any of the areas or levels listed above. Thus the "lowest" level of human behavior is endowed with its own complexity and consciousness; and the "highest" level of behavior articulates a vast complexification and expanded consciousness, with integrating mechanisms penetrating to all lower levels.

Students of human nature have periodically turned their attention to an even more characteristic mode of behavior, the interpersonal. Some attempts have been made in psychiatry, social psychology, and anthropology to establish a descriptive science of interpersonal behavior — the relations and transactions between man and men. As a dependent variable the human person vis-a-vis others is poorly predictable no matter how much the independent variables both within and without the subject are manipulated or controlled. The science of a human response to a particular drug is more exact than the science of human response to another person or constellation of persons. Teilhard's notion of the spontaneity of highly centered particles, over against the atomicity and statistical adherence of poorly centered particles, is pertinent here.

The idea of personalization faces the behavioral scientist with this new dimension in the multilevel center of complexity/consciousness which is man. On the other hand, the scientist within his discipline needs to remind himself, from time to time, that his findings and theories also exist in the organic flux of a noosphere, which of itself is evolving towards greater clarity, differentiation, centricity, and synthesis.

For the purpose of discussing some recent theories and their relevance to the thought of Teilhard de Chardin, descriptive levels of behavioral science might be conceived of as falling along one or the other of two axes. First, there are those levels of intrapersonal organization which fall along a biological-psychological axis; second, there are levels of interpersonal process which fall along a psychological-social axis. From an ontogenetic point of view, personality maturation can be visualized as progressing along both axes simultaneously.

The Biological-Psychological Axis

Von Bonin has summarized most modern neuroanatomical studies on the cerebral cortex of the brain.[10] A comparative embryological investigation of vertebrate brains shows that structures will be derived from an arencephalon or a chordencephalon. The former corresponds to the telencephalon and diencephalon of classical morphology and in the lower vertebrates is primarily concerned with olfaction and vision. The latter comprises the mesencephalon, metencephalon, and myelencephalon of classical morphology and contains preponderantly segmental structures associated with peripheral nerves of a given level. From the phylogenetic point of view, in reptiles and lower mammals, the motor activity of extremities becomes more and more intricate and, of course, in higher forms hand and foot tend to become independent. Control of these variegated melodies of movement is regulated by higher centers in a developing arencephalon. The dorsal portion of this endbrain structure, the pallium, expands and falls back on the midbrain in the course of vertebrate phylogenesis.

In mammals the cells of the pallium of the endbrain form a distinctive rind or cortex, which can be differentiated into three regions: a palaeopallium, an archipallium, and a neopallium. During phylogenesis the neocortex increases in size. Throughout the mammals the volume of the neocortex is directly proportional to the increasing volume of the brains. The cortex remains the same thickness but increases its surface tremendously by throwing itself into folds or sulci.

The evolution of the neocortex ushers in those higher centers that control the total pattern of activity inherent in lower centers and, at the same time, allows the emergence of new partial patterns of much greater flexibility, as in fine hand movements and, in man, the set of cranial muscles which serves speech. The neocortex also allows for the finest discrimination of all sensory information, and, in the frontal sector of the cerebral hemispheres, the neocortex is adapted to functions of prediction and preparation for action.

A comparative neurology of the central nervous system is the study of an expanding complexity. The evolution of the neopallium suggests an expanding consciousness. In evolutionary time, however, this brain structure is a recent development. Cephalization, according to Teilhard de Chardin, would be a phenomenon in biogenesis long before the appearance of such a highly differentiated brain formation as the neopallium.

A widely held interpretation of brain function is that the neopallium is involved with higher intellectual functions and learned behavior, while the phylogenetically older structures are concerned with instinctual or generally more primitive patterns of behavior. Karl Pribram presents an interpretation of comparative neurology which casts doubts on the classical correlations of changing brain size and structure with increasing complexity of behavior and capacity for learning.[11] He hypothesizes that the medial and basal forebrain structures, i.e., the palaeopallium and archipallium, partake in the increasing evolutionary differentiation of the forebrain.

Pribram argues for a modification of the classical dichotomy between older forebrain structures and new formations. He proposes a new dichotomy, founded on a significant functional separation, between an inner central core of neuronal systems and an external portion. Each of these parts, internal and external, would contain both old and new formations. A new taxonomy of behavior is derived from this dichotomy. The internal forebrain core is concerned with behavior sequences; the external rind is concerned with behavior involving discrimination.

These concepts of comparative neurology tend to validate Teilhard's law of complexity/consciousness. Consciousness is a corollary of complexity in the neuronal systems of the forebrain core and exterior portion. Consciousness is manifest in behavior involving the sequential dependency of responses and in behavior involving discrimination, and, we might add, in even more basic behavior.

A law of complexity/consciousness is further supported by Bullock's contention that all neurophysiological properties known in the vertebrates, man included, also occur widely among invertebrates. Since the differences of behavior are radical, the differences must be either architectural or numerical in neuronal distribution or dependent upon unknown, undiscovered parameters of neuronal systems.[12]

Much attention has been paid in recent years to neurophysiological research of a reticular formation within the brain stem, which phylogenetically appears, not so much as a new development, but as a rostral enlargement and specialization of interneuron collections. Functionally this central reticular system is capable of grading the activity of most other parts of the brain. Magoun [13] has conducted experimental observations that indicate an ascending reticular activating system, which particularly exerts influences upwards in the brain upon the cerebral neocortex. This system contributes to the initiation and maintenance of the wakeful state and the focus of awareness. This work demonstrates an integrative transactional core, operating vertically, between lower levels of the central nervous system and subserving the state of consciousness. This is further evidence that primitive consciousness, understood in Teilhardian terms, involves even more elementary integrative neuronal formations than the forebrain structures by themselves.

Pertinent to Teilhard's reading of a drift or direction within evolution is an article by Nissen.[14] A scan of the total range of animal life, with special regard to its early and end points, leads to the impression that there has been consistency in the direction of evolution. Nissen proposes a test of this orthogenetic hypothesis. He would compare different species along a curve derived from pooling quantitative data obtained from scoring each species in respect to six classes of adaptational behavorial traits and capacities. The categories of behavior he suggests for scoring are sensory capacities, locomotion, manipulation, perception, sensorimotor connections, and reasoning. The final step would be to choose points on the geologic time scale, and, on the basis of available scores, to select several of the highest scoring species at each point. The orthogenetic hypothesis would be substantiated if the average-score curve showed a rise from the earliest to the latest time points, with no intermediate reversals. Man, of course, would represent the highest scoring species on at least four geologic time curves.

Teilhard's definition of orthogenesis, as the manifest property of living matter to form a system in which terms succeed each other experimentally following the constantly increasing values of centrocomplexity, would provide a theoretical explanation of the validating experiment.

Turning our attention to psychological theory we are immediately confronted with the problem of consciousness as it figures in intrapersonal organization and interpersonal processes. Nuttin's discussion of this problem is most illuminating.[15] A representational theory of consciousness, rooted in philosophical and physiological problems about perceptual functions, is to be avoided or we face the consequence of introducing the concept of a double stage in our world, or even a double world. Consciousness, in the primary sense of the word, is the exposure of the organism to the world or the direct presence of the world to the organism. This exposure, this presence, is a psychological or behavioral fact.

If the fundamental capacity of the organism to be open or exposed to the outside world is lacking, the lack of consciousness means enclosure in the realm of physical and biochemical interactions. Consciousness is psychophysiological activity underlying all behavioral processes, in so far as they are intrinsically directed towards objects. In these terms consciousness has nothing to do with introspection.

Any psychology of man must consider the facts that man can call into play the vicarious presence of an object and that man can operate with a reflective consciousness. Man can think and imagine; he can also be present to his own activities, thoughts, and feelings in reflection.

These properties of animal and human consciousness fit nicely with Teilhard's concepts, although Teilhard suggests a preconsciousness or latent consciousness in nonliving matter. Consciousness is truly operative when the *within* of an organism is open or exposed to the world, or when the world can be felt as present to the *within* of an organism. Reflective consciousness or reflective thought in man might be conceived of as a more complicated function; however, it presupposes consciousness in its primary sense of direct presence of an outside world to man. Exposure to the world is already implicit behavior. Instead of an opposition between behavior and consciousness, the two human realities are inseparably united.

The Psychological-Social Axis

Contemporary scholars of the psychology of personality, from divergent schools of thought, have been reminding us over and over again that personality is more than an internal organization of drives, traits, attitudes, and behavioral levels. As Nuttin has written: "Personality is essentially a structure which goes beyond its internal organization. Its most characteristic feature consists in the fact that an outlook on and exposure to the world is included in its constitution. . . . The fundamental structure of personality is an ego-world unity." [16]

Human consciousness requires consciousness of something, the world, or more significantly, other human consciousnesses distributed in the world in varying degrees of relationship to the person. Personality is not only an ego-world structure, but also an ego-others structure.

The recognition of the importance of these concepts to personality studies has been indicated by many theorists, writing from a variety of viewpoints. Thus the ego-world unity of personality is an idea expressed by Kurt Lewin in his psychological field theory, by Ludwig Binswanger in his *Dasein-analyse,* and by psychoanalytic writers elaborating revisions of Freudian psychology. Among this latter group the psychosocial developmental theory of Erik Erikson is particularly significant and influential.

The ego-others unity of personality, with interpersonalist concepts given great emphasis, can be found in Harry Stack Sullivan's psychiatric theory of interpersonal relations, in Carl Rogers' client-centered therapy with its self-theory implications, and in a host of writings by contemporary personality scholars variously grouped together as culturalist or social psychological theory.

The currents of influence along these lines, in both American and European psychology, have been examined in a recent collection of essays, *Perspectives in Personality Theory.* [17] This book, like so many of its kind, is the child of an international psychological congress. Although the viewpoints expressed at such a meeting are inevitably diverse, a trend is visible, as Allport suggests. [18] Psychology itself is arriving at a new anthropological focus, in which its formulations accommodate personal patterns of functioning, personal attitudes, and personal projects. The general psychological theories of the future will be theories of personality. In the language of Teilhard de Chardin the behavioral science of psychology is undergoing a hominization and, in consequence of this, progressive personalization continues to provide man a deeper insight into his own anthropological space and the establishment of more coherent perspectives on human realities and human interrelatedness. Psychology, behavioral science, all human knowledge, Teilhard would insist, is becoming centered in a new dimension of complexity/consciousness. The evolutionist outlook is not towards chaos, but towards differentiation, synthesis, and unity of human knowledge.

Teilhard's concept of personalization provides the basis for a theory of interpersonalization, which is also emerging in contemporary psychiatric thought. An interesting parallel movement exists in philosophy, where the problem of intersubjectivity is a contemporary preoccupation. The inter-centric arrangement in Teilhard's picture of mankind making its evolution-ary transformation on human knowledge and human love has already been mentioned.

Nowhere is this interpersonalization, steeped in knowledge and love, more dramatically projected than in concrete dyadic life situations. The primary person-to-person relationships in the family are obvious cases in point. Teacher-student and friendship relationships are also examples. In the psy-chotherapeutic relationship the therapist has repeatedly demonstrated a unique laboratory of interpersonalization, within which he works and serves, not without some risk on his part. Carl Rogers has dealt with these problems and the tensions that might be expected to exist within the therapist, as person and as scientist.[19] The resolution of the question lies in a Teilhardian personalization of the psychological or psychiatric science. For science, too, as Rogers reminds us, is an I-Thou relationship with the world of objects; and the behavioral science of the consulting room is an I-Thou relationship with a person.

The mention of Martin Buber's I-and-Thou[20] brings us to the pene-trating and provocative thought of a man who is deeply influencing those areas of behavioral science which must consider the interpersonal matrix within which man exists. This influence on psychiatry is discussed by Farber[21] and Friedman.[22] Farber, in his article, draws a comparison between Buber's thought and the theory of interpersonal relations of the American psychia-trist, Sullivan. He also shows the relevance of Buber's ideas to the studies of schizophrenia made by Sullivan and Fromm-Reichmann. Friedman reviews Buber's importance to several schools of psychotherapy, stressing the psy-chological significance of the I-Thou relationship and genuine dialogue.

The philosophical anthropology of Martin Buber, with its emphasis on encounter, meeting, and dialogue between man and man, seems to me essen-tially complementary to Teilhard's ideas of man's personalization, hyper-personalization, and unification. Teilhard's evolutionist theories sketch out the contemporary human direction and its goal; Buber's thought elucidates the startling details of the interpersonal universe in which we live and grow. Teilhard indicates the inexorable advancement and centering of human knowledge and love; Buber describes the transpersonal context in which knowledge and love expand. If there is a visionary or prophetic trait shared by each of these men, it is because each realizes that mankind has evolved to an anthropological epoch and that man is no longer merely a part of the natural order, but the master of it.

The Swiss theologian Hans Urs von Balthasar writes that man may be viewed as undergoing a threefold evolution in his relation to and knowledge of the universe. Man evolves through three periods: a primitive cosmological epoch, a philosophical epoch, and our present anthropological epoch. The consequence and *leitmotif* of our present epoch is formulated by Von Balthasar: "Man can be the epitome of the cosmos only if he himself keeps the epitome of man before his eyes in his life, thought and behavior, even though he cannot completely embody it." [23] Urs von Balthasar, following Buber, sets the norm of all knowledge as the meeting between persons, which depends upon forms of personal openness. The highest objectivity can be attained only through the highest personal risk by the man who opens and surrenders himself to things.

Teilhard de Chardin appears as the first important creator of system and synthesis in our current anthropological epoch, where all science, all knowledge, all evolution itself, has come to be centered in man. Teilhard appears as the most heroically "open" of modern thinkers. His work is not a cosmology as understood in the older scientific sense. A law of complexity/ consciousness, once formulated, leads him directly to man. Man is not to be apprehended in part: the whole phenomenon of man must be grasped. Here is Teilhard's importance to the behavioral scientist, who is cautioned to remain open to the whole phenomenon.

11

HISTORY IN THE PHENOMENON OF MAN

John V. Walsh

History, the word, its origin, meaning, and uses, has been defined many times. Sometimes it has been considered objectively, as the process and development of nations, of movements, of peoples and cultures. At other times it has been conceived of subjectively as the painful reconstruction of this thronging activity through memory and source and insight, through disciplines, technique and criticism. It is the knowledge of the past, or again, the guide to present and future. History: the art, the science, the literary form, the narrative — what can be added in renewal of this ceaseless and unfruitful search? From Herodotus to von Ranke to Toynbee there have been stressed in repeated variety the investigation, the vivid recounting, the objective reconstruction, the comparative and cyclical recurrence and differentiation of human cultures and their plausible mechanisms. The historian has been by turns under the shadow of the rhetorician and the humanist, the statesman and the scientist. Prophets, too, of older and latter days, have raised their voices in mastery over history. Must we but add another to the long procession? or has not the naturalist already had his day of ascendancy? For, perhaps, to many, the new dimensions claimed in Teilhard's vision of history may be only a heightened version of the discredited scientific view, colored and intensified by a kind of poetry. But must this really be so? Again, what is history and what new dimensions and fresh ingredients of its reality and understanding are afforded in the depth and sweep of Teilhard's thought?

"Seeing" History

History is the totality of the cosmic process as this is lived and re-seen by humankind. This grasp of history is a vital and creative union of the thing and the thought, which are equally history. This incandescent fusion of the process and its meaning transcends the attempt to understand by a separation of the events and their reconstruction. Man in nature and beyond nature is alike actor and spectator: the culmination and the promise in a process wherein he is participant and observant, concentrating the whole in himself and projecting himself outward into the whole. This Teilhardian illumination is not so much a new dimension of history as it is a complex of dimensions converging to transform every ingredient of the universe into human and historical meaning. This achievement is comprehended in Teilhard's eminent sense of "seeing"; for, "fuller being is closer union," but "union can only increase through an increase in consciousness, that is to say, in vision." At the end of the most refined scientific analysis the structure of the object and the mind of the subject are virtually identified. "Object and subject marry and mutually transform each other in the act of knowledge; and from now on man willy-nilly finds his own image stamped on all he looks at." This net of seeing and being would remain a bondage save that in man these convergent relations are equally visual and structural.

Man stands at the center of the perspective, and of the constructing of the universe. Both the realization and the effect of this compenetration are being attained through a long millenial awakening awareness of immensity and depth, number and proportion, of quality, movement and the organic. These provide man with a unity of knowledge and of being and a capacity through this community which is necessary for action and achievement. Each one of these "senses" comprehends whole areas of experience and knowledge; but, to the extent he lacks any of these multiple dimensions, man remains imprisoned within an illusory anthropocentrism that keeps him from seeing his being as it truly is, "a simple and continuing trajectory, the curve of the phenomenon of man." The diminished and specialized view of man which is the anthropologist's, the jurist's, the sociologist's, and even the psychologist's, a view that the overindividuality of man's appearance permits and encourages, must be supplanted by a grasp of genuine inner and outer growth of the universe — a grasp that achieves "the inclusion of man in his wholeness in a coherent picture of the world." The moment of this grasp is the decisive moment in the life of an individual, of a group or of all mankind, a moment wherein the scales of isolation drop from the eyes and there supervenes the realization "that a universal will to live converges and is hominised" in each and all — but only as awareness and actuality and activity are fused into an axis of evolution. It is this "moment" which is captured in Rodin's "Man of Primal Times": heavy with the burden and the acceptance and the determination of life, but setting out on a journey which in this twentieth century of a particular era is only on the threshold of its destiny.

This plurality and concentration of dimensions are the creative contributions to history which Teilhard's *Phenomenon of Man* offers. To pursue and secure these insights one must see as causative — now, at each moment, as well as primordially — the preorganic and the inorganic: leading from chaos through cosmos into consciousness, through reflectivity of consciousness into an expanding co-operative control of the ever deepening process. Each of these phases will give us a new and constructive element of the problem — and our question — what is history? We shall see that Teilhard's vision of man does at last take us further into the inner complexities of history and into its unlimited possibilities as well.

Elemental matter is neither existent nor knowable save as fundamentally *in evolution*. The ineluctable historicity of the universe is revealed in the infinitesimal initiation of things — in the texture of its continuum — providing a matrix that is itself historical for the movement called human history. The players move, while the stage and setting and very floor beneath their feet move also, ceaselessly beyond their awareness. Such is the decisive bearing of the stuff of the universe upon the fabric of history, as we look closely into it, searching out our question, What is history?

Evolution: Matrix of History

The characteristics of plurality, unity, and energy which become manifest in system, totum and quantum, are fully revealed and meaningful only in that continuous transformation which is cosmogenesis. Yet, even in these elemental aspects, no one of which is as such isolable, there is already present and operative a certain historical tendency, a feature of succession or duration. In fact one is tempted to say of plurality alone, that in its polarity of disintegration and configuration, it parallels, prefigures, and indeed embodies one of the most persistent properties of human history. In equivalent fashion, unity and energy as tendencies of the smallest and the greatest historical segments are impressively present, so that one may say that the three faces of matter are also in themselves and by anticipation and analogy the three faces of history in any phase, as well as overall. "In its own way, matter has obeyed from the beginning that great law of biology to which we shall have to recur time and time again, the law of 'complexification.'"

Here, again, one must emphasize in looking at the stuff of the universe, in its incipient and suggestive historicity, the heterogeneity and developmentality of the whole from the atom to the star. "All science of the real becomes a history." We deal not with points in a structure, but rather instant and successive sparks in a temporality of space. The myth of the cosmic tree with its root and trunk plunged in the abyss and its branches rising beyond limit and visibility may still be the most effective image of the universe. The sidereal immensities, no more than the atomic infinitesimals, may be excluded from the life and the destiny of man, whether individual or the race — and even in tracing only the outer lineaments. There is not only a genetic connection of the atom with the star, but there is a constant necessity of this concentration in the stuff of the universe as a continuing condition of those intricate material complexes that are ultimately the organisms of consciousness. The genesis of man and the genesis of cosmos, merely as seen and scanned from without, are intimately interwoven in an operative and indestructible unity.

This structure in its contours is subject to those numerical laws customarily summarized under the names conservation and dissipation of energy, or, more generally, constancy and loss, diminution drawing toward death. In this sense, history in its sequence of syntheses is haunted by the nemesis of dissolution, although it is by this very limiting essence that nature is enabled to become history. "From time it passes into duration, and finally escapes from geometry dramatically to become, in its totality as in its parts, an object of history." It is in this passage of history into ever more improbable combinations, the terms of whose syntheses are bound to dissolve into ever more probable and shapeless elements, that the burden of tragedy and pathos always felt in the conflicts and the activities of historical events consists. But cannot science see beyond the contours into the inner dimensional configurations? Yes, says Teilhard, for even in the primordial stuff there is a *within*, and into this realm of actuality the fullness of the question, What is history, must be pursued.

The coherence of structural arrangements into an inner existentiality of variable but definable entities is Teilhard's bridge of the *within* and the *without*: a doctrine providing a comprehensive phenomenology. Just as its insight enables us to see how the granular atomicity of the primordial stuff is sustained from pressing dissolution, so this universal inwardness of events, manifoldly compounded as they must be, illumines history as a fabric rather than a raveling of threads. The primary problem at this level is the paradox of the two energies, as well as the apparent inverse relation between the physical and the psychical energy. At this point, Teilhard introduces a concept of vivid utility in historical thought, the distinction namely between tangential energy, itself twofold, and radial energy. It is suggested here that the compulsive tendency of institutions and movements, of persons, as of states, to behave by turns and simultaneously as centering on themselves, as well as peripherally, and to dissolve into successive phases, each radiating anew and toward fresh patterns, is so striking an instance of Teilhard's principle operating in the socio-historical sphere as to warrant its description as an historical law. It may also be remarked, by way of applying another Teilhardian observation to the historical process, that "to discover the universal hidden beneath the exceptional" is alike the most pervasive possibility and the most productive procedure in historical phenomena and analysis. There is therefore a universal inwardness of things — as distinct from persons — as there is an outwardness, and the properties of each aspect parallel and compenetrate, as do the concavity and the convexity of a mirror. These properties coexist as well as pre-exist in the earth as the scene of life and history. The physical cosmos in all its movement and immensity is then a prime factor in history and its understanding, and its early stages must be evoked in pursuit of our continuing question, What is history?

The Unity of History

There is no such thing as the earth before history, for both primevally and now, both *without* and *within*, the earth is history. This is the burden of what Teilhard calls the period of "pre-life": the crystallization and the polymerization of matter in such wise as to fashion an involution of the globe upon itself, concentrating an ever deeper cycle of energy into centers of emergent consciousness.

An aggregate of relatively stable atoms detached from the sun constitutes the nucleus of what shapes itself into the globe. An enclosure of inward intensification, constituting a possibility of a *within* and a consciousness, is not only present *ab initio*, but is genuinely both origin and continuity. Involution contains and sustains evolution. This immensity of process is merely expressible and sensible within the measure of time, hence in no way can creation be known, but only revealed, and even in the phenomenal universe that alone is experience, actual origins can be seen only in the flux and form of consequence. The earth, therefore, perilously balanced between the atomic and the galactic, is the vessel that holds and manifests in its symbols an abyss of reality which life and history adumbrate. The plentitude of the cosmos in its laws and its activities fashions the tissues and the happenings of history out of itself which is already history. This is accomplished by the supervening of the radial and expanding upon the tangential and limited (energy). In this formation of a pre-biosphere there is a simultaneous multiplicity of molecules and an intersolidarity of their effects. The mass of infinitesimal centers represented by the deposits of protein megamolecules is interactive by the very condition of its rise and continuance, namely, a new and sharper phase of unity within plurality. This heightening of level and deepening of emphasis mark the passage of pre-life into life, the very birth of the stuff and the form of history: what a great poet has called the rhythm and the color of life, discernible in the deeps of a past now become direction and destiny.

This discernment in the piercing of the past, that in the midst of continuity there is innovation, supplies, on the scientific and phenomenal level, the next Teilhardian contribution to a fresh illumination of history. For, in the plunging of the cell into the prolonged deeps of the barysphere and into that past commonly considered inorganic and azoic, there is afforded, in dawning glory, an ultimate linkage of life to pre-life and onward to that consciousness which, as reflection, becomes at last the fullness of humanity and history. In this vast area of the advent and the expansion of life to the brink of consciousness, Teilhard's scientific vision soars beyond the arrested insights of the historian. Just as the cell is climax and origination, so man will be seen anew as culmination and initiation of a vivid adventure whose stages are barely now begun and whose term is beyond comprehension.

The cellular revolution is among those major movements before and since which mark the distinctive advances in complexity and concentration characteristic of historical growth. The power and the meaning of inner and dynamic analogy are pervasive and penetrating in this particular presentation of Teilhard's and hence this discussion of life, its rise, fruition and piercing passage into consciousness is unusually overwhelming in its bearing on history as substance and knowledge. The mind leaps forward in illumination not only to the great organizational developments of human history, but also into the modern cybernetic possibilities of future mastery in concentration and control of consciousness. The cellular awakening is an achievement in the paramountcy of radial over tangential energy. It is therefore a cardinal instance of the *within* compelling itself by outer correlation upon our awareness and hence marking the actual start of an historical series. Simultaneously the impossibility of ever strictly observing the initial phase in an historical growth emerges as equally compelling and hence the formulation of Teilhard's doctrine: "This is a law running right through history which we shall later be calling the 'automatic suppression of evolutionary peduncles'."

It is clear then that the proliferating manifestations of primitive life can only be envisioned indirectly, but that the exercise of this method is analogously imperative for the scientist and the historian. The renewal of historical imagination as a refined and exacting instrument of analysis as well as in synthesis, and not as the vague and arbitrary literary description practiced by the popularizer, is one of the unique necessities of future science, a realm that Teilhard may fairly be seen as embodying. Accordingly, the reconstruction in perspective of milieu, microscopy, and multitude of the organisms in time-space as the enveloping foundation of life and consciousness, thought and history, is the condition of reaching origins, in so far as man's knowledge may hope to summon and resuscitate them. The fullness of life flowering into reflective consciousness is both the substance and the awareness of history: reality embodied not only in reconstitutive memory but even more in creative hope.

The interactive ramifications of life are but a special branch of the antecedent and accompanying shooting out of all physical and material existence. The dominant factor in all this immensity of phenomena is the linearity and irreversibility of the total process, despite the recurrence and periodicity of many structural phases within its progress. Herein lies a key to the nature of history and the actuality of its direction. "An ever-ascending curve, the points of transformation of which are never repeated; a constantly rising tide below the rhythmic tides of the ages — it is on this essential curve, it is in relation to this advancing level of the waters, that the phenomenon of life, as I see things, must be situated." Life and history are a unity and a continuity and a perspective of innumerable and complex, but not rewinding skeins.

The Ascending Spiral

It is perhaps essentially in this idea of an immense, but not vague, futurity of fulfillment that the unique illumination of history and its meaning by Teilhard's thought consists. For, as one passes from his treatment of the expansion of life and the rise of consciousness and duration to the birth and development of thought as embodied in mankind, the realization gradually deepens and clarifies that the modern earth and its survival are a matter of millenia slowly, but utterly, reformed and compenetrated by mind and spirit. It is in this very process itself that plentitude is continuous and concomitant, and that there is supplied the natural foundation for the supervenience and re-creation of redemptive grace. Man must grasp, share and, in this sense, ever more completely control and co-operate in the achievement of the universe which is equally an individual and a collective destiny. Humanity from a *massa damnata* will find anew its lost possibilities of organic life and spiritual immortality and become a *massa redempta. Hic labor, hoc opus est.* So in this toil and task man must see and share, and may, of course, fail and fall, but must accept the burden and the magnitude if he is ever to have the chance of finding his meaning and his greatness. Some of the profound insights in this panorama of psychogenesis are evoked in the latter portions of *The Phenomenon of Man.*

The importance of origins lies not in themselves, but in their bearing on the totality that includes the future, so that the more deeply man comprehends origins, the more illuminedly does he move into the activities of the present and the future. This insight into the life that is history, when translated into every distinct discipline and science and skill, completely revivifies and revolutionizes the sense and the use of history, giving value to every demanding detail of research and documentation, as well as hope to the higher uses of accumulated knowledge. Thus, one may see in the understanding of what Teilhard calls "the neolithic metamorphosis," the key to an interpretation of an atomic metamorphosis and an intellective-spiritual renovation for the whole of mankind. The transformative power of analogy and the recreative synthesis of ever accumulating activity reach dimensionally in a fourfold direction, besides forward and backward in time, downward into roots and upward into parabolic infinitude. "It was only in the Neolithic age that the great cementing of human elements began which was never thenceforward to stop. The Neolithic age, disdained by pre-historians because it is too young, neglected by historians because its phases cannot be exactly dated, was nevertheless a critical age and one of solemn importance among all the epochs of the past, for in it Civilization was born." And one might add, as Breuil and Teilhard himself remark, that the current cycle of centuries is but an extended interlude and transition between the waning Neolithic and the dawning Cosmopolitan age. Neo-humanity, germinated in the Mediterranean out of the Neolithic complex, has become the nucleus of a continuing noo-genesis which includes all the peoples of the earth.

It may be said in brief, drawing our position from the concept of dura-tion just discussed, that in Teilhard's synthesis anthropology has become his-tory, and both have become life. The remote worlds of the past and the future are brought together into a vivid and deepening present. Consciousness and continuity compenetrate, illuminate, and control each other in an ever more comprehensive activity and reality. The dominant questions in this conver-gence become a composite of survival and ultimates. In pursuit of these we shall find some beginnings of reply to our question, What is history? and some refreshment in the strengthened synthesis of natural and socio-cultural and intellectual-spiritual phenomena. The pressure of problems in their mani-fold form may be reduced to two fundamental themes, namely, collectivity and personality. Moving through these areas are the questions of knowledge and love, research and religion, growth and conflict. It will be seen how these are soluble deeply and developmentally in the light of the profound unitive phenomenological approach of Teilhard — the constant absorption (without loss of energy) of complexity into consciousness, and the unlimited intensification of this awareness into a glow of centrality, the reverse of dif-fusion. So considered, it becomes clear that collectivity compels the growth of personality, indeed that the person is a process concomitant and created only in the light of its polarity in the whole.

Knowledge is the deepening union of objectivity and consciousness. It is both an end in itself and a source of power and an agent in the evolutionary process. "The truth is that, as children of a transition period, we are neither fully conscious of, nor in full control of, the new powers that have been un-leashed. Clinging to an outworn habit, we still see in science only a new means of providing more easily the same old things . . .; (one must en-visage) a world in which, as happens already, one gives one's life to be and to know, rather than to possess." Knowledge and the radial energy which is love must mutually compenetrate, producing inevitably within one realm of their activity *"a science of human energetics."* This discipline is today adumbrated in combinatory sciences such as cybernetics, at once speculative and practical, but, above all, the interfertile result of sciences contiguous and conjoining. In just such a way there must arise many new sciences, few of which have yet even been imagined. A paramount instance of fruitful union must lie, above all, in the vast embrace of science and religion in whose his-torical and persistent opposition is clarified a vivid proof of the yet primitive perversity of mankind. "In the mutual reinforcement of these two still opposed powers, in the conjunction of reason and mysticism, the human spirit is destined, by the very nature of its development, to find the uttermost degree of its penetration with the maximum of its vital force." Knowledge and love, religion and science — these belong together.

Love as energy and the doctrine of the Omega bring us to the heart not only of the phenomenon of man, but in themselves and for that very reason to the essential conditions and ultimate liberations of mankind's historical life. They are the reversal of entropy and the escape from immanence. Interwoven in the entire thought of Teilhard's work, from the first discussion of the elemental inorganic stuff, there runs the parallelism of the two energies, tangential and radial, the one down-spinning, the other ever regathering and growing. The activity and interplay of these two energies culminate in that manifestation of energy in its 'hominised' form which is love. It is marvelous to behold just the historical realization of this tremendous force and form from Plato to Cusa and expressed in all the profusion of great imaginative composition. "Love in all its subtleties is nothing more, and nothing less, than the more or less direct trace marked on the heart of the element by the psychical convergence of the universe upon itself. . . . Love alone is capable of uniting living beings in such a way as to complete and fulfill them, for it alone takes them and joins them by what is deepest in themselves . . . personalisation by totalisation." And, be it noted, "a universal love is not only psychologically possible; it is the only complete and final way in which we are able to love." The paradox and the scepticism that such doctrines express and evoke are soluble in the surety that the person exists, rather than is lost in the collectivity, but, above all, in the realization of Omega which is not only the recognition of "some vague future existence, but the radiation *as a present reality* of that mysterious centre of our centres . . . ".

The Pleroma

Love and survival, of the cosmos and of man, demand Omega. If this radial energy be real in any of its forms, and above all in the form of love, there must coexist and sustain it at each present moment a center and a source and structure which not only hold from chaos, but draw the elements of whatever level together and upward. So the whole concourse of human institutions is imminently in danger of dissolution, but kept in hand and in ascent and ultimately even in defiance of death by the coactive drawing of an Omega whose impact is discernible inescapably in the infinitesimal and insistently throughout the structure of totality in all its bewildering manifold. "In Omega we have in the first place the principle we needed to explain both the persistent march of things toward greater consciousness, and the paradoxical solidity of what is most fragile." One must above all note that in this doctrine of Omega Teilhard is proposing a metempirical principle and not covertly verbalizing theism or the Incarnation — though, naturally, the profound precompatibility is significant. "Contrary to the appearances still admitted by physics, the *Great Stability* is not at the bottom in the infra-elementary sphere, but at the top in the ultra-synthetic sphere." So both in nature and in history there is at each moment and overall a phenomenal suggestion of completion hovering within and above complexity. The importance of this doctrine for the student of history is incomparable. It is, in fact, in this phenomenological perception that Teilhard himself is constituted a profound expositor of history from inception to its constantly receding as well as ever present vistas, the patterned compenetration of origins and ends. "The only universe capable of containing the human person is an irreversibly 'personalising' universe."

The vast sweep of Teilhard's mind and vision and synthesis clearly opens new lines of insight and scope to the materials and the science of history, even as our question was raised in the introductory paragraph of these reflections. Some breath of the deep spirit bringing light to those questions we have tried to evoke. For it is overwhelmingly clear that the bringing of his method to the sources of the historical period would revolutionize their treatment, just as the illumination rising from the immense geochronological approach in all its content, not obscuring the least item of the details, also would renovate the entire narrative and meaning of human history. Let us *see,* as Teilhard says, in epitomizing his thought, how this vision compenetrates and unites the immensities of the past, the actualities of the present, and the infinities of the future.

The Phenomenon of Man grasps and illumines the immanence and the import of process throughout the structure of reality. This is a fact and a doctrine still of little weight in the counsels of mankind despite the out-pouring of evolutionary ideas and images in recent generations. Therefore any work which like Teilhard's attempts to establish a complete and consistent phenomenology of man is of decisive bearing on the understanding of history and the character of human decisions. Unusual as it may seem, Teilhard's thought establishes so creative a dimension for the areas of natural and human history as to bring a fresh innovation to Sir John Seeley's famous identification of politics and history. For it is precisely in his revolutionary urges to research and innovation in human society that the amazing depth and vision of Teilhard's scientific synthesis are demonstrated. There is here a genuine sketch of human destiny which is based on knowledge and yet totally transcends intellectualism. Yet it actually disavows a claim to provide a philosophy of history. It falls into that void of demand for a new correlation of modern knowledge which the exponents of general systems theory have been so pressingly urging, something which the world has not had since the Middle Ages and for which it was not then ready, namely, a truly creative synthesis of spirituality and materiality. It opens a path for which the Cartesian system was a call rather than an answer, as has now been shown by the historical failure of its oversimplified parallelism.

It is then initially in the area not of simple theory, but of organic inter-relation, a field wherein philosophy has been largely sterile and the sciences basically inadequate, that a work like *The Phenomenon of Man* is both light and prophecy. The arbitrary divisions between the various sciences are elimi-nated by constructive combination and application to their common objects whose meaning and knowledge are thereby deepened. Teilhard's creative accomplishment may prove in the deepest sense Copernican, the establishment of a genuine origin in a new way of thought which has already long been looked for, but has had only a few harbingers. Besides the essays of the anthro-pologist Loren Eisely, *The Immense Journey* and *The Firmament of Time*, perhaps there should be mentioned *Human Destiny* of Lecomte du Noüy and that remarkable but as yet apparently little known work of the economist Kenneth Boulding, *The Image*, which is actually an essay in metempirical epistemology. These works, Teilhard's and a few others, are transitional signs in a broadening and deepening movement in world history which is driving toward the need of increasing union between knowledge, activity, and values.

Human Energetics: Love

This has been a process under way in broad sweeps since the pre-Socratic phase in Western thought, as today one witnesses the long and extended crea-tive agony of mergence between West and East — in far beyond the current political sense of those terms. Man is rooted in the stuff of the universe, and so he is a composite of its ramifications and diversifications alike. As the proof of evolution, man is the point at which the curve turns back upon itself. It is precisely and profoundly in the coalescence of human branches, biologically and culturally, that the direction of growth since the rise of man is now evidenced as a convergence rather than a divergence.

Humanity is a unique species which, unlike those others that move either to exhaustion or monstrosity, stretches gradually like a membrane over all the earth. It grows and deepens and will not break. The immediate contiguity of this embracing general concept and the most pressing concrete actuality is shown in the fact that the whole world is now needed to feed each man and that man now, thanks to electricity, radar, radio and whatever, is ubiq-uitous throughout the whole earth, in his voice, his image, and his move-ments. Each and every member of mankind, and humanity as a whole, are coextensive with the earth.

This polarity of each and all supplies another approach to the understanding of history newly illumined in Teilhard's vision. For just as we cannot know the part until we know the whole, so we cannot know the history of man save we see him in his origin and his end, and these seen immanently on the basis of the physical evidence, which provides a reconstruction and a prognosis of the total process. One does not know either cell or tissue without the organism, one does not know either tribe or nation without humanity, one does not know past or future without unison.

The historian therefore, to write a history of man or any phase thereof, must exercise a Teilhardian knowing of the past and seeing of the future in order to serve at all adequately for any perspective; otherwise fact and comment are scraps and pieces patched together without pattern or compass. It is such a composite projection in depth which alone will enable the historian and the statesman to employ and to concentrate the totality of acquired knowledge on the continuing problems of the present and the future. The challenge now of global and regional problems will demand the intensest possible evocation and application of scientific information and learning, but unified and vitalized by spiritual wisdom. Man must learn to think and to act at once evolutively and spiritually.

Indeed it has been the restriction of the evolutional concept to its material component and the assimilation of the spiritual into that limited dimension by scientists of insufficient vision which have tended to alienate many philosophers and theologians, as well as truly religious spirits, from a genuine insight into evolution as a whole. For rather than the contradiction of creation, it veritably *is* creation, as man beholds and becomes aware of its unfolding in the dimension of time which is but the moving image of eternity, as Plato has so wondrously said. The way of evolution is from matter to non-matter, physics to hyperphysics, with man the bridge between these worlds. Man is both creature and master of either world, as also he passes from them into that other world wherein he has no claim other than gratuity. The fact of living in both worlds of matter and spirit simultaneously and concomitantly constitutes the paradox and tension of human existence and the suggestion of its further coexistence in eternity as well as in time.

It is in this climactic eloquence of Teilhard that some of the profoundest and yet most practical utterances of his whole vision of man are to be found. For in recalling the pre-Socratic and Empedoclean division of force into that love and strife that unite and repel, we are reminded that there is no such thing as the energy of despair, but that ultimately all energy is love. It is love that unites and that gives, whether the self or the consuming of the self, as "the moth in the flame" which is the flame of life, so that love is both the end of man and his coming to birth: all births and consummations being but symbols thereof, and hence in the starkest moments and concrete harshnesses of life and history demanding ever to be kept vividly in mind, and meditated unto always deeper understanding.

The realm of politics and diplomacy with all its bitterness and conflict must be seen as the outer face of an inward drama. As we watch the spectacle, in so secular a setting as the United Nations, of new peoples and fresh struggles, we must forcibly bear in mind the overwhelming significance of this phase in world history, a passage, namely, from an Atlantic and European period to a continental era of human development. This is but the dawn of changes destined utterly to transform and to revolutionize the centuries and millenia before us. If the accompanying dimensions of thought and spirit are equally and comprehensively in growth, the entire process of history in all its complexities will assume a character of varied determination and manifold variety, complementary and simultaneous, in which the co-operative and conscious deployment of evolutionary possibility will at once humble and exalt man, preparing him for the fuller reception of divine gifts. "No evolutionary future awaits man except in association with all other men" — so, Teilhard in a sentence so simple as to slip by unnoticed, heavy at once with warning and hope. Also, and above all, "the crown of evolution (is) a supreme act of collective vision obtained by a pan-human effort of investigation and construction." These words embody concepts which contain a master-vision embracing and transcending the mere physical line of evolution which in all its fullness may be said to comprehend the essence of Christianity as shadowed forth in the profundities of Pauline oracle.

In the human and the divine scale, it must be remembered in patience and in labor that all advance — especially in big things — is imperceptible. "Nowhere among the men I met or about whom I was told did I see the smallest grain which might be destined to grow for the future life of mankind; . . . (yet) . . . beneath the universal movement of things, something is being formed . . . (so that) . . . nothing here below, none of man's travail, is lost to him." So we must (sometimes in the midst of bitterness) remember when we despair of the struggles and the tragedies that seem to be of destructive essence in man's attempts to pass beyond the bounds of nationalism and imperialism in the long journey and toil toward regional and world community.

The import of this international and global redeployment is borne in on us currently by the sight of the many new nations and the multicolored hues of the human race in the assembly of the United Nations. These new members begin now to constitute this assemblage into a genuine token gathering of humanity. This organization, which is the present phase in the growth of the international community, begins to approximate the goal of universality and at least to prefigure the hope of achieving the purpose implied in the name of unity. As the Oriental peoples and the increasing portions of the entire globe begin to symbolize Teilhard's curve of humanity turning upon itself, we become aware of the coming transcendence of the nation-state in a form that is to retain its vitality and to obviate its limits. Something of this transcendent awareness is in the statement of American policy as centered about the typifying realities of the coming world, namely, the atom and space, the upper and lower limits of the *without*. If these are the tangibles, the *withoutness* that man must work with and face, the *within of things* has reached that degree of consciousness such that the curve turns on itself and men are being fashioned into man; and through the terrors of our history, humanity in the union of new and old peoples will at length discover its dignity.

Light for the Historian

History is the story of man: a story that began with time and will end with time. Each generation, indeed each man, must fill in that inestimable gulf if he is to know what human life is, indeed what life itself is — estimating the beginning, weighing the past, anticipating the future, and finding his place somewhere in that process. *Process.* The word implies not only movement but progress. We have come from somewhere, from something; we are going somewhere; where? when? why? Are we near to the end of time? or are we still in the beginnings of time? A theologian of our time, Evgenii Lampert, has reminded us that we are all always in the penultimate stages of history.

Not only is man's story limitless in time (or should we say limited only by Time?), but spatially it extends to the very limits to which a man might go. What are these limits? An Egyptian might have said to the headwaters of the Nile; a Greek to the Pillars of Hercules; a medieval sailor to the edge of the earth. We ourselves remember when the stratosphere was our upper limit. What is it now? the moon? Venus? What are the physical limits to human existence?

It is an answer to some of these questions that Pierre Teilhard de Chardin attempts in *The Phenomenon of Man*. He tells us whence man, beginning with the birth of matter from which man in time came; he tells us where and how he sees the lines directed: those lines clearly and evidentially drawn by the succession of forms and the development of potentialities. Following these to their logical and preordained conclusion he sees the end of man, the end of man's story, the end of History. It is no more different or strange from man as we see him today than we ourselves are from the atom-molecule-megamolecule-cell progression that science has seen and substantiated.

Every thinking man — and that is each of us — thinks to himself more often than he asks of his neighbor: Where am I going? what am I doing?

why was I born? What is more tragic than to have no answers to these haunt-ings, and worse, to find no teacher who can tell us? It is this unique thing that Teilhard has given us in his volume *The Phenomenon of Man*: an answer to Where and What and Why. Here is an answer to our anxiety, if we can take it. Here is the human situation, if we can understand it. Far from fantasy, his report is rooted in fact, in the physics of the earth whence man emerged in order himself to build that earth and which each man himself contains in the gifts of consciousness and reflection. Man having been given life must him-self choose to live. This is the challenge that faces each of us. This is the point to which evolution has brought us. If we refuse, we die, and the earth dies with us; for man is evolution.

It is frightening; it overwhelms; it is too terrible for man to be so great a god. And yet this is the way of it: this is the impossible role thrust upon that creature of the earth that the earth has brought forth — an utterly un-acceptable role that man in the fullness of reflective consciousness must will to accept. *Acceptance.* To know and to accept and to be and to love: this is the fullness of human life which man shall in time learn more and better to existentialize. In his so doing, and in his so doing well, the earth and time will have their end. For this was it begun.

Where, then, in all of this does the conventional historical narrative fit? The paleontologist and anthropologist are at home in its first chapters: the beginnings of human existence, the stone and metal ages, the rise of the West. But whereas the historian usually leaves it to the theologian and the philosopher to write the end of that story, the scientist-historian should draw his own conclusions from the facts. This Teilhard does with his scientific evidence; and this is what makes his account a fuller and deeper history of man and a philosophy of the history of man in more than the conventional sense.

There is no line in history which is not a vector line. Every line has direction; every line is a pointer. It is not too soon to look for the pattern and even to draw conclusions. Pierre Teilhard de Chardin has outlined them in his *Phenomenon of Man*.

12

THE ENERGETICS OF LOVE

Christopher E. Fullman, O.S.B. and Henry J.-J. D'Aoust, O.S.B.

> *"Un univers chargé d'amour*
> *dans son evolution . . ."*

Central to the mature thought of Teilhard de Chardin as summed up in *The Phenomenon of Man* is the desire to mediate between the mechanist and the vitalist points of view, to indicate the possibility of a reconciliation between the mutually antagonistic and entrenched positions of the determinists and the finalists, and to unite the views of those who take into account only the external aspect of the world and those who insist upon an exclusively internal aspect of things.

Discussing the phenomenon of consciousness in man, Teilhard refuses to see it as an isolated instance in the cosmos. He argues, on the contrary, that it has cosmic extension: "Since the stuff of the universe has an inner aspect at one point of itself, there is necessarily a *double aspect* to its structure, that is to say in every region of space and time — in the same way, for instance, as it is granular: *coextensive with their Without there is a Within to things"* (p. 56).

In a similar way, Teilhard does not consider the phenomenon of love as something peculiar to man. He would say rather that love "is a general property of all life and as such it embraces, in its varieties and degrees, all the forms successively adopted by organized matter" (p. 264). The present article will be an attempt to explain Teilhard's idea of cosmic love. The reader should be mindful, however, of the difficulties and possible pitfalls of such an undertaking. Teilhard himself does not pretend to formulate a dogma but simply to propose a possible line of solution. *"To see or to perish* is the very condition laid upon everything that makes up the universe, by reason of the mysterious gift of existence" (p. 31). Over and over again in the writings of Teilhard one hears the tone, not of arrogant assertion, but of humble inquiry. "I believe I can see a direction and a line of progress for life," he says, and generously invites us to share his vision with him.

The "Within of Things"

So great has been the modern experimental scientist's fear of regression into a primitive animism that he has confined himself entirely to observation of external aspects of reality. There are, however, exceptions. "We do not find obvious evidence of life or mind in so-called inert matter, and we naturally study them most easily where they are most completely manifested; but if the scientific point of view is correct, we shall ultimately find them, at least in rudimentary forms, all through the universe." This statement, by J. B. S. Haldane, Teilhard cites as a surprising and welcome confirmation of his own intuition of the nature of reality (p. 57). Teilhard addressed himself to an examination of what he calls the "within" of things, their inner aspect. To Teilhard the modern experimental scientist had bent over backwards to avoid any consideration of this aspect of reality, and he saw his own efforts as a means of bridging the gap between the positivist scientists, on the one hand, and the vitalists, on the other.

What is the *within* of things of which Teilhard speaks? To Teilhard all reality has an inner face and an outer face, which are duplicates of each other. He sees this parallelism existing at every level of reality from the most diffuse states to the most highly complex ones. In the highly complex forms Teilhard notes that their *withinness*, their inner face, their "psychic" character is readily observable, as for example in man. The *withinness* becomes more and more difficult to detect the farther one goes back from the complex forms to the most diffuse and disparate fragments of matter. Conversely, the greater the complexity of matter, and the greater the complexity of a given form, the more observable its psychic aspect. This led him to formulate his law of "complexity-consciousness," in which he states that the unorganized multitude develops gradually and imperceptibly into the unified multiple. To Teilhard, at every point along the line of reality from the most minute atom to the highly complex form of the primates, of hominoids, and of man himself, there is a gradual increase in the degree of *withinness*.

If we understand this *withinness* as psychic energy, then the complete study of reality ought not to ignore its presence. But as we have mentioned before, the modern scientist has generally ignored it as outside the scope of his researches. Teilhard suggests that it would not involve a regression to consider it. On the contrary, he says we must *advance* and face the problem of this mysterious energy. On man's level the interdependence of the two energies, physical and psychic, is evident. "To think, we must eat." Is this a tyranny of matter over mind? Or is it a manifestation of the spiritual power within matter? Physical energy is required for the expression of the loftiest thought and the highest love. Spiritual and physical energies seem complementary, interwined, interrelated. The problem is: Are they basically one? Is the soul a focal point of the transformation of physical and spiritual energies? To Teilhard spiritual and physical energies are not identical nor transformable into each other. Though closely related in their operation, they are independent of each other. Mere change of form, simple transformation does not explain the differences between matter and spirit, between physical and spiritual energies.

Teilhard sees, not an equivalence, but a proportion between the inner and outer aspects of inanimate being on the one hand and the inner and outer aspects of animate being on the other. The *withinness* of a stone and its *withoutness* are in relation to each other as are the *withinness* and the *withoutness* of a man.

To avoid the problem of dualism, Teilhard proposes a solution. If we assume that all energy is psychic,* we may establish an hypothesis that there are two types of energy: tangential energy, that energy which links elements on the same level to one another; and radial energy, which draws forward each element into the conjunctions that produce a greater complexity in the process of evolution. The following formula will help to illustrate Teilhard's thought:

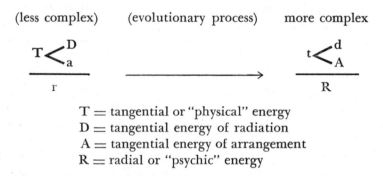

$$(\text{less complex}) \qquad (\text{evolutionary process}) \qquad \text{more complex}$$

$$\frac{T <^{D}_{a}}{r} \qquad \xrightarrow{\hspace{4cm}} \qquad \frac{t <^{d}_{A}}{R}$$

T = tangential or "physical" energy
D = tangential energy of radiation
A = tangential energy of arrangement
R = radial or "psychic" energy

Basically what Teilhard seems to say is that there is an inverse ratio between the degrees of tangential energy and of radial energy as we move from the simple to the highly complex forms. In the simple forms, tangential energy is at its maximum; radial or psychic energy is slight. In the most complex forms, tangential energy is at a minimum, whereas radial energy is at a maximum. He distinguishes further two functions of tangential energy: *radiation* and *arrangement*. These also are in inverse ratio as we move from the most simple to the most complex forms. In the simplest forms, the tangential energy of radiation is very great, while the tangential energy of arrangement is at a minimum. In the most complex forms, the tangential energy of radiation is at a minimum and the tangential energy of arrangement is very great.

*Erroneously rendered as "physical" in the official English translation. (*Editor's note*)

Turning now from the abstract concept of *withinness* to the manifestation of *withinness* on the earth, Teilhard assumes that "a certain mass of elementary consciousness was originally emprisoned in the matter of earth" (p. 72). He rejects the hypothesis that the origin of life on earth was the result of its impregnation by interstellar germs and insists that the earth, by its initial chemical composition, already contained within itself the elements of prelife. (It will be valuable to note in passing here that Teilhard's intuition is supported by the findings of the biochemists reported in Moscow in 1957 in the first international symposium on the origin of life. *The Phenomenon of Man* was written almost twenty years earlier, between 1938 and 1940.)

Teilhard worked within the classical frame of the history of evolution. This theory postulates a constant progression from the simplest to the most highly complex forms: atoms joining atoms to form molecules, molecules combining with other molecules to form megamolecules, megamolecules undergoing a process of polymerization which has its outcome in the emergence of viruses and finally the living cell. (Even the most casual observer will note the remarkable transition implied here in the leap from inanimate to animate matter, from the molecule to the living cell. The reader is referred to the article by Sidney W. Fox, "How Did Life Begin?" [1] Fox and his co-workers believe, on the basis of experimental data, that the first life involved a "simultaneous orchestration" of the following five stages of the origin of life: (1) synthesis of organic compounds; (2) synthesis of simple biochemical substances; (3) production of large molecules such as proteins; (4) organized cellular structure; and (5) evolution of macromolecules and metabolism.)

Looked at superficially, the tree of life seems to be a haphazard efflorescence. As Teilhard points out, most scientists would reject any notion of progression toward a definite goal. "Contemplated without any guiding thread, it must be recognized that the host of living creatures forms qualitatively an inextricable labyrinth" (p. 142). But Teilhard is convinced that evolution has "a precise *orientation* and a privileged *axis*." To him, the ultimate nature of evolution is not physical, but psychic. Evolution proceeds in an ordered pattern from geogenesis to biogenesis to psychogenesis. Recalling, at this point, Teilhard's distinction between tangential and radial energy, we can expect that, among the multitudinous forms the evolutionary process has produced, those have a pre-eminence which exhibit the greatest degree of radial or psychic energy. For example, in the arthropods we find this steady development of the external organism of the psychic: the nerve ganglia and the brain. The process is emphatically a development from a simple nervous system to a cephalized, highly complex one. From the centipede to the grasshopper the most striking element of change is this increased complexity of the nervous system and an increasing cerebralization. To Teilhard the shape of teeth, the disposition of limbs and other such elements belong to the secondary level of evolution. He considers the elaboration and development of the nervous system as the proper parameter or measure of the evolving phenomenon and the guidepost to its direction.

The Darwinian evolutionist attributes to external forces and change the changes and mutations that have resulted in the innumerable variations observable among living things. To the Lamarckians, however, some inner principle in living things is the agent responsible for their great variety. Teilhard sees an interplay between these two forces. He speaks in fact of a "symbiosis" of chance and anti-chance, of determination and spontaneity, of the *without* and the *within*. He suggests that external stimuli can be productive of change only if there is a consciousness to acknowledge them. "Beneath the 'tangential' we find the 'radial,'" he reminds us. The more complex the living being, therefore, the more freedom it manifests in its response to environment.

At the plateau of the mammals, one observes both a great variety and a remarkable similarity. The variety lies in their obvious special adaptation to different environments. One has only to think of the radical differences manifested in the giraffe, the elephant, the hippopotamus, and the antelope to realize the degree of special adaptations possible. But all mammals have a striking similarity to one another in the structure and cerebralization of their nervous system. Among the mammals the primates have achieved the highest degree of cerebralization. Teilhard points out that in them the main thrust of the evolutionary force has been the development of the brain. If, as he holds, the main axis of the evolutionary process has been the development of consciousness, then it is in the primates that we find this movement approaching its maximum fulfillment. Biogenesis has led to psychogenesis; and the highest degree of *withinness,* or radial energy, of complex interiority manifests itself in the most conscious of all the primates: man.

Human Consciousness

We have already seen in his study of the lower forms how Teilhard's concentration on the *within* of things provides us with a guide to the direction of evolution. The development of the nervous system and the process of cerebralization indicate the steady deepening of psychic or radial energy. When we come to man, we are able to study the manifestation of this energy on a remarkably higher plane, the realm of consciousness converging upon itself. To the positivist, man is a bafflingly mysterious section of the evolutionary labyrinth. In his physical structure man is only slightly different from the higher primates. But here is a primate who knows and who knows that he knows, who engages in intricate research, who writes poetry, who composes great music, who elaborates philosophical and theological systems. If there is a leap from the molecule to the living cell, there is an even greater leap from the anthropoids to man, a leap that the positivists cannot account for. Teilhard does not pretend to solve the mystery of man. Far from it. Admitting the mystery, he tries to penetrate its meaning. "To see, . . . and not to explain — this, . . . is the sole aim of the present study" (p. 58). For him, the most important clue to the solution of the mystery is the progressive complexification of the brain and the concomitant and parallel intensification of radial energy which manifests itself in reflective thought.

Having described in detail the long and arduous process of hominization and megasynthesis whereby primitive man becomes increasingly aware of himself and of his relations to others in the steady march from family to tribe to nation, Teilhard reminds us that the development of reflective thought is not an unmixed blessing. For each advance, there is a price exacted. For with the development of self-consciousness come the manifestations of egoism, the fragmentation of consciousness in a million individuals as opposed to the convergence of consciousness in the personal.

Let us recall that Teilhard envisions the process of evolution continuing through modern times and into the future. With regard to the phenomenon of egoism, he notes that it can take the form either of individual or of group isolation. He considers, for example, the doctrines of racial superiority propounded in the 1930's as inimical to the main drive of the evolutionary current. Isolation of any kind, whether the existentialist isolation of the individual or the group isolation of racism, is in conflict with the grand movement of convergence we have observed from the first agglomerations and syntheses of the remote past to the social megasynthesis of the present and the future. To Teilhard, the formation of the United Nations was not only a geopolitical event of the first magnitude but also the fulfillment in our time, however groping and tentative, of the main current of evolution.

If isolationism of the individual or of the group represents a cul-de-sac, a *No Exit* for man, there is a corresponding danger in collectivism:

> At no period of history has mankind been so well equipped nor made such efforts to reduce its multitudes to order. We have "mass movements" — no longer the hordes streaming down from the forests of the north or the steppes of Asia, but "the Million" scientifically assembled. The Million in rank and file on the parade ground; the Million standardized in the factory; the Million motorized — and all this only ending up with Communism and National-Socialism and the most ghastly fetters. So we get the crystal instead of the cell; the ant hill instead of brotherhood. Instead of the upsurge of consciousness which we expected, it is mechanization that seems to emerge inevitably from totalization (pp. 256–57).

If isolationism destroys the common good, raw collectivism destroys the personal. The central problem facing man in modern times, therefore, is how to serve the need of society without destroying the individual.

Cosmic Love

We have seen that Teilhard distinguishes between individuality and personality. "The goal of ourselves, the acme of our originality," he says, "is not our individuality but our person; and according to the evolutionary structure of the world, we can only find our person by uniting together" (p. 263). The affinity of being with being, of center with center, is a phenomenon parallel to the phenomenon of *withinness* and like it an energy which steadily intensifies from the simplest forms to the most complex. *Withinness*, then, is cosmic in extent and all-pervasive. So, too, is love, the prime expression of the personal.

Teilhard is, of course, not the first thinker to expound a theory of cosmic love. It is an intuition as old as civilization. Empedocles, for example, postulated love as a driving force underlying the activity of the universe. Love, says Eryximachos in the *Symposium* of Plato, "is not only in the souls of mankind, . . . but he is in all the rest, and directed towards many other things; he is in the bodies of all living creatures, and in what grows in the earth, and, one may say, in everything there is." For Aristotle, there is a natural appetite in all things, the impulse and movement that direct all things back to God. Lucretius opens his *De Rerum Natura* with an invocation to Love (Venus), "the life-giver" without whom nothing "comes forth into the bright coasts of life." Aquinas looks upon all things, mineral, vegetable, animal, human, as possessing the capacity of natural love in an analogical way: "Natural love is found not only in the powers of the vegetative soul, but in all the potencies of the soul, and indeed, in all parts of the body, and universally in all things."[2] Nicholas of Cusa (1401–64), in *De Docta Ignorantia*, speaks of the spirit of the universe "without which there is no unity, without which nothing can subsist. . . . This is the movement of a love that links all in one with the result that all things form one universe." [3] A modern thinker, Pitirim Sorokin, speaks of love as being "like an iceberg: only a small part of it is visible, and even this visible part is little known." With reference to the qualitative and quantitative infinity of love, he cites Paul Tillich: "I have given no definition of love. This is impossible, because there is no higher principle by which it could be defined. It is life itself in its actual unity. The forms and structures in which life embodies itself are the forms and structures in which life overcomes its self-destructive forces." Sorokin sees love ontologically as

one of the highest forms of a unifying, integrating, harmonizing, creative energy or power. . . . Subsequent thinkers [after Empedocles] viewed even the unifying physical forces of gravitation, of the unification of electrons and protons in the atom, of chemical affinity, of magnetism, and so on, as the manifestation of love energy acting in the *physical* world; the "instincts" of sociality or gregariousness, biological mutual aid and cooperation, as the manifestation of love energy in the *organic* world; conscious love, sympathy, friendship, solidarity, as its manifestation in the *psychosocial* world. Everywhere in the inorganic, organic, and psychosocial worlds, the integrating and uniting role of love functions incessantly. Untiringly, it counteracts the dividing and separating forces of chaos and strife.[4]

For Teilhard, love is the highest function of consciousness. And just as we have traced the presence of conscious energy from its most rudimentary level (e.g., the affinity of atom for atom, of molecule for molecule) to its powerful radiations in man, so, too, says Teilhard, "to be certain of [the presence of love] in ourselves, we should assume its presence, at least in an inchoate form, in everything that is" (p. 264). One might say, at this point, that perhaps Teilhard's chief contribution has been to attempt to reinforce through scientific data the fundamental intuitions of earlier philosophers. While salvaging some of the best thoughts of the past and reinterpreting them in the light of modern scientific research, he has essayed to build a bridge between philosophy and science.

Nowhere is this of greater value and significance than in his examination of the relevance of the idea of cosmic love to the personal relations of individuals in the present state of human evolution, the megasynthesis of man in the supersociety that lies just over the horizon. Let us recall that man, by reason of his reflective consciousness, has discovered his own ego. Let us recall further that man can retrograde either by the isolation of the ego in a withdrawal from human society, or by the annihilation of the ego in the ant heap. What is to prevent either catastrophe? Love. A love "capable of uniting living beings in such a way as to complete and fulfill them, for it alone takes them and joins them by what is deepest in themselves" (p. 265). A love that is not merely a source of inspiration for poet and artist and composer, not merely an attractive Utopian ideal, but a *biological* necessity for the survival of man, a fulfillment of the evolutionary process.

Teilhard insists on the personal aspect of love. It is a relation between beings, between "centers," but, above all, where man is concerned, it is a relation between persons. Love is suffocated by the impersonal. Therefore, not even the idealizations of recent thinkers who have spoken of "mankind," "humanity," "society," the "collective" — none of these provides a sufficient focus for the energies of personal love, because they are too impersonal. "There is a tide," Shakespeare remarks, "in the affairs of men which taken at the flood leads on to fortune. . . ." Instead of riding on this tide, men find themselves caught in the undertow of repulsion and hatred, and dragged into the tumult of the antipersonal. Teilhard says that

> we should overcome the "anti-personalist" complex which paralyzes us, and make up our minds to accept the possibility, indeed the reality, of

some *source* of love and *object* of love at the summit of the world above
our heads. . . . It is impossible to give oneself to anonymous number. But
if the universe ahead of us assumes a face and heart, and so to speak per-
sonifies itself, then in the atmosphere created by this focus the elemental
attraction will immediately blossom. Then, no doubt, under the heightened
pressure of an infolding world, the formidable energies of attraction, still
dormant between human molecules, will burst forth" (pp. 266–67).

What is this "source and object of love" to which Teilhard refers? It is
what he calls the Omega Point, the point of convergence which draws to itself
the innumerable personal energies of time-space. At first we are left under
the impression that the Omega Point is even less personal than expressions
like "mankind," "humanity," and so on. Teilhard himself is somewhat confusing about the nature of the Omega Point. He speaks of the universe
assuming "a face and heart" and personifying itself (p. 267). But in a caution-
ary footnote on the same page he says, "Not, of course, by becoming a person,
but by charging itself at the very heart of its development with the domi-
nating and unifying influence of a focus of personal energies and attractions."
Later on, when he speaks of "The Christian Phenomenon," Teilhard identifies the Omega Point with God, "the Center of centers." We realize then that
he has attempted to postpone the use of a terminology that would make the
evolutionary process a kind of allegory of Christian theology. He plainly
admits (on page 294) that he finds a complete congruency between the evolutionary process at the human level and the Christian doctrine of man's
ultimate destiny, viz., personal union with a personal God.

To Teilhard, in fact, the emergence of the concept of Christian love in
the consciousness of man is one of the more recent phases in the long unfolding expressed in his law of complexity/consciousness. Returning to something
like his earlier terminology, Teilhard speaks of "Christic" energy, and of
"Christogenesis" as "nothing less than the extension, both awaited and un-
hoped for, of that noogenesis in which cosmogenesis . . . culminates" (pp.
296 and 297). Obviously his vigorous Christian faith has influenced Teilhard's
thought. In a sense, he has read the history of evolution through Christian
eyes. But one feels that he has not permitted the Christian vision to distort
his observation of reality as a scientist, that the congruency he marks is not
subjective but objective when viewed in the context of his careful study of
the progressive development of the organism of consciousness, and of love:
the nervous system.

The radial energy that deepens into reflective consciousness and produces
the person finds its fulfillment in the hyperpersonal love, the affinity between
persons drawing them toward each other and toward God-Omega. Thus one
is "able to say literally to God that one loves him, not only with all one's body,
all one's heart, and all one's soul, but with every fibre of the unifying universe" (p. 297).

In Conclusion

Teilhard deserves careful study and good criticism. He has often been misread by both the positivist scientists and the "orthodox" theologians. But he has also won a host of friends in both camps. A man who was both a distinguished scientist and a Jesuit priest and who chose, moreover, to labor in the no man's land between the mounted hosts of religion and science seeking common ground between them — such a man was not taking the easy and ready way. He was an explorer, not a real-estate man. He was not fencing in a field, but opening an avenue. What he has presented to us is a working hypothesis, not a dogma. "I believe I can see a direction and a line of progress for life, a line and a direction which are in fact so well marked that I am convinced their reality will be universally admitted in the science of tomorrow" (p. 142).

If it is at all possible to build a bridge between mechanism and vitalism, to bring about a fruitful association between science and religion, Teilhard has shown us the way by revealing to us "a universe charged with love," a world in which biochemistry and adoration seem to be, not divorced and conflicting activities, but appropriate and complementary human manifestations of the energetics of love.

13

THE PHENOMENON OF TEILHARD DE CHARDIN

Gustave Weigel, S. J.

Ever since the mid-twenties the name of Pierre Teilhard de Chardin has been known to paleontologists and anthropologists. Those who were members of that scientific brotherhood read his reports and studies, of which there were many. Teilhard's complete espousal of the notion of evolution drew the attention of his brother Jesuits. Yet he was not well known to the world at large until after the second World War. His lectures in France during that era distinguished him as a man of profound vision. Books and articles appeared to explain the man and his thought. He went into comparative silence after he left France in 1951 to live in New York, where he died suddenly in 1955. After his death his works on themes of interest beyond the limits of formal paleontology were published, first in France and finally throughout the world. The English translation of *The Phenomenon of Man* has occasioned real commotion in the English-speaking world of ideas.

Catholics have shown a timorous attraction toward Teilhard. He was one of them, frankly and authentically so. Yet his ideas and language are so different from those in common Catholic currency that many wondered whether he was true to the faith once delivered to the saints. Those who knew the man personally gave eloquent testimony to his deep piety and religious conviction. If indeed it were true that his ideas could not be reconciled with the orthodox doctrine of Christianity, at least they were not inspired by disloyalty or treacherous intent. That much was certain beyond any doubt.

This primary datum did not solve the question whether this good Catholic's conception of the world and man was in harmony with the authentic expression of Catholic faith. Pierre Teilhard was certainly no fool — all the world was agreed on that. Likewise, he wanted above all to be a Catholic. How then could his ideas cause suspicion in some Catholic circles? It is to this question that the present study addresses itself.

For Teilhard *The Phenomenon of Man* was his principal essay at communicating his own understanding of human reality. He had written it as early as 1940 but retouched it during the years that followed. By 1948 he was anxious to publish it. His superiors did not feel that this was prudent and they refused him permission. He gave his manuscript along with manuscripts of other books to some friends. They published the works after his death. One may consider *The Phenomenon of Man* Teilhard's *summa*; his *Meisterwerk*.

Reading the book is an exhilarating experience. It is one of those books that cause deep and inspiring stirrings in the reader. It is not only logically structured but also rich in isolated golden phrases that excite the spirit, shooting lightning flashes on whole areas of human concern. The essay has its difficulties because it combines different modes of expression. Teilhard is primarily a scientist but not exclusively so. He is also a poet, a prophet, a veiled philosopher, and even a mystic.

But above all, we must remember his basic stance. He is examining reality in so far as it is related to man. He is discussing the *phenomenon* of man, and the title of the work was chosen with care so as to make it clear what was under discussion. The work is an essay in phenomenology. Man as he *appears* according to rigorous scientific examination is the theme, and no other. No ontology is presented nor is there any theological consideration of the subject. Theological and metaphysical relevances do become manifest, but the methods of these two disciplines are not employed. A scientist who is doing a scientific work of synthesis cannot avoid betraying his own concerns beyond his chosen field, but he is not willing to allow these concerns to interfere with his proper method of approach to the problem. Hence it would be most unfair to consider any statement of Teilhard as either philosophical or theological, even though strictly phenomenal positions are taken under the pressures of anxieties which are indeed theological or philosophical.

Teilhard invents many new words. He feels that he must do so, because he has found no other words in the current vocabularies which can express what he has in mind. He has no hesitation to speak in images just as the poet and the mystic do. He believes that this is the safest way for him to communicate his message accurately. Like a true scientist, he believes that the work of synthesis goes beyond mere description of data. He states quite explicitly that synthesis rests on an intuition freely accepted as the guiding light for the ultimate intelligence of the phenomenon. He believes that the intuition actually shows up the wealth of phenomena as a unity but he knows that it itself cannot be deduced with mathematical rigor from the data.

The central position of the author is that the world is man: man in different stages of becoming; and this becoming has by no means ended. Evolution for Teilhard is synonymous with cosmic reality. He presents no cosmology but describes in terms of understanding the cosmogenesis (a neologism Teilhard often used). The evolution of the cosmos is for him as clear as the world itself. He describes evolution; he does not prove it, because it is as evident to him as the existence of the cosmos we see. He merely thinks that the scientists have not investigated evolution sufficiently. It can explain much more than the mere origin of a present species.

Teilhard gives his account of the meaning of evolution by tracing quickly the outline of the history of the universe. He rightly insists that history is a necessary dimension of scientific investigation. To understand an object, its genesis must be understood, even though indirect evidences are all we can rely on.

Many thousands of million years ago, he tells us, clouds of cosmic dust moved in masses in what we call the heavens. (Scientific analysis cannot discuss its first cause, which is beyond the phenomena.) This dust was made up of protons, electrons, neutrons, and photons. In their whirlings, they joined up with each other to produce simple atoms. This was not merely a matter of chance, though chance had a part in the operation. Any cosmic entity has an outside action that can be seen from above; but it also has an inside action that can be seen only from within. This inside action is centered about an élan, a phenomenal impulse pushing the thing to consciousness. It is phenomenal but analogous to the form that philosophers call a soul. To avoid ambiguity, Teilhard calls this principle in the nonliving a pre-soul. This impulse is toward consciousness; and under its thrust, simple elements formed molecules. Bunches of such molecules became suns, and from the suns molecular masses were torn off to become independent planets. One such planet is our earth.

Since in every element there was an impulse to consciousness and unity, all the elements moved to ever more complicated forms of union, ever closer to consciousness, though in the beginnings infinitely far from the consciousness that was ultimately to arrive. In every element and molecule there was a double action; one expending *tangential* energy, moving outward with impact and influence on other elements and molecules, and the other with *radial* energy building up within the agent, producing ever closer approximations to the state of consciousness. Consciousness does not stumble on matter; matter is by inner compulsion groping for it.

In this way the earth historically built itself up in layers or spheres. First there was the barysphere, where simple atoms pushed forward to produce complicated molecules, which in turn formed a stable lithosphere capable of holding water, thus creating a hydrosphere. The condition for life was now produced and the molecular beings could move on to preliving unions like the viruses. When these came into existence, the protozoa in the form of single living cells were brought forth with the power of the reproduction of their kind. Cells clustered and combined so that organisms came forth from the seas. Millions of years ago, by reason of the inner radial energy, such simple organisms combined with others in the ceaseless groping for forms that nervous tissue could co-ordinate. Ganglions grew to become a system of brain and nerves. At this point consciousness was achieved, but it was still an imperfect thing because it was incapable of self-reflection. Brain space had yet to grow larger, and in doing so, hominization (Teilhard's word) was in its embryonic stage. There finally came a form with large enough brain power to permit matter to support the activity of thought. Life gave the earth a biosphere, and reflective consciousness in the hominized combinations produced the noosphere, that layer of our earth which spreads thinking around the world.

This upward nisus was not in a straight line. It was the formation of a spiral around a cone. On this vine-like spiral, buds shot off at many points. From these buds new forms in fan-form were essayed, but not all led upward. When they did not move toward consciousness, they withered away or remained static to show the paleontologist a fruitless chance taken by evolution. Yet one of the buds on the vine would be on the way up in the spiral course of matter seeking spirit. The relics of some are found, but hardly all. We have no direct evidence of the complete movement of species to species up to the appearance of *Homo sapiens.*

Teilhard supposes on grounds of observation that each new sphere was a once-and-for-all event. Once matter had achieved a higher stage of complication it did not bother to continue the process on the lower levels. Only at one period did the large molecules form. Once and only once did life take over on the earth. Once and only once did reflective consciousness form its own sphere. This does not mean that only a single new form was produced siring all of its kind, but it does mean that it occurred only at one period of geological time, to be continued by survival rather than through the continuing evolution of lower forms. Evolution today does not produce new men from a pre-human level nor does life proceed through the evolution of inorganic agents.

The question of entropy commanded Teilhard's attention. He thought that it applied only to the tangential energy of earth beings. This energy decreases more and more as time goes on, and this fact spells the inevitable death of the material globe. Teilhard found, however, that as tangential energy is reduced, radial, spiritual energy is increased. Thought and its action supplement and even supplant the external action of the material agent.

So far Teilhard is creative only in details. His great contribution lies in his insistence that evolution is still going on in man. Isolated men give way to man in association, where the power of thought is increased by the accumulation of thinkers in collaboration. The earth is being changed not merely by unconscious gropings but through the planned orientations of the thought of communal thinking, preserved in cultures and tradition.

His greatest contribution is the discovery of an "Omega Point" in the phenomenon of human evolution. This is the point on the cone of evolution.

This point meets a superior plane which limits the cone and which is always there, attracting the very bottom of the cone through radial energy to climb up to the Omega Point. Of course, Omega itself is what Christians call God, and the doctrine of the Omega Point opens up the possibility of a new theodicy based on the scientific study of phenomena. Teilhard does not limit the order of phenomena to the external material object. He believes he has observed the inner nisus of radial action in phenomena through scientific, i.e., phenomenal, observation. Concerning Omega itself, which is no phenomenon, he can say nothing as a scientist. But the Omega Point, where matter meets God and toward which all earthly reality tends, is observable because of its attractive influence on evolution upwards. Teilhard is anxious to keep all metaphysical and theological reasoning outside his own approach to the phenomenon of man. Concerning the Omega doctrine, Julian Huxley, who is so eulogistic of Teilhard's work, is far from being convinced. He thinks that it is a valiant try of Teilhard to be at once an orthodox Christian and a sincere scientist. But he feels the try has failed.

The foregoing sketchy summary shows us the thought outline of Teilhard's message. Little details come into the book which show us the breadth of mind of the man. Long before Sputnik went into space, he saw the high probability of man's early voyage into space. He makes room in his collectivization of the last stage of man's evolution for other groups of human beings on other sidereal bodies, and sees the possibility of fullest development of man as a single flower formed by petals gathered from all the worlds of space. He wrote a distinct chapter on the phenomenological meaning of Christ and the Church, pointing out the heights to which Christianity has brought the human race. There is something winsomely mystical in the way he paints the action of God as a call of love and the response of creation as love's response.

Many a Catholic theologian has studied this vision communicated by Teilhard. Some became angry at once and judged the whole idea a betrayal of the doctrine of the Church of which Teilhard was a priest. Others were not so much angry as worried and puzzled. They could not judge the man on the level of scientific competence because they were not at home in that field, nor could they even validly raise the question because the luminaries of biological science have given fulsome praise to the merits of the French paleontologist. But some felt sincerely that too many basic dogmas of faith were irreconcilable with Teilhard's phenomenal scheme.

Can any positive judgment be passed on the meaning of Teilhard's work? Certainly no definitive verdict can be made at this moment. Too much must yet be considered in three fields: science, philosophy, and theology. Yet certain recognitions of merit can be offered in our time.

First of all, we see that a wholly committed Catholic accepted science for its own sake with loving honesty and integrity. Teilhard has proved that there need be no schizophrenia in the Catholic who is enamored of scientific contemplation. He can love both his faith and scientific truth without inner conflict. If Toynbee could write a work on the religion of an historian, Teilhard could equally well write about the religion of a biologist. He found his scientific and religious commitments mutually corroborative and he realized in himself his own prophecy that religion and science will in the future collaborate wholeheartedly instead of fighting each other to no avail. It is an inspiring thing to find in Teilhard no trace of nervousness when he speaks of man and his meaning in terms of scientific method. In this enterprise he suspects no possibility of conflict with his tranquil acceptance of faith.

Secondly, philosophers and theologians are hard put to dispute with the man. He has made it explicitly clear that he is not doing philosophy or theology. His affirmations are not to be fitted into a theological or philosophical framework of discourse. There they may have no sense because those disciplines and methods are orientated differently with different starting points and different modes of procedure. Of course philosophers and theologians who have not yet discovered that disciplines differ, with the consequence that a proposition in one field cannot be extrapolated into another without losing its meaning — such thinkers will find all kinds of inadequacies in Teilhard's work. But the current progress in the disciplines makes such men fewer as the days go by. To a theologian the Eucharist is truly the Body and Blood of Christ; to a chemist it is homogeneous in phenomenal structure with bread and wine; to a philosopher it opens the doors of speculation on the possibilities of accidents without substance, reality with alien appearance, direct divine action in a natural milieu. We do not expect the three disciplines to make the same affirmations, and the disparity of their statements invalidates none of them.

Since Teilhard essays no theology or philosophy he cannot be criticized for his philosophy or theology. Yet it remains true that the theologian and the philosopher will be stimulated by his nontheological and nonphilosophical statements. Teilhard makes it quite clear that he finds present theology oblivious of an important phase of human existence. The cosmos in which man is rooted has immensity as its setting in space and duration in the thousands of millions of years of its history. Yet theology concerns itself at most with some four thousand of these many years restricted to our little earth. The kinship of man with all the past and with the present realities of an expanding universe are not considered by theologians, and yet these factors are of human concern because they influence us through the past and in the widespread present. Time and space need theological study to make theology adequately relevant to modern man.

One lacuna in Teilhard's reflections especially is of theological concern. This has already been felt, and Teilhard himself foresaw it. He was exuberantly optimistic about the present and future of the human species. Humanity came from humble beginnings but it has been a glory for the universe and it is still on its way upward. Teilhard had to write a chapter on the evil in the world. He merely defended himself for not giving the matter much discussion on the ground that he is tracing the positive benefits of evolution and therefore he had no need to consider all the suffering and immorality involved in the history of the world. This defense may certainly be accepted, but evil is as much present in evolution as glory, and it needs explanation. Perhaps paleontology and anthropology cannot explain it, but theology must make the attempt.

The basic solution of the theological tradition is the doctrine of Original Sin which entails the notion of a devolution of man, rather than his evolution. It seems to assume that in the beginning man was perfect and culpably fell into abiding imperfection. The basis of man's first perfection is described in dogma as an extraordinary direct and free action of God from without history and evolution. Man's imperfection needed the graciously given divine Incarnation in order to be overcome. The Christian hope is that in spite of the present decadence of man, he can in faith look forward to a future happy state for a remnant of mankind, bestowed not by the innate power of natural evolution but through a catastrophic action of God. No matter how Original Sin is explained by the various schools of theology, the outline here given is accepted by all.

Can such a theological position be reconciled with the phenomenal vision of Teilhard? To be candid, it must be admitted that at first sight the two schemes *seem* contradictory. History, however, has shown us that answers flowing from first sight are not to be trusted. First of all, Teilhard's scheme is not a theology. It is confected outside the theological circle. Hence on analysis it is clear that he contradicted no theological doctrine, for the simple reason that he did not speak theologically at all. What is more, he accepted the totality of the Church's dogma sincerely and without reserve. That is a primatial fact.

What is under question is not the formal validity of Teilhard's vision. By the rules he chose — the rules of phenomenal observation of empirical science — it is valid enough. The question is whether the vision is compatible with Teilhard's first commitment, his Catholic faith.

It is well to remember that faith must not be identified with theology. The direct object of faith, the dogmas of the teaching Church, must not be identified with theology. Theology is the human science that explores dogma and faith. Dogmas are not made by theology; theology only examines them rationally and then in an explanatory synthesis proposes them to the believer in search of understanding. Theology as a living tradition undergoes great changes in its long life. The temporary use of one philosophic insight rather than another, gives theology new vitality and a "new look."

This is quite evident in our time. The majority of theologians at the beginning of our century, following the thought of their predecessors in the 19th century, rejected the possibility of using the then new theory of the origin of the human species through biological evolution. Many a theologian was hotly insistent on this rejection. Since 1950 this stand is no longer possible. The encyclical *Humani generis* of Pius XII explicitly declared that such a theory could be legitimately used by Catholic theologians. Teilhard began his own work long before 1950, and his own employment of an evolutionary theory exposed him to the attacks of not a few theologians. Today this is no longer possible. Teilhard cannot now be censured for holding a theory of evolution.

But there remains a problem. Granted that *Humani generis* makes it licit to employ some form of evolutionary hypothesis even for the theologian and Scripture scholar, is Teilhard's conception of evolution one of the acceptable forms?

The encyclical did not permit the use of an evolutionary theory that supposes polygenism, i.e., the actuation of evolution to produce more than one central source of the human race. Teilhard expressly declares for monogenism rather than for polygenism. But he understands monogenism to permit either the production of a single pair of true humans or of different individuals in different places in one and only one defined geological period. Teilhard holds for monogenism in the sense of monophylism. Whatever may be objected to this conception, it must be yet admitted that the true unity and unicity of the human race are being affirmed. Whether or not Teilhard's conception meets all the requirements of theological monogenism can be debated, but we must not begin with the supposition that he stands for polygenism, when as a matter of explicit fact he expressly declares for monogenism.

Even though Teilhard is unimpeachable in his use of an evolutionary theory for the explanation of the origin of man; even though a case can probably be made for his understanding of monogenism; the problem of Original Sin, the role of the Incarnation of God in Jesus Christ in the development of mankind, the distinction of natural and supernatural, are all theological preoccupations that find little solace in his phenomenology. But this does not mean that the theologian must immediately condemn Teilhard's image of the world. The history of theology ruefully shows that such a short shrift for a scientific creation can produce embarrassment for later theologians, and even for the whole Church itself. We want no more Galileo cases. One was too much, even though the real benefit it did to the Church was to make her cautious in her pronouncements concerning the reconcilability of scientific observation with theological stances.

The true task of theologians in the presence of Teilhard's ideas is to examine diligently their own position with the greatest care in order to discover the precise content of their formulas. In the past this type of investigation has proved very fruitful. Today with the serious work being done in Scripture and the Fathers such work should be congenial. Above all, they must not consider Teilhard an adversary but only a stimulus to renewed study of the matter of their own field. Teilhard does not even pretend to be a theologian, but he has expressed the hope that theologians would fill the many lacunae of his own thought.

If theologians are called on to go more deeply into their own sources, the scientists have a similar invitation. Teilhard's great desire was the collaboration of the two disciplines, not their opposition. Scientists are called on to deal with the phenomenological work of the French scholar, to prune, to criticize, and to expand what he has done. No one expects theological contributions of them, but they are competent to tell us to what degree they themselves can subscribe to the scheme of Teilhard. It is not to the point for them to discuss his religious preoccupations in his work. He obviously had them. But he wanted to do a job according to the scientific method and he presented his ideas as true to the observations of science. His work can be evaluated by scientists on the level on which Teilhard himself placed it.

Teilhard made an implicit suggestion at one point which could help both disciplines. Recognizing that his own view of natural history seemed to suggest an ever better situation for the human race with a kind of utopian finale, he proposed the idea that this final upward thrust in the end time could be contingent on the acceptance of an invitation from Omega. Such an invitation would not coerce all the members of the species. Some would decide to accept it and others would decide against it. Those who accepted would rise to the highest expression of humanity, and those who rejected it would wither away as so many species and subspecies have done before them. This kind of thinking was obviously provoked by the Christian conception of an ultimate judgment and of a previous divine call to faith. In this form the hypothesis is certainly not scientific because it cannot be derived from the observation of phenomena. For the theologian, however, it shows clearly how the notion of an ever-ascending evolution of man can be harmonized with the notions of faith. It indicates a conceptual possibility, even if it does not present us with a fact.

Along such lines the theologian can do much to bring theology and science into an effective union. It is certainly true that theology by the very antiquity of its discipline must make heroic efforts to transpose its categories of the past into categories relevant to the present. We hear much criticism of the introduction of non-Hebraic modes of thought by Greek theologians of the first five centuries. But this criticism is often wall-eyed. These Greek theologians were not creating revelation, nor even re-creating it. They were presenting the doctrine originally expressed in Hebraic literary forms, in styles and modes proper to the Greek way of life and thought. What the Greek theologians did, must be done in every new cultural situation. If Thomas Aquinas could use the Aristotelian framework for the elaboration of the Gospel, later theologians can use other hypotheses and postulates.

St. Thomas did not make a natural science for his time. He supposed one, and created his theology to harmonize with what he found at hand. Today when we go to St. Thomas, we are not concerned with his scientific world image because we know that he used the one suggested by the Aristotelian sages of his own day. That image has lost its appeal for us because we do not find it sufficiently reflective of the world we know. We go to St. Thomas to find his atemporal theological or metaphysical statements. We have to demythologize St. Thomas, in the good sense of that word. In this process St. Thomas is more useful than ever. But it is not a Talmudic study of Thomism which helps us; instead we must engage in a construction of the medieval doctor's ideas to produce a viable structure for our day. It is hardly a serious investigation to search for what St. Thomas had to say about Freudian psychoanalysis. Patently he had nothing to say about a theory he knew nothing about. He did, however, have metaphysical principles and theological positions that can be supremely useful in our own current discussion and elaboration of the Freudian theses. We want to understand St. Thomas as he historically existed in order to understand better the moment in which we live. Nor do we identify the two historical moments; rather, we believe that the two moments can illuminate each other. According to the evolutionary concept of Teilhard, in *Homo sapiens* tradition and culture supplement human instincts. What was good is not lost but moves into a fuller synthesis with the goods discerned in the lengthening of time.

Whatever is defective in Teilhard must not overshadow the high merit of his work. He wished to excite theologians to recognize the basic outline of the scientific image of our time. His presentation of an evolutionary scheme was not an apologetic reconstruction to the end that it might emerge theologically acceptable after a kind of plastic surgery. He wanted to be faithful and loyal to it for its own sake. There was no treachery in his use of it. He presented it as he found it, with brilliance and imagination. This is what the scientists recognize when they praise Teilhard.

Teilhard wanted the theologians and philosophers of our day to take evolution seriously so that they would express their own findings in a way relevant to an age that has spontaneously accepted the evolutionary image of the cosmos. He himself portrayed that image from a perspective readily achievable by theologians and philosophers. He was not an apologete. Rather he was the voice of one anxiously urging theologians and philosophers to tasks which are truly theirs and which they have, by and large, refused to undertake.

Teilhard is no enemy of theology. He is its true friend, even though outside its preserve. He is shouting to the theologians to enlarge the borders of their highly significant discipline.

14

COSMOGENESIS AND THEOLOGY

J. Edgar Bruns

The theological vision of Teilhard de Chardin awaits the masterful brush of some great artistic genius. Teilhard has painted the vision in words: "Starting with an evolutive Omega placed where we suppose it to be, not only does it become conceivable that Christ shines above the frightening totality of all things, but even more that it is inevitable that this radiance attain the highest degree of penetration and activation." [1] "It is *He* who consummates: the plenitude of the world is reached only in the final synthesis where a supreme consciousness will appear above the total complexity supremely organized — and Christ being the organic principle of the harmonization, the whole universe finds itself, by that very fact, marked with the structure he imparts to the whole edifice of matter and spirit." [2]

Faith and Cosmogenesis

Teilhard was convinced, then, that the dogmas of our faith once seen in the light of cosmogenesis would assume an astounding clarity and coherence. No one, friend or foe to his point of view, can deny that cosmogenesis gives Christian doctrine a new dimension, but it is probably this very transposition that prevents many from accepting it as true. Can this be the meaning of the Apostles' Creed, they say? Can all this reference to physics, biology, and evolution have anything to do with the questions and answers in the catechism? Does it not rather seem like some new kind of Gnosticism conjured up for the intellectual gymnastics of an ultrasophisticated elite? It should be obvious to any thinking person, on the contrary, that the God of nature is also the God of revelation and that, consequently, these two manifestations of Himself cannot be unrelated. We have to discover the connection when and where possible and, if we do, we must also expect to be startled by the coincidence.

If in the words of one of Teilhard's brilliant contemporary compatriots, "the Church came to an understanding of its pronouncements only in the light of the event," [3] it is equally true to say that the progress of the natural sciences can also illuminate the deposit of faith. Christian philosophers admit, for example, that the doctrine of creation *in time* is not demonstrable philosophically. Yet well-informed people today know that only two theories on the origin of the universe are scientifically admissible. One, proposed by Lemaître and seconded by Gamow, Herman, and Alpher, envisages a universe beginning five thousand million years ago with the explosion of a single primordial atom. The other, advocated by Hoyle, Bondi, and Gold, suggests that matter is and has always been continually created throughout the universe. Both these theories are based on the data of astrophysics; they are neither theological nor philosophical speculations.

If eventually, as could well happen, the first of these two theories should prove to be scientifically demonstrable, we should be faced with an example of Nature's telling us something that had previously been known only through Revelation. Moreover, it would be telling us something we could have known centuries or milennia previously had we had at our disposal the knowledge and instruments that now enable us to penetrate the secrets of the cosmos. It is in some such similar way, then, that we must regard the parallel drawn by Teilhard between the postulates of cosmogenesis and the revealed mysteries of Christian dogma: they are not isolated but complementary sources of knowledge.

No theologian would deny that human contemplation and human analysis down through the ages have contributed immeasurably to the development and understanding of the articles of faith. There has been no increase in the basic content of revelation, but, beneath the penetrating rays of scrutiny and the enriching deposits of scholarship, it has, like a seed, burgeoned into a towering tree. Who is so naïve as to believe that the *Summa Theologica* could have been written in the Apostolic Age? No more could a book like *The Phenomenon of Man* have been conceived before the 20th century; so that it is absurd to dismiss this book simply because traditional catechetics have not heretofore related Christian doctrine to the relevant aspects of biology, physics, and astronomy. The Church, writes Yves Congar, "has still much to learn and to reveal about herself by growing organically through the assimilation of all the marvellous wealth and variety of human values she has not yet incorporated." [4] These remarks could not currently be applied more appropriately than to the work of Teilhard de Chardin.

Teilhard speaks of man as "nothing else than evolution become conscious of itself." There is a true though analogous sense in which it might be said that dogma, too, becomes conscious of itself, i.e., progressively reveals more and more of its meaning, content, and ramifications. And, as with man, this progress comes about over a long period of time through development. Unlike natural species, however, dogma does not undergo transformation, and this is the essential criterion whereby to distinguish growth from distortion. An enlarged comprehension of Christian doctrine must, nevertheless, be at least implicitly recognizable in the sources of revelation. In so far as the apparent novelty of Teilhard's phenomenological approach to theology has led not a few to suspect it of, or equate it with, heterodoxy, the Catholic theologian, realizing the immense loss an abandonment of Teilhard's views would entail, has an obligation to examine those sources and to decide not only whether "cosmogenetic convergence" does not contradict defined truths, but whether, in fact, it possesses therein substantial support. This is what we hope to ascertain.

Transcendence and Immanence of Omega Point

For the enlightened Christian, Teilhard de Chardin's concept of God as Omega is perhaps the most important and at the same time the most controversial contribution he has made to theological thought. Its importance arises from the evident relation it establishes between the process of evolution and the necessary existence of a God. Whether or not the type of argument employed by Teilhard will ever wholly replace the traditional "proofs" laid down in the theological manuals is beside the point. What is certain is that Teilhard has constructed a synthesis of scientific and religious elements which makes an undeniable appeal to the 20th-century mind. This concept of God-Omega has, however, disturbed the more conservative and cautious in our midst, because, to them, it seems to imply a denial of the creative act and a diminution of the divine transcendence. Actually, Teilhard's views on creation are tentative (as, in accordance with his modesty, are most of his suggestions). It has been conceded that, in the last analysis, he has done no more than revive an ancient mythology according to which God fulfills himself, finds himself again as it were, in creating the world through engaging in a struggle with the many (the "chaos" of Assyro-Babylonian cosmogony).[5]

It is necessary to appreciate the reason for Teilhard's departure from the classic presentation of creation. The idea that the world, ontologically, is superfluous, seemed to him destructive of all motivation for human participation in the work of creation. To envision the creative act as arbitrary and utterly gratuitous is to vindicate the Marxist criticism of religious belief as an "opiate." These fears and strictures of Teilhard are recognized as far from baseless, but there are approaches to the problems involved which satisfy the traditional teaching and would, nonetheless, it is reasonable to suppose, reassure Teilhard.[6] In any case, his essential notion of creation as involving God's union with and immergence in it can be retained. It is here, of course, that the charges of immanence and pantheism are made. Yet Teilhard's position on God's transcendence is unequivocal: "While being the last term of its series, it (Omega) is also *outside all series*. Not only does it crown, but it closes. . . . If by its very nature it did not escape from the time and space which it gathers together, it would not be Omega. Autonomy, actuality, irreversibility, and thus finally transcendence are the four attributes of Omega" (p. 270).

What Teilhard demands in the name of convergent cosmogenesis is that we no longer regard God as an artisan and creation as merely His handicraft. It is impossible to look upon the magnetic "Center of centers" who directs the course of evolution and who has, historically, actually taken His place in it, in this way any longer. And without attempting to draw the line at which transcendence disappears — something for the philosopher to decide — we can affirm unhesitatingly that the God of biblical revelation is such a one as Teilhard's synthesis postulates. Transcendent He is, but immanent too both personally and dynamically: "He is not far from any one of us. For in Him we live and move and have our being" (Acts 17:27–28); "My Father works even until now" (John 5:17). If He is not to be identified with His creation He has at least, and repeatedly, associated Himself with it in such ways as to suggest that it projects and expresses Him (Ex. 3:1–6; 19:16–21; 40:34–38; III Kings 8:10–11; 19:11–13; Ez. 1:26). Most important of all, He is indeed an Omega Point in whom and through whom creation is converging.

It has been said that whereas the mythologies of other peoples look backward to a golden age in the past, Hebrew prophecy places it in the future as the consummation of the divine plan.[7] Faith in the ultimate moral, spiritual, and intellectual refinement of man, in the subjection and pacification of nature, and in the focal attraction of God for all men is characteristic of Messianic expectations (Isa. 2:1–4; 65:17–25; Jer. 31:34; 33:16–18; Ez. 34:24–26). These themes reappear in the New Testament with the difference that they are described there as already inchoate (John 4:19–24; II Cor. 3:18; Acts 2:14f.; Rom. 8:19–22). But their complete realization awaits the Second Coming (I Cor. 15:22–28; Apoc. 21:1–4, 22–27; II Pet. 3:9–13). This is entirely in accord with Teilhard's opinion that human and religious evolution had to reach a certain degree of maturity before the Incarnation could take place but that it must yet attain a certain level of "unanimasation" before the Parousia will be possible.

Unanimasation as the process of and prelude to total convergence at the Omega point deserves special consideration. For reasons that underlie the whole (theory) of cosmogenesis, Teilhard proclaims that "biologically speaking humanity will not fulfill itself, and will not find its internal equilibrium (not before some millions of years perhaps) until it finds itself psychically centered upon itself." [8] The organic principle of this harmonization, moreover, must be personal, and the Christian knows that, in fact, it is none other than Jesus Christ, "principle of universal vitality because sprung up as man among men," he "put himself in the position (maintained ever since) to subdue under himself, to purify, to direct and superanimate the general ascent of consciousness into which he inserted himself. By a perennial act of communion and sublimation, he aggregates to himself the total psychism of the earth. And when he has gathered everything together and transformed everything, he will close in upon himself and his conquests, thereby rejoining, in a final structure, the divine focus he has never left" (p. 294).

It is Teilhard's thesis that by different paths faith and science arrive at the same conclusion: "The universal center of Christ, determined by theology, and the universal center of the cosmos postulated by anthropogenesis: these two focal points, all things considered, coincide (that is to say, they overlap each other) necessarily in the historical milieu in which we find ourselves." [9] Teilhard says elsewhere that "till now and despite the dominant place that St. Paul gives it in his vision of the world, . . . this third 'nature' of Christ, a nature neither human nor divine but 'cosmic,' has not attracted much explicit attention from the faithful and the theologians." [10] He is speaking, of course, of Christ considered as Omega; and although it is true that the concept has not been developed theologically, this is naturally due to the relative newness of the notion of anthropogenesis.

We have already seen, however, that Revelation delineates for us a God who is close to His creation, who is directing it and moving it toward a glorious consummation in Him. What we must examine now is the extent to which this same revelation has intimated the validity of Teilhard's concept of unanimasation in Christ. Teilhard cites St. Paul frequently in confirmation of his views, and unquestionably the Apostle to the Gentiles phrases the doctrine of the (Mystical) Body of Christ in language easily suited to this purpose: but the doctrine had a long and interesting period of development antecedent to its full Pauline exposition. We may, perhaps, trace the first faint outline in that strange passage, Gen. 32:25–31. Here we meet one of those many instances in the Old Testament where the transcendent God becomes an immanent "someone" and engages in a wrestling match which He cannot win without resorting to a divine stratagem. Then He changes Jacob's name to Israel because the latter had "contended with God and men" and "triumphed."

This story appears very primitive in its anthropomorphisms and yet at the same time it is capable of a most profound interpretation. God strives with a man who stands here for a nation, a whole people, but it is a struggle of love and union, physical and intellectual ("I will not let you go. . . . What is your name?") in which God reveals himself as willing to be possessed (did He not initiate the match?) and man as seeking to possess Him. The name given to Jacob and consequently to all his descendants is meant to perpetuate the tableau so that this people would know that its vocation was to contend thus with God.

In the prophets the relation between God and His people is described as that of husband and wife (Hos. 2:19–20; Isa. 54:5; Jer. 2:2); and although this metaphor lacks the relevantly interesting aspect of progressive endeavor, it is even more strongly indicative of loving union. Israel also appears as a vine in the prophetical (Isa. 5:1–7; 27:2f; Jer. 2:21; Hos. 10:1) and sapiential books (Ps. 79:9f), as does Divine Wisdom (Sir. 24:17). This highly suggestive implication of organic life and growth in God is, of course, made explicit in the New Testament (John 15:5). In one place the vine, which is Israel, is also called "the son of man" (Ps. 79:16) and although this identification may be due to a textual error, its retention from the most ancient times reflects general acceptance of the idea which in any case is confirmed by the famous passage in Dan. 7:13–18, 27:

> I saw in the night visions,
> and behold, one like the son of man
> came with the clouds of heaven,
> and came to the Ancient of days,
> and they brought him near before him.
> And there was given him dominion,
> and glory, and a kingdom . . .
> which shall not be destroyed.

The explanation of the vision given in the text is that "the saints of the Most High," "the people of the saints of the Most High," are the recipients of the everlasting kingdom. The "Son of Man," then, is a collectivity, the Messianic people pictured here as an individual endowed with quasi-divine attributes and approaching the throne of God. Though loftier in tone and more specifically developed as a theme, this is basically an echo of the dialogue between Jacob-Israel and God. In fact popular Jewish belief, which found its way into the apocrypha, transformed Jacob into a heavenly figure, "higher than the angels," not unlike the "Son of Man";[11] but whether under the influence of this passage in Daniel or vice versa cannot be known. The significance of the image is its correspondence to the idea of unanimasation: a human collectivity so united as to be described as a single man and moving in one direction: Godward.

That this unity in multiplicity was actually to be accomplished through some kind of future physical incorporation is not taught in the Old Testament. The election of Israel, already one in flesh and faith, is all that concerns the hagiographer. It is in the New Testament that all these revelatory images take on a universal, a cosmic import. The title by which Jesus most frequently calls Himself (69 times in the Gospels) is "Son of Man," not chiefly, as has been pointed out, because it was a widely recognized Messianic title — though the book of Enoch may have contributed towards this to some extent — but because it connoted a connaturality with man that was also a hegemony. "If He is identified with humanity in its weakness, they must be identified with Him in His glory." [12] His words concerning the Sabbath certainly "seem to suggest some participation by men in (His) privilege as Son of Man" (see Mark 2:23–28). The meaning of the title, then, as first formulated in the book of Daniel, rather than any subsequent synonymic implication, underlies Christ's use of it. It shows that "the mystery of our incorporation into Christ is present" just as surely in the simplicity of the Synoptic Gospels as it is in Paul's mysticism.[13]

If confirmation of this were needed it would be sufficient to refer to the institution of the Eucharist, whose purpose is total incorporation, and to the discourse on the metaphor of the vine already mentioned. There is only a difference of coloring between the eschatological "Son of Man" of the Gospels and the cosmological Pantocrator of St. Paul. What St. Paul does is to lift the image from its purely Hebraic expression and frame it in language more suited to his mission.

The Cosmic Body

It is difficult not to agree with those who maintain that St. Paul developed his doctrine of the Mystical Body under the impact of the impressions his journeys had made upon him. Here was a Jew who, under ordinary circumstances, would most probably never have set foot beyond the stretch of land between Tarsus and Jerusalem. But through his conversion he came into contact with new lands and new races, new cities and new civilizations, whose existence he had scarcely suspected. The world had become an immense place for him, and the variety and dispersion of mankind something to stagger the imagination. Even, or rather especially today, we can relive his experience by confronting the milling midday crowds of a vast metropolis and ponder the destiny of this teeming multitude. In these circumstances Paul's understanding of the Lord's salvific identification of Himself with mankind acquired its full perspective; this diversity and multiplication have no meaning in themselves; they are destined to converge: "There is neither Jew nor Greek; there is neither slave nor freeman; there is neither male nor female. For you are all one in Christ Jesus" (Gal. 3:28).

Seeing mankind from a biological and anthropological standpoint undisclosed to Paul, Teilhard was deeply impressed by the human phenomenon in what was qualitatively the same, though scientifically or quantitatively an immeasurably more extensive way. The Son of Man is indeed the ladder between God and the cosmos (John 1:51) inasmuch as He is the frame enclosing the entire upward surge of creation in the process of evolution, a process into which He has Himself entered in order to lead the way: "If . . . according to what is established by the facts, our universe . . . truly forms a sort of biological 'vortex,' dynamically centered on Him, then how can we not see that a unique and singular position discloses itself at the temporal-

spatial summit of the system in which Christ, without deformation or strain-
ing, becomes literally, with an unheard of realism, 'the Pantocrator.'" [14]

In the Apocalypse St. John writes of God as "him who is and who was and
who is coming" (1:8). It is tempting to see an obscure trinitarian formula
here, a reference to the Father-Creator who *is* from all eternity; to the Incar-
nate Son who *was* made flesh at a point of time; and to the Indwelling Spirit
who *is coming*. St. John writes in his Gospel that "that which is born of the
Spirit is Spirit" (3:6) and St. Paul speaks of the Christ in whom we seek incorporation as "a life-giving Spirit" (i.e., really, one who spiritualizes) in I Cor.
15:45. We shall see that this vision of a universe raised to the level of spirit
through unanimasation in Christ ("Do you not know that you are the temple
of God and that the Spirit dwells in you?" [I Cor. 3:16]) corresponds exactly with Teilhard's view of the state of mankind at the time of the Parousia.
This lofty condition represents, however, the ultimate stage of human progress. What, in Teilhard's view, was its beginning? What are the humble origins, the basic and simple constituents of this universe which is destined to be
diaphanously divine?

The Realm of the Spirit

Although Teilhard has summed up the entire evolutionary process in
the single word "spiritualization" it is unquestionably his concept of spirit
which presents traditional Christian philosophy and theology with the most
formidable difficulties. In *Le Coeur de la matière* he states unequivocally
that "matter and spirit are not at all two things — but two states, two aspects
of a single cosmic stuff"; that "matter is the matrix of spirit, spirit the superior
condition of matter"; and that "matter irresistibly transforms itself into
psyche." It would seem from such precise statements that spirit, in his views,
owes its existence to matter and makes its appearance only after matter has
achieved a certain degree of development or organization. But this conclusion would oversimplify and misrepresent his position. In *The Phenomenon of Man* he speaks of life and consciousness (or "mind," the term used by
J. B. S. Haldane in a passage endorsed by Teilhard) as existing in some attenu-
ated or rudimentary form from the very beginning of the process he calls
cosmogenesis: "Refracted rearwards along the course of evolution, consciousness displays itself qualitatively as a spectrum of shifting hints whose lower
terms are lost in the night" (p. 60). Conversely "a consciousness is that much
more perfected according as it lines a richer and better organized material
edifice." Hence, it seems that matter and spirit have always coexisted; they
are, we must deduce from his words, nothing other than the two distinct components of all physical (*sic*) energy: "a *tangential* energy that links the element
with all others of the same order (that is to say, of the same complexity and
the same centricity) as itself in the universe, and a *radial energy* that draws

it towards ever greater complexity and centricity — in other words, forwards" (p. 65).

If then we are to identify spirit with "radial energy" the nature of this energy must be carefully studied. At the risk of further oversimplification (but not, in this case, misrepresentation) we might say that radial energy is goal-seeking, purposive, directing and organizing; in short, it gives meaning to matter. Teilhard acknowledged that the Aristotelian theory of matter and form, when translated into the equivalent notions demanded by a science based on an evolutionary perspective, "is almost indistinguishable from our own speculations on the development of nature," [15] and one of his more benign critics admits that the idea of an "emergence" of forms ordered according to their complexity is acceptable if, as is possible, it "is interpreted in the framework of hylomorphism." [16] In other words, radial energy in its various manifestations may be compared to the "substantial forms" of Scholastic philosophy. The evolutive character of this energy distinguishes it, however, from the rather static and abstract "form" of Aristotelianism and enables Teilhard, I think, to speak of it as spirit, i.e., as something not only vital but progressive.

When spirit, so understood, achieves or accomplishes a high degree of organization it becomes "conscious," and let us confine ourselves for the moment to the consciousness or awareness of, say, the animal. A recent commentator on Teilhard puts it this way: "There is but a *single* reality, organized matter, which, the more organized it is, permits the manifestation of a greater spirituality. Organization is the material aspect of the spiritual just as the spiritual is the specific aspect of organization." [17] It would seem, from this, that consciousness must be compared to the spoken word: it is the goal of spirit seeking realization and expression of itself in terms of matter, just as the thought is materially represented by the word. There is, consequently, a strong temptation to liken the purposive drive of Teilhard's spirit to instinct, and it may be suggested that Teilhard himself would approve the idea that spirit is indeed the instinct to lead and return all creation to God the Omega, the instinct whose intermediary goal is to produce consciousness. It is at this point that we must insist that spirit, thus conceived, and the human soul are not identical. Spirit brings organized matter to the stage of neurophysical development where reflection becomes possible. The intervention of God at this step is perfectly compatible, Teilhard declares, with this phenomenology. But how are we to conceive of this intervention without destroying either Teilhard's synthesis or the defined dogmas of the Church?

Perhaps a solution can be found along these lines. Creation is continuous; to create is for God to unite himself with, to immerge himself in, creation. Teilhard speaks of the Divinity in *Le Coeur de la matière* as fire, "c'est-à-dire, que devenu capable de se glisser partout, *de se métamorphoser en n'importe quoi*, il se trouvait désormais apte, en tant qu'universalisable, à faire irruption, pour l'embraser, dans le milieu cosmique." (The image has, of course, excellent biblical substantiation: see Dt. 4:24; Ex. 3:2; 13:21; 19:18; Mal. 3:2; Matt. 3:11). May we not think of God so uniting himself to spirit (or radial energy, call it what you will) at the moment it has brought "the anthropoid . . . 'mentally' to boiling point" (p. 168) that His consuming and purificatory embrace actually *transforms* spirit into soul, while *phenomenologically*, it appears that spirit has merely advanced to a higher level of psychic development? In this view, spirit would actually have returned to Omega, would have fulfilled its larval purpose and achieved its destiny in a metamorphosis that at once foreshadows and prepares the ultimate metamorphosis of "Christification." In this way does God "make man in His image and likeness." The human soul emerges from the molten crucible of Divinity and, thus transformed, begins anew the path of convergence.

Note that in this proposed solution radial energy or spirit becomes a secondary cause of the soul's creation. It is this element which, while preserving the essentials (I believe) of Teilhard's view, does not conflict with the official teaching of the Church; for although most theologians deny the co-operation of any secondary cause or causes, "there has never been any formal definition on the point by the Church." [18] Moreover, the phenomenological emergence and continuity which this hypothesis allows is in accordance with biblical terminology. The Hebrew word *nephesh*, which we translate as "soul," has many differently nuanced meanings, the most basic of which is "breath" or "life," applicable to man and beast alike. The special creative activity of God relative to man's *soul* is not indicated in the text of Gen. 2:7 by the words "Then the Lord God formed man out of the dust of the ground and breathed into his nostrils the breath of life, and man became a living being" (often incorrectly translated as "a living soul"), but by the phrase "God created man in his image" in Gen. 1:27.

There is a curious parallel, in fact, between Teilhard's concept of the organizing powers of radial energy and the Hebrew rejection of any dichotomy of body and soul. "Unhampered by the body-soul dichotomy, the Hebrew calls this tangible, sensible, expressive, and living reality that is man, a soul. I perceive, not a 'body' which contains a 'soul' but, directly, a living soul. Within the sensible that I am shown I may decipher all the wealth of its intelligibility." [19] In Hebrew thought "the very ideas of matter and of 'body' as a substance other than the soul" [20] are ignored. For this reason Sheol, the abode of the dead, receives not the "soul" but the whole person, though in a relatively lifeless and weak state (Isa. 14:9–10). The admittedly imperfect concept of a future life accepted in pre-exilic Israel contains within itself, nonetheless, the elements of a solution to the problem of bodily resurrection. This has always been a difficult doctrine for the scientifically minded, but a further question is raised by Teilhard's assertion that the ultimate goal of organization is the abandonment of an "organoplanetary foothold" (p. 287). Is there room for resurrection in his view? The answer must be yes — when the dogma is understood in the very way that eliminates all the difficulties posed by biochemical considerations: "In the context of the Bible, the problem does not exist. Since the soul is the body's essence, since soul and body are but one, the resurrection of bodies is the resurrection of souls, that is, the resurrection of men." [21]

Returning to what was suggested above regarding the soul's creation, we can perhaps derive from this some aid to a proper understanding of the place of original justice and original sin in the vision of cosmogenesis. With "spirit" emerging from God's transforming touch as "soul," the additional elevation accorded to it by sanctifying grace seems appropriate indeed. As the human psyche comes from God, He enables it to return to him in a meeting of loving friendship. Since this is a religious and moral relation it does not, of itself, imply more than the most elementary or primitive intellectual development. Adam "may have been morphologically and culturally a primitive — but a primitive to whom God communicated knowledge adequate for his condition in life and capable of being directed toward his supernatural end." [22] Theologians today are prepared to acknowledge that their predecessors "often exaggerated the privileges of Adam and Eve . . . unquestionably overstated the perfection of Adam's knowledge." [23] The Bible itself indicates that technical and artistic inventions appeared long after our first parents (Gen. 4:20–22), so that there is nothing to prevent us from recognizing that "the cultural level of life in the Garden (of Eden) could have been very elementary" [24] — as the data of anthropology suggest. In the light of these observations we can better appreciate the Fall. "There has been too much consideration of original sin as a proof of superiority whereas sin is a sign of insufficiency and weakness." [25] St. Irenaeus, one of the Church's earliest theologians, stated that man (Adam) was not capable of the perfection with which God had endowed him: "The Son of God, who is perfect, became a child in the midst of men, not for His own sake, but because of the childishness of man." [26] Such words correspond exactly with Teilhard's approach to the mysteries of Incarnation and Redemption.

The Human Peduncle and the Incarnation

We are taught, however, that Adam also received the gifts of bodily integrity and immortality, and it is these privileges that seem to contradict the physical picture of primitive man proposed by the natural sciences. But there is no real conflict here either. As far as integrity is concerned, "it is not unlikely that in early times man experienced the procreative instinct only at a certain season of the year and that human nature has undergone progressive derangement in this regard, failure to resist the impulse within the bounds of right reason having increased its intensity." [27] The sources of revelation do not tell us how God would have preserved man in immortality, the tree of life being a symbolic representation. It seems to me that this gift of immortality can be compared to that abandonment of man's "organoplanetary foothold" posited by Teilhard as the consummation of noogenesis and referred to earlier in connection with the doctrine of bodily resurrection. Surely the moral and spiritual perfection with which man entered into the world were guarantees — had they been preserved — of a far swifter movement of convergence than that which sin has retarded and the Redemption alone accelerated again.

The objectively redemptive character of Christ's sacrificial death is barely mentioned in Teilhard's works. For him, as for the Greek Fathers, redemption is effected by the Incarnation. This implies no denial on his part of atonement through the Cross, any more than it did on the part of so many illustrious names in the past, but it does indicate his conviction that "something essential is lacking, for our generation, in a Gospel tinged with Manicheanism in which the progress of knowledge and technology is still presented not as the primary co-condition but as a simple addition to the human spiritualization in which defeat has as much sanctifying value as success, if not more; in which the Cross is constantly placed before our eyes to recall to us the initial failure of the world we live in." [28]

Strictly speaking, the work of redemption was consummated on the Cross, but every theologian knows that human solidarity with Christ through the Incarnation renders His expiatory death effective: "For as in Adam all die, so in Christ all will be made to live . . . that God may be all in all" (I Cor. 15:22; 28). It was insistence on this principle which characterized the earliest statements about redemption. St. Irenaeus affirms that "it would not be possible for us to receive incorruptibility and immortality were we not united with incorruptibility and immortality." [29] More strongly still, St. Hippolytus declares that man is "deified and engendered unto immortality. . . . God has power enough to make thee God for His own glory." [30] When Teilhard exclaims, as he does, that "in truth, Christ saves," it is in this tradition of recapitulative Christology that he intends the words to be understood: "Christ comes right now in these days not only to preserve man from the legitimate revolt against life — confronted by naïve suspicion with the stark menace of a total death — but also to bring to him the supreme excitation without which thought apparently cannot attain to the planetary term of its reflection." [31] Insofar as the Incarnation is that "privileged point in which all the cosmic fibers tend to unite themselves by their natural structure," [32] the salvific work of Christ exists on two levels: "not merely the individual and 'supernatural' but the collective and terrestrial as well." [33] Salvation, in the fullest sense of the word, is Christogenesis, for "only at the end and summit of cosmic evolution" is Christ "fully attainable." [34]

Do the sources of Revelation lend any support to this soteriology of cosmic convergence and "supreme excitation"? Is it truly part of the Christian message? It is a curious fact that on three different occasions in the Fourth Gospel Jesus relates the consummation of His life to a movement of convergence: "I, if I be lifted up, . . . will draw all things to myself" (John 12:32); "If anyone eat of this bread he shall live forever; and the bread that I will give is my flesh for the life of the world" (John 6:52); "I lay down my life for my sheep. And other sheep I have . . . and there shall be one fold" (John 10:16). In the first of these texts the significant word is "things," giving us a precise parallel to that Pauline passage most often used by Teilhard: "In him all things hold together" (Coloss. 1:17). The Eucharistic flesh of Christ is, of course, essentially a unifying medium so that the second of these texts requires no explanation. Finally, the ultimate union of all men in Christ is promised as the fruit of His self-sacrifice. Hence, although it is true that all these citations refer, primarily, to a supernatural process, the end-term predicted is also on the phenomenological level, which, as Teilhard would be quick to point out, proves that they are moving toward the same goal.

St. Paul is full of relevant passages, the most important of which (Rom. 8:18f.) we have seen already. Highly suggestive also is II Cor. 3:18: "But we all, with faces unveiled, reflecting as in a mirror the glory of the Lord, are being transformed into his very image from glory to glory." It is the Christian, of course, who is transformed by grace, but in the light of Paul's universalist outlook, the notion of Christogenesis in the Teilhardian sense cannot be excluded. Very similar are the words of Eph. 4:13f., in which "unity of faith" and "deep knowledge of the Son of God" (is this not "supreme excitation" of thought?) will bring men "to perfect manhood, to the mature measure of the fullness of Christ" from whom "the whole body . . . derives its increase to the building up of itself in love." Indeed this text is a veritable synthesis of Teilhard's "Super-humanity — super-Christ — super-Charity."

The Whole Christ

The many references in the New Testament to the hallowing of *all things* in Christ — the subhuman as well as man himself (Rom. 8:18f.; John 12:32; Eph. 1:10; Apoc. 22:3) — clearly indicate the correctness of Teilhard's perspective. The function of Christ is far more extensive than the cancellation of Adam's debt.

When Teilhard writes that Christ comes to bring man the "supreme excitation without which thought apparently cannot attain to the planetary term of its reflection" he is expressing, from a theological point of view, a judgment he phrases elsewhere in purely scientific language: "Man is not yet zoologically an adult. Psychologically he has not spoken his final word." [35] In common with some other anthropologists — not all by any means — Teilhard anticipates an ultrahuman state induced by attraction and unanimity, but his specifically Christian contribution is in recognizing Christ as the magnetic center of this process — as the Omega toward which, as an unknown focus of personalization, mankind would, without Relevation, be but blindly directed. Without the "conviction, strictly undemonstrable to science, that the universe has a direction and that it . . . should result in some sort of irreversible perfection" (p. 283 f.), man will reach, not the Omega Point, but "an unscalable wall, on which consciousness would crash and then forever disappear." But Relevation affirms, what noogenesis logically demands, the Parousia, and on this subject Teilhard speaks with great forcefulness: "By habit we continue to think and portray to ourselves the Parousia (by which the Kingdom of God on earth is consummated) as an event of purely catastrophic nature, that is to say, liable to appear without any precise relation to any determined state of humanity and with no importance attached to what moment of history it will occur in. That is one point of view. But why not admit, in full accord with the new scientific views of a humanity in the actual process of anthropogenesis . . . that the Parousia could spring only from a physical and organic necessity, only between heaven and humanity biologically arrived at a certain critical evolutive point of collective maturation?" [36]

In order to avoid any misinterpretation of this and similar passages in Teilhard's writings I think it is essential to note, at once, that he is *not* saying that mankind as a whole will inevitably attain a collective state of spiritual and intellectual perfection by the time of the Parousia. What he postulates is a "certain critical evolutive point of collective maturation," but in *The Phenomenon of Man* he explicitly allows for a situation which, as he observes, is "more in conformity with traditional apocalyptic thinking." In other words, he envisions a possible conflict, in which case "the noosphere, in the course of and by virtue of the processus which draws it together, will, when it has reached its point of unification, split into two zones each attracted to an opposite pole of adoration." He admits, however, that an alternative hypothesis of the final convergence taking place "in peace" conforms "most harmoniously with our theory" (pp. 288–89).

In relation to the data of Revelation two questions must be raised and answered here. The first is: Does the "traditional apocalyptic thinking" referred to by Teilhard represent the indubitably authentic teaching of the Scriptures? and the second: Does revelation contain any basis for the assertion that the Parousia will take place when humanity has "arrived at a certain critical evolutive point of collective maturation"?

There is a text in the third gospel which seems, at first reading, to preclude any "peaceful" final convergence: "Yet when the Son of Man comes, will he find, do you think, faith on the earth?" (Luke 18:8). These words suggest that few men, at the time of the Parousia, will be disposed to accept Omega. But the text is, first of all, interrogative, not declarative, and it must be interpreted in the light of what precedes it. The faith spoken of here is confidence in God's providence: spiritual imperturbability. It is this quality about whose pervasiveness at the end of time Our Lord wonders. Wholly in accord with this is Teilhard's observation that convergence in peace, since it coincides with the approach to "a critical point," will take place *"in extreme tension"* (p. 288), and he disavows any intention of resurrecting the "old millenary dreams of a terrestrial paradise at the end of time" (p. 288). Similar words of Christ's referring, this time, to the diminution of "charity" may be found in the famous eschatological discourse (Matt. 24:12). But the exegetical difficulties involved in attempting to determine which words in this discourse refer to the period preceding the fall of Jerusalem, and which to the period preceding the Parousia, free us from the obligation of relating it either to an "apocalyptic" or to a "peaceful" convergence. Were it certainly pertinent to the circumstances of the Second Coming it would favor the apocalyptic interpretation.

The most colorful passage on the Parousia in the New Testament is unquestionably the second chapter of St. Paul's second letter to the Thessalonians. But the wealth of detail serves to obscure rather than clarify the ideas conveyed thereby. Exegetes resign themselves to the fact that although elements in this chapter reflect "traditional ideas current at that time," these are "now lost" to us.[37] Nevertheless, as it stands, the passage implies an "apostasy" and a "misleading influence" which would, of course, militate against a peaceful convergence. Yet it should also be noted that these circumstances are not spoken of as accompanying "the brightness of his (the Lord's) coming" but as preceding it by what appears to be some length of time. Even less conclusive are the many vivid and dramatic tableaux painted in the Apocalypse itself. There the situation is complicated by the interposition of a symbolic thousand-year period in which "those who had been beheaded because of the witness to Jesus . . . came to life and reigned with Christ" (Apoc. 20:4). Yet this is not the Parousia, for "when the thousand years are finished, Satan . . . will go forth and deceive the nations" (Apoc. 20:7). Then, without any real indication of immediate sequence, John describes the Second Coming in a moving literary crescendo of great beauty which owes much to the prophecies of Isaias (Apoc. 20:11 — 22:5). No one can question, however, the general impression of joy and peace implicit in this final description.

As to the second question, whether revelation says anything about the "critical evolutive point of collective maturation" demanded by Teilhard's thesis, I think we may find an answer in a striking text from the first epistle of St. John: "Beloved, now we are the children of God, *and it has not yet appeared what we shall be. We know that, when he appears, we shall be like to him,* for we shall see him just as he is" (I John 3:2; italics added). No one can presume to say exactly what St. John had in mind here, but it is certain that he envisions a veritable "Christification" of the faithful at or by the time of the Second Coming. If, as is possible, we are to understand it as meaning "*by* the time of the Second Coming," then Teilhard's view is solidly based on Revelation.

"*Decentration*" *and Sin*

The whole idea of excitation through Christ to a point of collective maturation is, I think, intimately linked, at least implicitly, to the question of moral evil. Teilhard's critics, even those who are largely well disposed, tax him with having ignored the presence and significance of sin: "Père Teilhard appears to forget evil *par excellence*, namely *sin*, the revolt of man against God under the impulse of Satan." [38] Teilhard's "theory of evil" is called a "glaring inadequacy," his "most serious" "doctrinal" error.[39] I do not think a profound reading of Teilhard's work leaves this impression. What is the "egoism" which Teilhard calls "retrograde" and which, he says, "seeks to drag the world backwards towards plurality and into matter" (p. 263) if not the principle of all that we call sin? Is it not precisely the "ego" that St. Paul exposes as the cause of all sin, in Rom. 7? "What shall we say then? Is the Law sin? By no means! Yet I did not know sin save through the Law. For I had not known lust unless the Law had said, 'Thou shalt not lust'" (Rom. 7:7). And it is by losing the self in Christ that we are freed from sin: "There is therefore now no condemnation for those who are in Christ Jesus" (Rom. 8:1). When Teilhard insists that "we must advance — towards the 'other'" i. e., "in the direction of convergence" (p. 263), he is equivalently saying the same thing.

Human resistance to convergence, which Teilhard recognizes as a formidable obstacle, can be nothing other than the selfishness that derives from our fallen nature and is the root of all moral evil. It is then a distortion of his views to say that sin does not appear in them. Moralists are currently aware that sin must be described and explained as an attitude rather than as a thing. The decidedly untheological presentation of sin as a "stain" or "disfigurement" to which earlier generations had been exposed has left too many psychological scars to be sustained. Teilhard ignores this "entitive" concept of sin indeed, and correctly so, but if the word "sin" does not often appear in his pages, "every egoistic solution of life" (p. 263), a phrase covering everything from serious sin to imperfection, does, and as an attitude it is rejected. Be it noted, also, that the divergent effect of egoism is, ultimately, nothing less than a turning away from union with Omega, i.e., with Christ.

The affirmation of an ultimate convergence of the universe in Christ corroborates the radical orthodoxy of Teilhard's perspective while it challenges the strength of the Marxist appeal to many genuine humanitarians of our era. Indeed it has been said that Teilhard's presentation of Christian doctrine is the only one in which doctrinaire Communists recognize any serious competition for the minds and hearts of men. In their respect for the properties and potentialities of matter, their faith in the aims and results of scientific endeavor, and in their vision — though it is differently conceived and orientated in each case — of increasing collectivization, the Marxist and Teilhard are on common ground. They part company at a point where the Marxist must also terminate his dream.

The classless, utopian society promised by dialectical materialism is actually a static, and therefore unrealistic, goal. As long as social and economic conditions demand amelioration, such an ideal can impel and inspire, but in so far as they are attainable ends, what further motivation do they provide for man upon achievement? "There is neither an escape towards the future permitting it to avoid total death nor a supreme focus of personalization by which love can shine among the human cells. A world entirely disintegratable, a world of ice. A universe without heart or goal. So powerfully propelled that it finds itself departing from the biological evolution in which it is inserted, the Marxist anthropogenesis cannot succeed in justifying or maintaining its *élan* down to the end because it excludes the existence of an irreversible Center at its end." [40] The Christian, however, can and must take up again "the idea (or, if you prefer) the 'myth' of progress" [41] because he is committed to looking forward to the Parousia.

The Parousia

It would hardly be an exaggeration to say that Teilhard has invested the belief in a Second Coming with an importance and significance it has not possessed since the end of the first century. But whereas for the Christians of those early days it loomed on the horizon as an imminent event against whose expectation they had to be cautioned (II Thess. 2; II Pet. 3:10–13), for us it appears — especially in the light of cosmogenesis — as a culmination necessarily delayed but ever present as a hope that will not be disappointed. In Apostolic times there were not wanting those who sought to discredit faith in Christ by asking "Where is the promise of his coming?" (II Pet. 3:4). In subsequent centuries, including our own, Christians themselves have asked this question because they have judged the world and found it worthy of annihilation. Both groups stand convicted of spiritual myopia, and to them Teilhard says, "Arrière . . . les pessimistes athées et les pessimistes chrétiens!" [42] The future will be made by "those who are united in the common faith of the world's spiritual destiny." [43]

The Christian who looks about him at a world alienated from religious faith and who, accordingly, turns his back upon it, leaves tomorrow in the hands of Marxism. He is content to think that as long as a faithful few, like himself, are left in the world, the divine promise that the gates of hell shall not prevail against the Church remains fulfilled. He forgets, as Karl Rahner has recently pointed out, that "the Church is not merely a large or a small number of people, as chance may see fit to decide; she is a 'sign lifted up amongst the nations,' and she must bear the sign of her divine foundation plainly for all men of good will to see." [44] And, we might add, in order that the process of "Christification" continue, increase, and consummate itself.

Yet as a sign the Church and her teachings must be intelligible. From all sides today the Christian theologian is urged to translate the message and meaning of the Gospel for modern ears. The old formulas have lost their appeal and the voice from the pulpit is heard but not understood, as though the miracle of Pentecost had suddenly been reversed. "We have, too, an unpleasant sense, whenever we hear the sound of our own voice, that it is not particularly surprising that nobody listens to us. Doesn't a great deal of what we say sound strange in our own ears — outmoded, utterly out of date?" [45] This frank confession by Karl Rahner, an echo of similar words uttered by men of his standing all over the world, points to the general awareness among Catholic intellectuals of a pressing need for a new presentation of eternal truths.

Teilhard, too, has voiced the same sentiment, but he has done much more, he has made the effort to give theology this new direction. He has seen that "the Christian faith . . . by the sole fact that it is rooted in the idea of the Incarnation, has always left a large place in its structure for the tangible values of the world and matter. A part too humble perhaps and too accidental it seems to us now . . . but a part so intimately bound in the very structure of dogma that like a living bud it only asked for a signal or a ray of light in order to develop." [46]

It seems nothing short of providential that our age, which is so clearly one of transition, has been provided with a synthesis of faith and science that is viable. That it requires further development, clarification, and even, in some respects, revision, no one, least of all Teilhard, if he were alive, would deny. This man, who spoke of Rome as "the principal ascensional pole of what I call, in my 'jargon,' hominisation," [47] and whose whole life was an example of obedient submission, would be the first to acknowledge the doctrinal authority of the Holy See in any definitive appraisal of his contribution. But we may be equally sure that in the face of an ideological struggle with the forces of atheism the Christian world will render a tremendous debt of gratitude to the man who diagnosed the weakness in contemporary theology and then prescribed the remedy: "The only means of overcoming Communism is to present Christ as He ought to be presented: not an opium but the essential stimulant of hominisation." [48]

15

A PRELUDE TO FURTHER THOUGHT

The Editor

It seems to me that the task of the modern scholar is to be an expert and specialist in one area of truth while keeping in view the whole field of truth and knowledge. This statement of his task may seem an oversimplification, but the challenge and implications are tremendous. With our scientific knowledge increasing as fast as it is, the real scientist cannot do anything but become a specialist. To be an expert in general genetics or in any other general field is impossible, for the fields are far too extensive today. But granted that specialization is unavoidable, we must avoid the prime danger that threatens any specialist: the loss of balance and perspective, and the inability to assimilate and co-ordinate the findings of other fields.

The question in this study has been to determine whether Pierre Teilhard de Chardin, specialist in mammalian paleontology and human evolution, maintained his equilibrium and perspective in relation to the whole complex of modern thought. For this purpose we have invited scholars in various branches of modern knowledge to give their considered evaluation and judgment of his writings and thought. The preceding essays, presenting their views, have been prepared seriously, after much background work, though the views are offered as personal and tentative.

Teilhard has been praised and criticized both in this work and in numerous others. Sometimes the criticisms have seemed to preclude any hint of praise; occasionally praise has seemed to leave no room for criticism. Actually, no such appraisals are intended as precise measurements of the mind of a great scholar.

Serious objections have been raised in this study and elsewhere to the methodology of phenomenology as found in the writings of Teilhard, and to his "Lamarckian" genetics. The reader will find the question of scientific phenomenology also treated quite extensively in a work by Dr. Paul Chauchard, neurophysiologist and director of the École des Hautes Études at the Sorbonne.[1] Chauchard asserts that the scientific phenomenology of Teilhard is "a new domain of scientific thought" in the tradition of the great plant physiologist Claude Bernard. We agree with Chauchard that Teilhardian phenomenology is not science in the strict sense of the word as used today by the experimental scientists. But it does seem to fall within the realm of science in a wider sense that is becoming more and more acceptable even to the strictest experimental scientist.[2] This question, however, will require much more study.

The Lamarckian aspect of Teilhard's thought is no doubt due to his preoccupation with the sociopsychic evolution of man. The extrapolation that Teilhard made, whether consciously or not, will bear much more careful study before a final answer can be made as to its validity. The work of Dr. Sonneborn and Dr. Dippel at Indiana University, only recently reported at the 1960 Vanuxum Lectures, along with the whole study of cytoplasmic heredity, may throw some light on the question in the future. For the present we can only say that modern genetics is not favorably impressed by subhuman Lamarckian genetics.

Much of the criticism of Teilhard's theory seems to be founded in a problem of semantics. We seriously wonder if, when all the writings of Teilhard de Chardin have been examined, scholars will not agree with Nicolas Corte that the "Teilhard controversy" is basically a misunderstanding of terminology.[3] Teilhard's neologisms, his evolutionary and scientific approach to old problems that concern also the philosopher and the theologian, his "poetic" style, his *mystique* of science" — all these pose problems for the reader primarily, I believe, because Teilhard is first of all a prophet.

What the fate of this man's thought will be, no one today can say. We suspect, however, that scholars of the future will find much fruit in the writings of Teilhard de Chardin just as we can today. What he attempted and yearned for, others, following in his path, may be able to attain in the years to come. Perhaps some of us may live to see his desire accomplished. This, I am sure, would be his earnest wish.

NOTES AND REFERENCES

All quotations within the chapters for which only a page reference is given are taken from the English translation by Bernard Wall of The Phenomenon of Man *(New York, Harper, 1959). Thus, the bibliographical entries to follow do not include references to* The Phenomenon of Man.

Chapter 1   Introduction

1. Fothergill, P., *Historical Aspects of Organic Evolution* (London, Hollis & Carter, 1952).
2. Messenger, E., *Evolution and Theology* (London, Burns, Oates, & Washbourne, 1931), pp. 56–58.
3. De Solages, Bruno, "Christianity and Evolution," *Cross Currents*, I (Summer, 1951), pp. 28 f.
4. Guitton, J., "Le Phénomène Teilhard," *Informations Catholiques internationales*, III (January, 1960), 28 f.
5. Lecomte du Noüy, P., *Human Destiny* (New York, Longmans, Green, 1947). A comparison of consciousness in Bergson, Teilhard and Lecomte du Noüy can be found in the *American Benedictine Review*, XII, 2 (June 1961), 206–219: "Evolution and 'Panpsychism' in Teilhard de Chardin," by Robert Francoeur.
6. Wald, G., "The Origin of Life," *Scientific American*, 191 (August, 1954), 44–53.
7. Polanyi, M., "An Epic Theory of Evolution," *Saturday Review*, XLIII, 5 (January 30, 1960), 21.
8. Viallet, F.-A., *L'Univers personnel de Teilhard de Chardin* (Paris, Amiot-Dumont, 1956).
9. The recent discoveries made by Dr. Juan Armenta Camacho in the valley of Puebla, southeast of Mexico City, may cause some change in our idea of the date of man's first appearance in the New World.
10. Teilhard de Chardin, P., "Psychological Conditions of Human Unification," *Cross Currents*, III (Fall, 1952), 1–5. Also, "Building the Earth," *Cross Currents*, IX (Fall, 1960), pp. 315–30.
11. Movius, H. L., "Pierre Teilhard de Chardin, Paleoanthropologist," *Science,* 123 (1956), 92.

Chapter 4   An Augustinian Approach to Natural History

1. There is so much of the psychological *argumentum ad hominem*, of clinical name-

calling, in materialistic philosophies that it would be only too tempting to apply the same method for the opposite argument!

2. I once participated in a radio debate with a well-known scientist who was a professed atheist. Our subject was "Science and Faith" or something like that. We came to talk about "communication" and I ventured the remark that a fugue by Bach contained more truth than quite a few verbalized items of this morning's newspaper. At this my adversary was genuinely amused, and corrected me, stating that a fugue by Bach was a "purely emotional experience" which had nothing to do with truth. We forget only too easily that with the fearful dichotomy of our modern minds the values, aesthetic and moral, become not only arbitrary but also expendable. After a five-course feasting on European civilization we can either retire to the drawing room to discuss serious business or to the *salon* to look at lovely paintings and listen to *nocturnes*. The aesthetic as a pleasant emotional cloud is a romantic notion, and romanticism was the corollary of the first wave of industrialism.

3. I am using the terms "explaining" and "comprehending" in the sense in which Karl Jaspers has used them in a different connection; the meaning is obvious from the present content.

Chapter 5   A Student of the "Phenomena"

1. There should be no need to insist that this is an exploratory essay. Since much of Teilhard's writing is as yet unpublished, this article, based on the available texts, particularly *The Phenomenon of Man*, is necessarily tentative.
2. Tresmontant, Claude, *Pierre Teilhard de Chardin: His Thought*, (Baltimore, Helicon, 1959), p. 16.
3. Bosio, G., "Il fenomeno umano nell' ipotesi dell' evoluzione integrale," *Civiltà Cattolica*, CVI, 4 (December 17, 1955), 622 ff.
4. *Nouvelles lettres de voyage* (January 11, 1951), as cited in Tresmontant, *op. cit.*, p. 16.
5. *Le Cœur de la matière* (1950), as cited in Tresmontant, *op. cit.*, p. 18.
6. Tresmontant, *op. cit.*, p. 21 f.: "Teilhard's entire scientific work can be characterized as an effort to read the direction of evolution in reality itself, without recourse to any metaphysical presuppositions, in order to elucidate its immanent intentionality in the very order of phenomena, and using the scientific method alone."
7. *Esquisse d'un univers personnel* (1936), as cited in Tresmontant, *op. cit.*, p. 22.
8. Bergson, Henri, *Creative Evolution*, trans. A. Mitchell (New York, Scribner, 1944), pp. 274 ff.
9. *L'Union créatrice* (1917), as cited in Tresmontant, *op. cit.*, p. 51: "Whereas in Bergson's *Creative Evolution*, the cosmos is revealed as a widespread irradiation as from a spouting center, the shape of the universe as disclosed in the 'creative union' is that of a reduction or a leading back of a convergence, of a centripetal confluence from some sphere infinitely distended. Equally evolutive, the two theories are the reverse of each other."
10. Tresmontant, *op. cit.*, p. 51.
11. "La Place de l'homme dans l'univers, réflexions sur la complexité" (1942), as cited in Tresmontant, *op. cit.*, p. 14: "Perhaps I may go so far as to hazard an 'ultraphysics.' But no one should look for a metaphysics here."
12. *Résumé de la pensée du Père* (1948), as cited in Tresmontant, *op. cit.*, p. 15: "Essentially P. Teilhard de Chardin's thought is not expressed in a metaphysics, but in a sort of phenomenology."

13. Viallet, François Albert, *L'Univers personnel de Teilhard de Chardin* (Paris, Amicot-Dumont, 1955), p. 72: "Il prétend ne faire qu'une phénoménologie (au sens étymologique du mot, pas au sens de Husserl)."

14. Teilhard de Chardin, *Le Groupe zoologique humain* (Paris, Albin Michel, 1956), p. 3: "Comme leur titre même l'indique, les pages qui suivent ne prétendent absolument pas donner une définition exhaustive de l'homme. Mais elles cherchent tout simplement à fixer de celui-ci les apparences 'phénoménales,' dans la mesure où (pour notre observation terrestre) l'humain peut être légitimement regardé par la Science comme prolongeant et couronnant, au moins provisoirement, le vivant."

15. As Teilhard put it, "Thus it would be mistaken to represent Omega to ourselves simply as a center born of the fusion of elements which it collects, or annihilating them in itself. By its structure Omega, in its ultimate principle, can only be a *distinct Center radiating at the core of a system of centers*; a grouping in which personalization of the All and personalizations of the elements reach their maximum, simultaneously and without merging, under the influence of a supremely autonomous focus of union" (p. 262).

16. Thus, "Autonomy, actuality, irreversibility, and thus finally transcendence are the four attributes of Omega" (p. 270).

17. De Solages, Bruno, "Christianity and Evolution," *Cross Currents*, I (Summer, 1951), 29 f.

18. Teilhard de Chardin, *La Vision du passé* (Paris, Seuil, 1957), p. 348: "Finissons-en donc une bonne fois avec la naïve conception, entièrement dépassée aujourd'hui, de l' 'hypothèse-Évolution.' Non, prise assez largement, l'Évolution n'est déjà plus, et depuis longtemps, une hypothèse, — ni seulement une simple 'méthode': ce qu'elle représente, en fait, c'est une dimension nouvelle et générale de l'Univers, affectant par suite la totalité des éléments et des relations de l'Univers. Non pas une hypothèse, donc, mais une condition à laquelle doivent désormais satisfaire toutes les hypothèses."

19. Breuil, Henri, *Bulletin de littérature ecclesiastique* (L'Institut Catholique de Toulouse, January 5, 1956), as cited in *La Vision du passé*, p. 350: "Le principe de l'Évolution n'est que la méthode scientifique elle-même, appliquée à toutes réalités de toute nature se développant dans le temps. C'est l'unique moyen à notre disposition pour essayer de saisir la loi de leur épanouissement et succession, quel que soit leur succession, quel que soit leur substratum ontologique. Sans lui, on ne pourrait qui'édifier un catalogue descriptif des choses, sans tenter de les comprendre."

20. De Solages, *op. cit.*, p. 30: "In so far as we can force a thought so modern into ancient categories, we must say that his fundamental point of view is what Aristotle would call *Physics*, and the Scholastics, Cosmology. Considering total reality from the objective point of view of the sciences, the author attempts to make a systematic presentation of it, and thus to derive its essential laws and postulates, including the existence of God. Did not Aristotle introduce in his Eighth Book of the *Physics* a demonstration of the Prime Mover?"

21. *La Centrologie* (1944), cited in Tresmontant, *op. cit.*, p. 14.

22. Viallet, *op. cit.*, p. 72: "Teilhard se refuse absolument à faire de la 'metaphysique,' c'est-à-dire à déduire le Monde de certains principes a priori."

23. *La Vision du passé*, pp. 347-48: ". . . tout ce que la théorie moderne de l'Evolution déclare c'est que, dan la réalité spatio-temporelle du Cosmos, le plus succède au moins. Et ceci est à la fois incontestable et in-condamnable. Un *processus* n'est pas une *explication* philosophique."

24. *Le Groupe zoologique humain*, p. 3: "Essayer de définir expérimentalement ce mystérieux humain en fixant structurellement et historiquement sa position présente par rapport aux autres formes prises autour de nous, au cours des temps, par l'étoffe cosmique, — tel est le but, bien circonscrit, de l'ouvrage ici présenté."

25. So Teilhard: "Is evolution a theory, a system or a hypothesis? It is much more; it is a general condition to which all theories, all hypotheses, all systems must bow and which they must satisfy henceforward if they are to be thinkable and true. Evolution is a light illuminating all facts, a curve that all lines must follow" (p. 218).

26. As Teilhard says, "To think 'the world' (as physics is beginning to realize) is not merely to register it but to confer upon it a form of unity it would otherwise (i.e., without being thought) be without" (p. 249, n. 2).

27. "Comment je vois" (1948), as cited in Viallet, *op. cit.*, p. 236: "Être, dit encore Teilhard, est s'unir soi-même . . ."; also *The Phenomenon of Man*, p. 293, n. 1.

28. Viallet, *op. cit.*, p. 235.

29. "Comment je vois," *loc. cit.*

30. De Solages, *op. cit.*, p. 30.

31. Gilson, E., *The Unity of Philosophical Experience* (New York, Scribner, 1950), pp. 248 ff.

32. Cornford, F. M., *From Religion to Philosophy* (London, Arnold, 1912), p. 138.

33. Tresmontant, *op. cit.*, p. 16.

34. Teilhard himself seems to admit this point when he says: "The universe fulfilling itself in a synthesis of centers in perfect conformity with the laws of union. God, the Center of centers. In that final vision the Christian dogma culminates. And so exactly, so perfectly does this coincide with the Omega Point that doubtless I should never have ventured to envisage the latter or formulate the hypothesis rationally if, in my consciousness as a believer, I had not found not only its speculative model but also its living reality" (p. 294).

35. De Solages, *loc. cit.*: "Nonetheless, though he assumes the scientific, objective point of view, the work of Father Teilhard de Chardin . . . is not exactly what we would call science in the restricted, contemporary sense of the term."

36. Lauer, J. Quentin, *The Triumph of Subjectivity* (New York, Fordham University Press, 1958), p. 164, n. 5: "Strictly speaking phenomenology does not provide a method of inquiry; in the concrete it is a method of justifying what one has thought all along, without, of course, denying that it can result in revising some of one's convictions."

37. De Solages, *loc. cit.*

38. As he says, "Man discovers that *he is nothing else than evolution become conscious of itself*, to borrow Julian Huxley's concise expression" (p. 220).

Chapter 6   The Excellence of Man

1. There are as many kinds of psychologists as there are individual minds. A short statement of my idea of psychology may help to account for the discursive style of my presentation:

The correlative terms *subject* and *object*, first exactly distinctified by the Scholastics, provide *the* all-important distinction in the science of psychology. It is the primary concern and work of mental science to discover the whole nature of the truth found under each of these names. The critical significance of each specifically pertains to its precise meaning with regard to the paramount truth: the inviolability of individuality, the incorruptible integrity of self. Specifically, it is one thing to state that "subject" means "self," but quite another thing to state that "object" means "not-self." Innumerable problems of the science of psychology stem from the investigator's unrecognized attempts thus to do violence to the existence of mind, in the name of studying the mind. Seemingly as a consequence of this mental block, a scientific psychologist may tend to devote his interest to apparently less insoluble difficulties. Meanwhile, a system of psychology that adequately observes the mind's oneness continues to be the most deeply felt want of each one who makes the conscious effort to use his mind. The "thinking subject" and the "object of (one's) thought" — each designates a local action occurring as the whole motion of the mind goes on, each is an integrant individuation of the total mind's individuality.

2. Baltimore, Helicon, 1959.
3. "Comment je vois," as quoted in Tresmontant, *op. cit.*, p. 94.
4. Tresmontant, *op. cit.*, p. 81.
5. "Le Milieu divin," *loc. cit.*, p. 86.
6. "La Vie cosmique," *loc. cit.*, p. 79.
7. Tresmontant, *op. cit.*, p. 108.
8. *Ibid.*, p. 23.
9. *Ibid.*, p. 51.
10. "Rugged Individualism," The Annie Talbot Cole Lecture, Bowdoin College, March 22, 1960.
11. Conscious acceptance and conscious exercise of my personal responsibility for being all of myself is the only kind of hard work that cultivates that mental hardihood designated as self-consciousness (self-insight). I submit that there is no other ethical absolute which does not arise from error and illusion. If I ask myself, "How can I make such a sweeping self-observation?" my reply is, "Only with the greatest of difficulty." It is only by hard and sustained work in my selfward direction that I have been able to evolve the creation of this kind of self-view. My viewing my "authoritarianism" as not my own living of it is my way of comforting myself with an anesthetic when I need it. I live comfortably other kinds of self-views, notably such ones that picture man as a member of this or that organization, as a cog in the wheel of state, as a speck in the cosmos. Being lived harmoniously by me, views such as these latter ones are readily renounced (lived preconsciously, as out of focus), or focused upon, as the occasion of my living may call for the one or the other consideration.
12. "La vie cosmique," as quoted in Tresmontant, *op. cit.*, p. 97.
13. *Op. cit.*, p. 86.
14. Self-unconsciousness is practiced regularly whenever self-consciousness is being practiced. To illustrate, my unconsciousness of all the rest of myself occurs whenever I live any portion of myself with consciousness. Furthermore, in the interests of my living whatever portion of myself that I can live consciously, I actively disregard other portions of myself which might threaten my sense of self-control. Self-consciousness, as such, is always accompanied by a sense of conviction of self-control. It is only when I am about to live parts of myself which I cannot see clearly as being nothing but my own living that I become uncomfortable and suffer, what is miscalled "an attack of self-consciousness." Contrary to the usual description of it, "stage fright" is due always to one's unreadiness to see his "audience" or "viewers" as being all, and nothing but, his own living of these parts of himself. Once he develops the strength of mind to be able to live his auditor or viewer as his very own — that is, self-consciously — he immediately recovers his sense of self-control.
15. The necessary organic unity underlying individual experience underlies the

history of man's effort to reduce his world (universe) to unity. This unity is based upon the actuality that only one life creates all that life's experience.

16. This discussion of consciousness is intended to emphasize the fact that individuality is thoroughly subjective, hence neither objective nor isolable. Thus, this view of divinity is clear of any sort of pantheism. I have examined but one facet of Teilhard's *Weltanschauung*. However, this essay is to be read with the whole view in mind.

Chapter 7   A "Gentile's" View

1. Preface to Marguerite-Marie Teilhard de Chardin, *L'Energie spirituelle de la souffrance* (Paris, Seuil, 1951).
2. March 18, 1934. *Lettres de voyage, 1923–1939* (Paris, Grasset, 1956), pp. 175 f. This and subsequent quotations in this essay are translated from the French by A. J. Knodel.
3. As quoted in Claude Cuénot, *Pierre Teilhard de Chardin* (Paris, Plon, 1958), p. 193.
4. April 10, 1934. *Lettres de voyage*, p. 176.
5. Cuénot, *loc. cit.*, n.2.
6. *Lettres de voyage*, p. 136.
7. *Ibid.*, p. 91.
8. *Ibid.*, p. 181.

Chapter 8   The Birth of Life and Consciousness

1. Smuts, J. C., *Holism and Evolution* (New York, Macmillan, 1926), pp. 1 f.
2. March 18, 1934. *Lettres de voyage, 1923–1939* (Paris, Grasset, 1956), pp. 175 f.
3. Cassirer, E., *Determinism and Indeterminism in Modern Physics*, trans. O. T. Benbey (New Haven, Yale University Press, 1956), pp. 212, 213.
4. See chap. 9 in this volume.
5. Simpson, G. G., review of *The Phenomenon of Man, Scientific American*, 202 (1960), 202.

Chapter 9   Beneath the Microscope

1. Simpson, G. G., *The Meaning of Evolution* (New Haven, Yale University Press, 1950), pp. 309–24.
2. Dobzhansky, T., *Evolution, Genetics, and Man* (New York, Wiley, 1955), pp. 357–79.
3. Huxley, J., *Evolution in Action* (New York, Harper, 1953), pp. 152–76.
4. Oparin, A., *The Origin of Life* (3rd ed.; New York, Dover, 1957).
5. Weisz, Paul B., *The Science of Biology* (New York, McGraw-Hill, 1959).
6. Lecomte du Noüy, Pierre, *Human Destiny* (New York, Longmans, Green, 1947), pp. 30–39.
7. Miller, S. L., and H. C. Urey, "Organic Compound Synthesis on the Primitive Earth," *Science*, 130 (1959), 245–51.
8. Huxley, *op. cit.*, 91–123.
9. Royce, J. E., "Life and Living Things," *The Modern Schoolman*, XXXVII (1960), 213–32.
10. Thomas, Aquinas, *De Potentia*, Q. 3, a. 8, ad 15.
11. van Melsen, Andrew G., "Philosophical Aspects of Evolution," *Symposium on Evolution* (Louvain, Nauwelaerts, 1959).
12. Sinnott, E. W., *Matter, Mind, and Man: the Biology of Human Nature* (New York, Harper, 1957).
13. Luria, S. E., and M. Demerec, "Mutations of Bacteria from Virus Sensitivity to Virus Resistance," *Genetics*, XXVIII (1943), 491–511.

14. Dobzhansky, T., *Genetics and the Origin of Species* (3rd ed.; New York, Columbia University Press, 1951), pp. 76–107.
15. Goldschmidt, R. B., "Evolution as Viewed by One Geneticist," *American Scientist*, XL (1952), 84–98.
16. Cannon, H. G., *Lamarck and Modern Genetics* (Manchester, Manchester University Press, 1959), pp. 48–66.
17. Corte, Nicolas (*pseud.*), *Teilhard de Chardin, His Life and Spirit*, trans. Martin Jarrett-Kerr (New York, Macmillan, 1960), Preface.
18. "Évolution zoologique et invention," *Œuvres de Pierre Teilhard de Chardin* (Paris, Seuil, 1957), III, 329–31.
19. Lysenko, T. D., *Heredity and Its Variability*, trans. T. Dobzhansky (New York, Kings Crown Press, 1945), pp. 5–9.
20. Cannon, *op. cit.*, pp. 67–84.
21. Simpson, *op. cit.*, pp. 130–59.
22. Teilhard de Chardin, "La vision du passé: Note sur la réalité actuelle et la signification évolutive d'une orthogénèse humaine," *Œuvres*, III, 351–62.
23. Lecomte du Noüy, *op. cit.*
24. Klubertanz, G. P., *Introduction to the Philosophy of Being* (New York, Appleton-Century-Crofts, 1955), p. 156.
25. Waddington, C. H., *The Strategy of the Genes* (London, Allen & Unwin, 1957), pp. 162–87.

Chapter 10   Man and the Behavioral Sciences

1. Simpson, G. G., Review of *The Phenomenon of Man*, *Scientific American*, 202 (1960), 201–207.
2. See Murphy, Gardner, *Human Potentialities* (New York, Basic Books, 1959). In this work, an American psychologist takes a close look at the sources within human nature for the outgrowing of human nature and the directions that on-going biological and social evolution may take. He emphasizes the possibilities of self-directed change in the biological nature of man, in human culture, and in human creativeness. Much of Murphy's thought coincides with neo-Lamarckian views and the Teilhardian ideas of an engendering noosphere and progressive hominization.
3. Erikson, E., "Identity and the Life Cycle," *Psychological Issues*, I (1959).
4. Hartmann, H., *Ego Psychology and the Problem of Adaptation* (New York, International Universities Press, 1958).
5. Teilhard de Chardin, P., *Construire la terre* (Paris, Seuil, 1958); and "The Psychological Conditions of Human Unification," *Cross Currents*, III (1952), 1–5.
6. Sherrington, C., *Man on His Nature*, (New York, Doubleday, 1955), p. 255.
7. Huxley, J., *Knowledge, Morality, and Destiny* (New York, New American Library, 1960), p. 98.
8. Strasser, S., *The Soul in Metaphysical and Empirical Psychology* (Pittsburgh, Duquesne University Press, 1957).
9. Rohrer, J. H., "The Research Team Concept and the Cultural Pattern of Science," *American Journal of Psychiatry*, CIX (1953), 677–83.
10. Von Bonin, G., *Essay on the Cerebral Cortex* (Springfield, Thomas, 1950).
11. Pribram, K., "Comparative Neurology and the Evolution of Behavior," in *Behavior and Evolution*, ed. by Roe and Simpson (New Haven, Yale University Press, 1958).
12. Bullock, T. H., "Evolution of Neurophysiological Mechanisms," *ibid.*
13. Magoun, H. W., *The Waking Brain* (Springfield, Thomas, 1958).

14. Nissen, H. W., "Axes of Behavioral Comparison," in *Behavior and Evolution*.
15. Nuttin, J., "Consciousness, Behavior, and Personality," *Psychological Review*, LXII (1955), 349–55.
16. *Ibid.*, pp. 353 f.
17. H. P. David and H. von Bracken (eds.), *Perspectives in Personality Theory* (New York, Basic Books, 1957).
18. Allport, G. W., "European and American Theories of Personality," *ibid.*
19. Rogers, C., "Persons or Science? A Philosophical Question," *American Psychology*, X (1955), 267–78.
20. Buber, M., *I and Thou*, trans. R. B. Smith (Edinburgh, Clark, 1937).
21. Farber, L. H., "Martin Buber and Psychiatry," *Psychiatry*, XIX (1956), 109–20.
22. Friedman, M. S., "Healing through Meeting: Martin Buber and Psychotherapy," *Cross Currents*, V (1955), 297–310.
23. Urs von Balthasar, H., *Science, Religion, and Christianity*, trans. H. C. Graef (Westminster, Newman, 1958), p. 29.

Chapter 12   The Energetics of Love

1. *Science*, 132 (July, 1960), 200–208.
2. *Summa Theologiae* I–II, art. 26, q. 1, ad 3.
3. Nicolas Cusanus, *Of Learned Ignorance*, trans. Germain Heron (New Haven, Yale University Press, 1954), p. 105.
4. *The Ways and Power of Love* (Boston, Beacon Press, 1954), pp. 3, 6.

Chapter 14   Cosmogenesis and Theology

(References to the unpublished works of Teilhard de Chardin are listed by title only.)
1. "Le Christique."
2. "Super-Humanité — Super-Christ — Super-Charité."
3. Congar, Yves M., *The Mystery of the Church* (Baltimore, Helicon, 1960), p. xi.
4. *Ibid.*, p. 143.
5. See Tresmontant, C., *Pierre Teilhard de Chardin: His Thought*, pp. 92–94.
6. Tresmontant, C., *A Study of Hebrew Thought* (New York, Desclée, 1960), pp. 58 f.
7. Greenstone, J. H., *The Messiah Idea in Jewish History* (Philadelphia, Jewish Publication Society of America, 1906), pp. 21 f.
8. "Une Interprétation plausible de l'histoire humaine; la formation de la Noos‧phere" (*Revue des questions scientifiques,* 1947), as quoted in Tresmontant, *Pierre Teilhard de Chardin*, p. 60.
9. "Super-Humanité — Super-Christ — Super-Charité."
10. "Le Christique."
11. Schweizer, E., "The Son of Man," *Journal of Biblical Literature*, June, 1960, p. 126.
12. Johnstone, L., "The Son of Man," *Scripture*, VI (1954), 183.
13. *Ibid.*
14. "Le Christique."
15. *La Vision du passé* (Paris, Seuil, 1957), p. 181.
16. Collin, Remy, *Evolution* ("Twentieth Century Encyclopedia of Catholicism," Vol. 30 [New York, Hawthorn, 1959]), p. 138.
17. Chauchard, Paul, *L'Être humaine selon Teilhard de Chardin* (Paris, Gabalda, 1953), p. 168.
18. Messenger, E. C., *Theology and Evolution* (Westminster, Newman, 1952), p. 89, n. 1.

19. Tresmontant, *A Study of Hebrew Thought*, p. 94.
20. *Ibid.*, p. 97.
21. *Ibid.*, p. 106.
22. Vollert, Cyril, in *A Symposium on Evolution* (Pittsburgh, Duquesne University Press, 1959), p. 114.
23. *Ibid.*
24. *Ibid.*
25. Chauchard, *op. cit.*, p. 197.
26. *Adv. Haeres.*, iv, 38, 1–2.
27. Johnson, H. J. T., *The Bible and the Early History of Mankind* (New York, McMullen, 1948), p. 73.
28. "Le Christique."
29. *Adv. Haeres.*, iii, 18–21.
30. *Philosophumena*, x, 33–34.
31. "Le Christique."
32. "Super-Humanité — Super-Christ — Super-Charité."
33. *Nouvelles lettres de voyage* (1939–1955), p. 52.
34. "Super-Humanité — Super-Christ — Super-Charité."
35. "The Heart of the Problem."
36. *Ibid.*
37. Burrows, Millar, *Outline of Biblical Theology* (Philadelphia, Westminster, 1946), p. 196.
38. Corte, Nicolas *(pseud.)*, *Pierre Teilhard de Chardin: His Life and Spirit* (New York, Macmillan, 1960), p. 90.
39. *Ibid.*, p. 93.
40. "The Heart of the Problem."
41. *Nouvelles lettres de voyage*, p. 62.
42. *Ibid.*
43. *Ibid.*
44. "The Prospect for Christianity," in Rahner, Karl, *Free Speech in the Church* (New York, Sheed & Ward, 1959), p. 68.
45. *Ibid.*, p. 55.
46. "The Heart of the Problem."
47. *Nouvelles lettres de voyage*, p. 96.
48. Letter of April 25, 1954, as quoted in Cuénot, Claude, *Pierre Teilhard de Chardin*, p. 448.

Chapter 15   Prelude to Further Thought

1. *L'Être humain selon Teilhard de Chardin* (Paris, Gabalda, 1959).
2. J. L. Russell has a short paper on the "ultraphysics" and its relation to metaphysics in *Heythrop Journal* I, 4 (October, 1960), 271–84, and hopes to expand this essay and a subsequent article into a book in the future.
3. *Pierre Teilhard de Chardin, His Life and Spirit* (New York, Macmillan, 1960), p. 85.

ACKNOWLEDGMENT

I wish to express my sincere appreciation to the many friends who are responsible for this project and without whom it would never have been completed. The assistance that Mlle. Jeanne Mortier, Claude Cuénot, and Msgr. Bruno de Solages — all of the Teilhard de Chardin Foundation — have given me over the past years has been an essential factor in laying the groundwork for this study. About eight years ago Walter J. Ong, S.J., urged me into a deeper study of Teilhard de Chardin at a time when that name was practically unknown to the American reader. That encouragement was no doubt the tap root of the present symposium. Inspiration and guidance are always vital in a work such as this, and that is why I have dedicated it to three inspiring teachers: the late Leo Buss, of the University of Detroit, Dr. Paul Stokely, chairman of the science department at the College of Steubenville, and Edward Wenstrup, O.S.B., former chairman of the biology department at St. Vincent College. The cooperation of the contributors is especially appreciated since they cheerfully worked under some very trying circumstances. I also acknowledge the kind permission to use excerpts from the writings of Teilhard granted by Harper and Brothers, Editions du Seuil, and Grasset, as well as permission to use Claire Huchet Bishop's essay, which appeared in *The Third Hour*, edited by Helen Iswolsky, Karl Stern's essay, which appeared in *The Wind and the Rain*, edited by Neville Braybrooke, and Gustave Weigel's study, which appeared in *Natural Law Forum*. For their generous assistance in preparing the manuscript I would like to thank Mrs. James Addy, Judith Icuss, Lynne McGoldrick, Jeanne Slivka, and Judith Visyak. To all these and many others who in any way helped bring this work to completion, I offer a sincere word of appreciation.

THE WRITERS

RICHARD W. BALEK, assistant professor of chemistry at the University of Detroit, received his B.S. degree in chemistry from St. Mary's College, Winona, and his doctorate in pharmacology from the University of Chicago. He has published several biochemical studies on the effects of colchicine.

GEORGE B. BARBOUR, M.A. (Cantab.), M.A. (Edin.), Ph.D. (Columbia), is professor emeritus of geology and former Dean of Arts and Science at the University of Cincinnati. Born in Scotland and educated in the universities of Great Britain, Germany, and the United States, he spent twelve years in China, where he worked with Davidson Black, Teilhard de Chardin and others. He was geologist with the University of California Expedition to Africa in 1947–48 and has traveled extensively in Europe, Siberia, Southeastern Asia, the Caucasus, and North America.

CLAIRE HUCHET BISHOP, born in Brittany, prepared at the Sorbonne, and married to an American, has an extensive list of published works to her credit, including stories and biographies for young people, poetry in French and English, and articles and books on intellectual and spiritual developments in postwar France.

J. EDGAR BRUNS, Director of the Institute in Comparative Religion at St. John's University, New York City, received his doctorate in theology from the Gregorian University in Rome, and his licentiate in Sacred Scripture from the Biblical Institute in Rome. He is a member of the editorial board of *The Bridge* (Institute of Judaeo-Christian Studies), consulting editor of *The Spirit* (Catholic Poetry Society of America), and a regular reviewer for *America* and the *Catholic World.*

HENRY JEAN-JACQUES D'AOUST, O.S.B., instructor in theology at St. Vincent College, Latrobe, received his B.A. and Ph.B. from the University of Ottawa and his M.A. from St. Vincent's. He has translated French articles in collaboration with Christopher Fullman for different philosophical and theological journals.

JOHN M. DORSEY, M.D., is professor and chairman of the department of psychiatry, College of Medicine, Wayne State University. In 1935 he received a Rockefeller Foundation Research Grant for work at the University of Vienna and the Vienna Psychoanalytical Institute under Freud. With numerous offices in psychiatric and mental health organizations, he is the author of several books and over fifty articles on mental health and related subjects in medical and popular journals to which he contributes regularly. He is now Wayne State University's first *University Professor.* His appreciation of the value of individual personality in mental health is seen in the way he vigorously keeps to an exactingly individualistic syntax.

PAULINUS F. FORSTHOEFEL, S.J., associate professor of biology at the University of Detroit, received his M.S. and Ph.D. from Ohio State University, and his S.T.L. from West Baden College (Indiana). In the field of genetics he has done much research on the mouse, having received grants for research study from the National

Science Foundation and the National Institutes of Health, as well as publishing many articles in scientific journals.

JAMES L. FOY, M.D., assistant chief psychiatrist at the District of Columbia General Hospital, instructor in psychiatry at Georgetown University School of Medicine and lecturer in psychiatry at The Catholic University of America, is a graduate of the University of Notre Dame and of the Loyola University School of Medicine.

ROBERT FRANCOEUR, a priest of the Diocese of Steubenville, received his M.A degree at St. Vincent College, Latrobe, and has done postgraduate work in the biological sciences at the University of Detroit, Pennsylvania State University, and the John Hopkins University, where he is studying for his doctorate. Besides teaching biology at Mount St. Agnes College, he has published a number of articles on Teilhard de Chardin and worked on the American edition of the Tresmontant study of Teilhard.

CHRISTOPHER FULLMAN, O.S.B., assistant professor of English at St. Vincent College, Latrobe, received his M.A. with honors and Ph.D. at the University of Wisconsin. He has done research in literature at Oxford University, has contributed to several periodicals, and collaborates with Henry D'Aoust in translations from French.

ARTHUR J. KNODEL, Ph.D., professor and chairman of the department of French at the University of Southern California, has followed the thought of Teilhard for many years, though better known for his monographs and articles on Jules Renard and St.-John Perse and for his collaboration in the translations of Igor Stravinsky's *The Poetics of Music* and Louis de Broglie's *Non-Linear Wave Mechanics*.

JOHN LAFARGE, S.J., was graduated from Harvard in 1901, took advanced degrees at Woodstock and Innsbruck, and was ordained priest in the Society of Jesus in 1905. He is a fellow of the American Academy of Arts and Sciences, a director of many socio-spiritual organizations, and author of several well-known works, including *The Race Question and the Negro* and the biographical *The Manner is Ordinary*.

JAMES P. REILLY, JR., associate professor of philosophy at the University of Detroit, received his M.A., L.M.S., and Ph.D. from the Mediaeval Institute, University of Toronto. He has published articles on philosophy and aesthetics in various journals.

KARL STERN, M.D., author of *The Pillar of Fire*, *The Third Revolution*, and *Through Dooms of Love*, of essays on various topics, and of over fifty scientific publications in medical journals, is psychiatrist-in-chief at St. Mary's Hospital, Montreal, professor of psychiatry at the University of Ottawa, and professeur agrégé at the Université de Montréal. From 1951 to 1959 he was Canadian representative on the UNESCO Institute of Education's Board of Governors. He received his medical degree in Frankfurt, Germany.

JOHN V. WALSH, Ph.D., is a full professor at Pace College, New York City. Research done with Professor William F. Albright at the Johns Hopkins University is presently being prepared for publication; and a study of Don Luigi Sturzo, the well-known social philosopher, is nearing completion. Dr. Walsh is also responsible for a fundamentally new academic program which will be initiated in the near future at Pace College.

GUSTAVE WEIGEL, S.J., present professor of ecclesiology at Woodstock College, was ordained in 1933 and received his S.T.D. in Rome in 1938. Since his return from the Catholic University of Chile, where he was professor of theology for a number of years, Father Weigel has concentrated on questions of ecumenism, and has been appointed by Pope John XXIII to the Christian Unity Secretariat in preparation for the 21st Ecumenical Council. His findings in this field have been given currency in many scholarly publications as well as in public lectures, and an extended work on the subject will be published by Helicon Press in the near future.

A PARTIAL BIBLIOGRAPHY OF WRITINGS
ON TEILHARD DE CHARDIN

Prepared by Judith Visyak

Barbour, G. B. "Memorial to Pierre Teilhard de Chardin, S.J. (1881–1955)," *Proceedings of the Geological Society of America, Annual Report for 1956* (New York), 169–76. Good account of his geological contributions, sprinkled with personal recollections.

———. "Pierre Teilhard de Chardin, S.J.," *Proceedings of the Geological Society of London* (London), MDXXIX (September, 1955), 132–33. Short account of his youth and work in China.

———. "Teilhard de Chardin," *Journal of the Palaeontological Society of India* (Lucknow), II (1957), 21–23. Personal recollections of his work in India.

Braybrooke, N. (ed.). *The Wind and the Rain Yearbook, I.* Baltimore: Newman, 1962; and London: Secker & Warburg, 1962. Contains two unpublished pieces by Teilhard: "Christ in Matter," a section of the appendix to *Le Coeur de la matière* dealing with a soldier's vision of Christ during World War I, and "The Meaning and Constructive Value of Suffering"; as well as essays by Lucille Swan, Canon C. Raven, George B. Barbour, Karl Stern, Bernard Towers, Vincent Cronin, Geoffrey Wagner, C. C. Martindale, D. M. Mackinnon, and others.

Brennan, M. "The Phenomenon of Man," *Studies* (Dublin), XLIX:194 (1960), 117–30. Excellent study of analogy and consciousness; faulty on "physical" energy.

Brunner, A. "Pierre Teilhard de Chardin," *Stimmen der Zeit* (München), CLXV (1959–60), 210–22; and *Theology Digest*, VIII:3 (1960), 143–47. "A personal vision rather than a presentation of established facts."

Bruns, J. E. "The Divine Milieu," *Catholic World*, CXCII (1960), 185.

———. "God Up Above — or Up Ahead?" *Catholic World*, CXCI:1, 141 (1960), 23–30. An excellent theological study.

———. "The Phenomenon of Man," *Catholic World*, XC:1, 139 (1960), 323–25.

Burkhardt, W., Ewing, J. F., Francoeur, R., and Walsh, J. V. "Evolution, Science and Religion," *Jubilee*, VIII:1 (May, 1960), 48–51. Transcript of a television program; brief, popular summary of present position, his contribution, and scope of appeal.

Collin, R. *Evolution.* Translated by J. Tester. New York: Hawthorne, 1959. Uses many of Teilhard's ideas in presenting a summary of evolution.

Connolly, F. M. *The Voices of France. A Survey of Contemporary Theology in France.* New York: Macmillan, 1961. Numerous references, especially pages 118–30; not completely accurate on some points such as polygenism, the "fact" of evolution, and the *imprimatur* problem.

Corte, N. (Leon Cristiani). *Pierre Teilhard de Chardin, His Life and Spirit.* Translated and with a Preface by M. Jarrett-Kerr. London: Barrie & Rockliff; and
New York: Macmillan, 1960. Reviewed by B. Towers in *Blackfriars,* XLI (1960),
351–52. An excellent short study of his life, the *Phenomenon of Man,* and
opinions pro and con.

D'Arcy, M. C. *The Meaning and Matter of History.* New York: Farrar, Straus &
Cudahy, 1959. Chapter 10, "Christianity and Historicism, II," is an excellent
study of Teilhard's "philosophy of theology and of history."

———. "The Varieties of Human Love," *Saturday Evening Post,* CCXXXI (1959),
38 ff.; also in Thruelsen, R. and Kobler, J. (ed.). *Adventures of the Mind.* New
York: Knopf, 1959. A discussion of love, consciousness and freedom with favorable comments on Teilhard.

Dehner, E. W. "The Phenomena of Christ and Man," *St. Louis Book Review Section*
(Monthly Book Supplement, March 4, 1960), 1. Worthwhile comments.

Donnelly, W. "The Thought of Teilhard de Chardin," *Clergy Review* (England),
XLV:6 (June, 1960), 324–49. A fine setting of Teilhard in the current theological trends and an appraisal of the criticisms in *Divinitas.*

Evans, J. W. "The Phenomenon of Man: Dilemmas and Limitations," *The Commonweal* (New York), LXXII:18 (1960), 439–41. Sane look at limitations.

Ewing, J. F. "The Human Phenomenon," *Theological Studies,* XXII:1 (March,
1961), 86–102. An excellent summary and comment.

Fehlner, P. D. "Teilhard de Chardin: Ambiguity by Design," *Homiletic and Pastoral Review* (New York), LX:8 (1960), 709–17. Confusing, and in the *Divinitas*
tradition.

———. "Teilhard de Chardin: 'Leading to Confusion . . .' " *Homiletic and Pastoral
Review* (New York), LXI:1 (1960), 35, 40–47. A bit clearer than the first article,
but still *Divinitas.*

Francoeur, R. "The Divine Milieu," *The Commonweal* (New York), LXXIII:18
(1961), 463–64. A review of his three passions.

———. "Flight from Time, No," *The Catholic World* (New York), CXCIII:1,158
(1961), 367–73. A study of the ultraconservative reactions to Teilhard.

———. "The Phenomenon of Man: a Call to Greatness," *The Commonweal,*
LXXII:18 (1960), 441–43. Historical background and analysis.

———. "Evolution and 'Panpsychism' in Teilhard de Chardin," *American Benedictine Review* (Collegeville, Minn.), XII:2 (1961), 206–19. A study of the concept of "consciousness" in Teilhard, Bergson, and Lecomte du Noüy.

———. "Teilhard de Chardin: Prophet of a New Vision," *Homiletic and Pastoral
Review* (New York), LXI:1 (1960), 34–40. An answer to Fehlner.

———. "The Witness of a Christian Scholar," *The Month* (London), CCXI:1123
[n.s. XXV:3] (1961), 179. Review of *Le milieu divin.*

Gilligan, B. B. "The Phenomenon of Man," *New Scholasticism,* XXXIV (1960), 515.

Huxley, J. "The Human Phenomenon," *Encounter* (London), VI (1956), 84–86.

Kenney, W. H. "Teilhard de Chardin, his Theory of Evolution," *Faculty Collo-
quium.* Xavier University, Cincinnati, Ohio, (March, 1960), 11 pages, mimeographed. A good introduction.

Knodel, A. "An Introduction to the Integral Evolutionism of Teilhard de Chardin,"
The Personalist (Los Angeles), XXXVIII (1957), 347–55. An excellent, early
summary of his thought.

Lafarge, J. "The Divine Milieu," *America* (New York), CIX:7 (1960), 224–27. An
excellent evaluation.

Lawler, J. G. "Chardin and Human Knowledge," *The Commonweal* (New York), LXVIII:2 (1958), 40–49. Teilhard's fight against Jansenistic Christian spirituality.

Maitland, B. "The Phenomenon of Man," *Downside Review* (England), LXXVIII:252 (1960), 227–29. Good summary and favorable review.

Martindale, C. C. "A Letter," *The Tablet*, CCV (1955), 460.

McKenzie, J. "Divine Milieu," *The Critic*, XIX:3 (1960–61), 29–30. A fine review by a biblical scholar of rank.

McNaspy, C. J. "A Theology of History?" *Worship*, XXXII (1958), 464–69. A study of Pieper, Guardini, Toynbee and Teilhard in respect to the theology of history.

Movius, H. L., Jr. "Pierre Teilhard de Chardin, S. J., 1881–1955," *American Anthropologist* (Manasha, Wisconsin), LVIII (1956), 147–50. Personal tribute from a fellow scientist and friend.

———. "Pierre Teilhard de Chardin, Paleoanthropologist," *Science* (Washington, D.C.), CXXIII (1956). 92. Short tribute to him as a man and as a scientist.

Musurillo, H. "Phenomenon of Man," *Thought*, XXXV (Fall, 1960), 450–54.

Neilson, F. "The Phenomenon of Man," *American Journal of Economics*, XX (October, 1960), 101–06. A review of the *Phenomenon of Man* from the economist's point of view.

Novak, M. and Alcorn, J., "Directions '61: A Catholic Perspective," (Show #111: Man in the World of Nature, February, 1961), ABC Television. Mimeographed television script, 7 pages, obtainable from Michael Novak, William James Hall 109A, Cambridge 38, Mass.

O'Doherty, E. F. "The Phenomenon of Man," *Philosophical Studies*, IX (December, 1959), 162–65. A question of the validity of scientific extrapolations.

Ong, W. J. *American Catholic Crossroads. Religious-Secular Encounters in the Modern World.* New York: Macmillan, 1959. Chapters I on cosmic history and V on research contain some interesting comments on Teilhard.

———. (ed.). *Darwin's Vision and Christian Perspectives.* New York: Macmillan, 1961. Essays on biology, philosophy and theology by James Collins, Robert Gleason, Vincent Hopkins, Walter Ong, and Alexander Wolsky, with occasional references to Teilhard.

———. *Frontiers in American Catholicism. Essays on Ideology and Culture.* New York: Macmillan, 1957. Some comments related to Teilhard indirectly.

———. "The Mechanical Bride," *Social Order*, II:2 (1952), 79–85. A review article; very early discussion of Teilhard in America.

———. "Personalism and the Wilderness," *Kenyon Review*, XXI:2 (1959), 297–304. Teilhard's contribution to existential philosophies; "often exquisitely articulate about the interior of consciousness but somewhat insensitive to consciousness' exterior setting and relation to cosmic history."

———. "Secular Knowledge, Revealed Religion and History," *Religious Education*, LXX:5 (1957), 341–49. The meaning and theology of history.

Osborne, H. F., "Explorations, Researches and Publications of Pierre Teilhard de Chardin, 1911–31. With map and legend showing chief fossil collecting areas of China, 1885–1931," *American Museum Novitates*, #485, 11 (+2) pages, 1 fig., 1 map, 1931. May be purchased from the American Museum for twenty-five cents. Has a list of all his early publications.

Pepper, G. "Le Phénomène Teilhard," *Cross Currents*, X:3 (1960), 289–93. A good review and summary of the main reactions to and criticisms of Teilhard.

Polanyi, M. "An Epic Theory of Evolution," *Saturday Review*, XLIV:5 (1960), 21. Favorable, but misses the point.

Pontet, M. "Evolution according to Teilhard de Chardin," *Thought* (New York), XXXVI:141 (1961), 167–79. An excellent study of human evolution and convergence on the Omega, his Christology, etc.

Poulain, D., "Christ and the Universe. The vision of the great Jesuit Paleontologist, Pierre Teilhard de Chardin," *The Commonweal* (New York), LXIX (1959), 460–64. An excellent report of the 1958 *Decades* of the Abbaye de Pontigny, which was devoted to Teilhard.

Russell, J. L. "Teilhard de Chardin: *The Phenomenon of Man*, Part I," *The Heythrop Journal* (Oxon., England), I:4 (1960), 271–84. The best study of his "philosophy of science and nature" available in English. "Part II," *ibid.*, II:1 (1961), 3–13. An excellent study of his theology.

Russo, F. "The Phenomenon of Man," *America* (New York), CIII:5 (1960), 185–89. One of the best summaries in English along with a fair appraisal of his limitations, by a close friend.

Schmitt, C. G. "The Environment of the Soul: Teilhard de Chardin," *The Catholic Messenger* (Davenport, Iowa), LXXIV:14 (1961), 13. A good review of the *Divine Milieu*.

Sheed, W. "Père Teilhard's View of Evolution. A Jesuit Paleontologist presents a unique statement about man's place on the evolutionary scale," *Jubilee* (New York), VII:8 (1959), 42–49. A fine popular presentation.

Simpson, G. G. "On the Remarkable Testament of the Jesuit Paleontologist Pierre Teilhard de Chardin," *Scientific American* (New York), CCII (1960), 201–207. A favorable review, but as "not science."

Solages, B. de. "Christianity and Evolution," *Cross Currents* (New York), IV (1951), 26–37. One of the earliest, best and still most quoted studies.

Stern, K. "Great and Controversial Priest and Scientist," *The Commonweal* (New York), LXXI:14 (1960), 400–01. Interesting comments of a liberal view; faulty on Lecomte du Noüy reference.

Taylor, H. "The Phenomenon of Man," *American Scientist*, XLVIII:1 (1961), 56A–58A. Favorable review by a leading scientist.

Teilhard de Chardin, P. "Building the Earth," *Cross Currents*, IX:4 (1959), 315–30. Reprint of *Cahiers I*.

———. "Psychological Conditions of Human Unification," *Cross Currents*, III:1 (1951), 1–5.

Towers, B. "Significance of Teilhard de Chardin," *Blackfriars*, XL (1959), 126–29.

———. "Teilhard de Chardin," *Blackfriars*, XLI (April, 1960), 119–26.

Tensing, R. H. "Evolution and Philosophy of Science," *The 1960 Lecture Series in the Philosophy of Science*. Graduate Program in Philosophy of the Athenaeum of Ohio. Cincinnati: Mt. St. Mary's Seminary of the West, 1961. Contains some references to Teilhard.

Tresmontant, C. *A Study of Hebrew Thought.* New York: Desclee, 1960. On the theory of Teilhard see pages 90–119.

———. *Pierre Teilhard de Chardin, his Thought.* Baltimore: Helicon Press, 1959. An excellent commentary/study, with a Foreword by Gustave Weigel, S.J., and a useful bibliography and glossary by R. Francoeur.

Vass, G. "Teilhard de Chardin and Inward Vision," *The Heythrop Journal* (Oxon., England), II:3 (1961), 237–49. A detailed analysis of the spirituality presented in the *Divine Milieu*, detachment, mortification, etc. The only one available in English, but also a faithful and fine evaluation.

Vollert, C. "The Phenomenon of Man," *The Modern Schoolman*, XXXVIII (1960), 72–76. He is more favorable in his later reviews.

————. "Toward Omega: Man in the Vision of Teilhard de Chardin," *The Month* (London), XXIII (May, 1960), 261–69; also in *The Catholic Mind* (New York), LVIII (October, 1960), 402–09; and in *Theology Digest* (St. Mary's, Kansas), VIII (1960), 133–36. A fine theological study; some of his criticisms have been modified lately.

Williams, R. "Aristotle and Teilhard de Chardin," *The Tablet* (London), CCXIV:6166 (1960), 599–600. Energy in Aristotle and Teilhard: very good.

AN INDEX TO
THE WORLD OF TEILHARD